Basic to Advanced Computer Aided Design Using

NX 10

Modeling, Drafting, Assemblies, Sheet Metal and Other Goodies

A Project Oriented Learning Manual

By:

Stephen M. Samuel PE

DESIGN VISIONARIES

**Superior Vision Yields
Optimal Products**

ISBN: 978-1-935951-07-0

Published by:

Design Visionaries

7034 Calcaterra Drive

San Jose, CA 95120

info@designviz.com

www.designviz.com

www.nxtutorials.com

Local Phone: (408) 997 6323

Fax: (408) 997 9667

DESIGN VISIONARIES

Superior Vision Yields
Optimal Products

Proudly Printed in the United States of America

Published August 2015

Dedication

We dedicate this book to Zelda Druce – an exceptional math teacher and an even more amazing person. Zelda taught Algebra at Samuel J Tilden High School in Brooklyn N.Y. from 1967 to 1982. She touched the lives of thousands upon thousands. She was a rock solid person with a "get down to business" exterior and an incredibly caring interior.

<u>About the Author</u>

Stephen M. Samuel PE, Founder and President of Design Visionaries, has over 25 years of experience developing and using high-end CAD tools and mentoring its users. During a ten-year career at Pratt & Whitney Aircraft, he was responsible for implementing advanced CAD/CAM technology in a design/manufacturing environment. He has trained thousands of engineers in Unigraphics, written self-paced courses in UG Advanced Modeling and Best Practices, and performed design work for numerous Fortune 500 companies. Stephen is the author of distinctive publications on Nastran, UGNX CAD, Sold Edge, SolidWorks, and Teamcenter Engineering PLM. Stephen holds several US patents and enjoys a life of creativity and intellectual challenge in the city of San Jose, CA. He happily shares his life with three amazing children, his wife and his 83 year old powerhouse of a mother that lives in a home right next door.

Editors

Huge thanks to Landon Ritchie. This book would not be what it is without his invaluable help and knowledge of the intricacies of NX.

Acknowledgements

We would like to thank the following people for their tireless efforts. Without the contributions from each of you, this book would be a mere shadow of what it has become.

Jennine Scott, Landon Ritchie.

What readers have to say about our previous books

"Practical Unigraphics NX Modeling for Engineers was extremely effective and much better than [other] textbooks. I would highly recommend this book to other professors and students alike."

Fred Dyen, Director of St. Louis University's Aviation Maintenance Institute (AMI)

"The UG NX textbook is well organized. Its tutorial style of learning is easy for students to utilize. The practice exercises are essential. From my experience in teaching students to use UG software, I have found that this is the best textbook currently on the market for teaching UG NX."

Dr. Pat Spicer, Professor at Western Illinois University

Preface

Dear reader,

Thank you for purchasing *Basic to Advanced Computer Aided Design Using NX 10*, the latest offering in our series of CAD training text books. Design Visionaries is an engineering consulting firm that performs many design projects great and small, including industrial design, product design and engineering analysis. Our customers entrust us with a wide range of designs, including medical devices, aerospace components, heavy machinery, and consumer products.

The methods outlined in this book go beyond an academic use of the software. They are tricks of the trade that come from thousands of hours of actual use of the software to design some of the most difficult products in the world. In addition, Design Visionaries offers world class on-site training which enables us to develop and evolve our training material to provide maximum benefit. Please enjoy this text, and we invite you to log on to our websites – www.designviz.com and nxtutorials.com, where you can download the part files pack that accompanies this book. There are also additional free materials, other advanced materials, products, and goodies.

Thank you,

Stephen Samuel

June 2015

Table of Contents

1 An Overview of NX 10

This book has been written with an underlying philosophy that comes from years of engineering design which we would like to share with you. Engineers are pretty bright in general, so we've written this book to take advantage of that fact. Our book begins with the basics and examples explained to every last detail. As the book progresses, more and more is left to the reader. We believe this enables faster learning as you won't have to sift through superfluous instructions. We hope you enjoy this material that we've truly poured our hearts into.

Using NX 10 is like playing a piano. In the same way that chords are as important as individual notes, NX commands are far more powerful when used in concert with others. Our book makes an effort to show not only the details of the most important commands, but the powerful combinations that we have used to bring about excellent designs.

All projects and practice exercises can be downloaded from www.designviz.com. Use them for your reference or as examples of how each project should look upon completion.

For even more tutorials, visit nxtutorials.com. There are some great tutorials on some very useful but esoteric NX functions. They even have some awesome projects with plans already available if you need a quick break from NX and want to get your hands on some real building!

1.1 Fundamental Concepts of Solid Modeling in NX 10

Siemens PLM Software NX 10™ (commonly referred to as *Unigraphics*, *UG*, or *NX*) is a 3D Computer-Aided Design (CAD) software that is used by companies all over the world to design state-of-the-art products. This manual teaches you the basics of modeling, assemblies, drafting, and sheet metal in NX 10. Each of these functions is organized into a separate *application*. This book concentrates on what is typically the most complicated task in NX 10: three-dimensional geometric modeling.

1. Parametric Models

A *parametric model* has variables (*parameters*) that control its geometry. Parametric models are "smart" models that remember how they were built and "rethink" themselves as their parameters or features change. Most models constructed in NX are parametric.

2. Non-parametric Models

A *non-parametric model* has none of the parameters or feature-driven geometry; it is sometimes referred to as a "dumb" model. To modify a non-parametric model, it is often necessary to rebuild a lot of the geometry, or to make use of the *Synchronous Modeling* tools.

3. Hybrid Models

A *hybrid model* is neither completely parametric nor non-parametric; rather it is comprised of both types of geometry. Portions of the geometry may be so complicated that it is more efficient to make it non-parametric, while some of the geometry is still feature-driven. This is a very flexible and powerful modeling technique.

Building a completely parametric model takes more planning and foresight; however, the extra effort can pay off if you are building multiple versions of a model, or if you can anticipate potential design modifications. The experienced NX 10 user will determine which modeling approach is appropriate for each design project.

4. Curves

Curves can be created in three-dimensional space. Basic curves are typically non-parametric, but NX 10 has the capability to create some *associative* curves like lines, curves, circles, and helices for which you can control certain parameters; plus, unlike the basic curves, they appear in the modeling tree. Each curve has a set of *control points*. For example, lines have control points at both ends and at the midpoint, while circles have a basic control point at their center. These control points are useful for a variety of tasks, such as selecting features, building new geometry, and making measurements of existing geometry.

Curves can be placed in many ways, such as at (x, y, z) coordinates, or they can be connected to another curve at control points. They can also be placed in relation to other curves (parallel, perpendicular, tangent, normal, etc.).

Note: NX 10 distinguishes between selecting a curve itself and selecting one of its control points. This can be a source of confusion to a new user. If you are having difficulty selecting geometry, pay close attention to your <u>selection technique</u>. To avoid the ambiguity between selecting a curve and its control points, you can zoom in closer to the area in question or rotate the model into a better orientation. You can also use the snap point tool bar to control the selection.

5. Sketches

Sketches are by definition, planar (two-dimensional) parametric features. Sketches are always defined upon a planar entity, with a reference that orients the sketch horizontally or vertically. As with curves, sketch entities also have control points.

The general approach in creating a sketch is to define its orientation, quickly create the curves that define it (do not worry about dimensions when creating geometry), and constrain it by placing dimensions or geometric constraints. At any point after the sketch is constrained, the dimensions that define the sketch can be changed and the model will then update.

Once a sketch is completed, it may be used to create other geometry. A typical use case involves sketching a profile and invoking the Extrude command for a specified distance to create a solid body. Sketches may also be used to define complex geometry, such as free-form surfaces.

6. Reference Features

Reference features include **Datum Plane**, **Datum Axis** and **Datum Coordinate System** features, which are used as construction entities and may be thought of as parametric reference geometry. A common use for reference features is to position sketches in order to create meaningful geometric relationships.

7. Design Features

Design features are used to create solids. They are typically based on either curves or sketches (e.g., the **Sweep** entity). Although design features are parametric in nature, they are only fully parametric if they are created upon parametric geometry, (i.e., solids created from sketches).

8. Surfaces

Like design features, surfaces are often based upon curves or sketches. They are the most powerful and mathematically complex of the geometric tools in NX and are often used when the desired geometry is too complicated to create using design features alone.

9. Feature Operations

Feature operations are used to add detail to the existing geometry. These are great tools and save a lot of time while creating complex geometry. The most commonly used feature operations are **Blend**, **Draft**, **Chamfer**, **Pattern Feature**, **Shell**, **Trim**, and the usual *Boolean operations* (**Unite**, **Subtract**, and **Intersect**).

10. Associativity

Associativity is an important concept to grasp when using NX 10.

1.2 A Basic Modeling Procedure

NX 10 allows the user a great deal of freedom to determine the method in which a model is built. The basic approach to building a model is outlined below.

1. **THINK.** Carefully consider the geometry that you wish to create and to develop a strategy for building it. NX 10 works best if you have a good idea of which operations you need to perform and in what sequence they need to be applied. Although you may not know the final configuration of what you are building until it is done, you will find that there are certain universal techniques that can be applied to almost any modeling situation.

2. **SKETCH.** The next step is to sketch the basic two-dimensional shape, or outline, of what you are building. Generally just a neat freehand sketch is adequate. Remember that the idea for this step is to save time – you do not need to sketch the perfect finished shape just yet. The geometry will take its accurate form later when you apply dimensions.

Note: Sometimes people like to use primitive features (block, cylinder, cone, or sphere) for this step, but in most cases, the use of a good sketch is a superior modeling approach. Defining the shape using non-parametric curves often does not work as well either, since defining them is harder than sketching and modifying the shape.

3. **CONSTRAIN.** Put all of the dimensional and geometric constraints on the sketch. Use enough to capture the design intent and constrain the sketch.

Note: If the sketch geometry changes color, you either have an overconstrained sketch or you have created conflicting constraints. This will be discussed in detail later.

4. **ENUMERATE.** Once you have a fully constrained sketch, input the actual numerical values of each dimension. At this time, you can also relate dimensions to one another (by referring to their variable names) in order to further capture design intent.

5. **POSITION.** You can position your sketch using the sketchers standard dimensioning and constraining tools. Each strategy comes with its own pros and cons.

6. **PERFORM SOLID OPERATIONS.** Once the first sketch is complete, you may Extrude or Revolve it to create the basic building block of your model.

7. **ADD FEATURES.** Now that you have the first solid object, you may proceed by adding detail features such as bosses, pads, holes, or even more sketches (to be used for uniting, subtracting, or intersecting).

8. **REPEAT THE ABOVE.** A model may consist of many sketches or form features, each created in the above sequence. Mastering these modeling steps will make you far more productive.

9. **DRAFT, ANALYZE, AND MACHINE.** Once you have iterated the steps above enough, you may now begin using the associated functions. You can derive a huge benefit from taking advantage of the associativity between the various functions in NX9. For example, if you begin the modeling phase and shortly thereafter another person begins with the analysis phase in a WAVE geometry linked version of the model while simultaneously another copy is being drafted, you can shorten the design cycle to an amazing degree.

2 First Steps in NX 10

Our philosophy in writing this book is that you will only learn the material by *doing*. Let's get started right away with the first project! Begin by launching NX 10.

NX 10.0

When NX is completely loaded, your screen should appear as below.

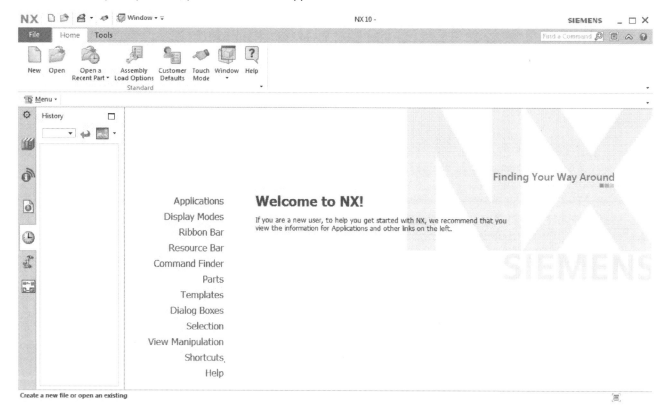

If your color scheme doesn't match ours, you can change it by visiting the User Interface preferences menu at File / Preferences / User Interface.

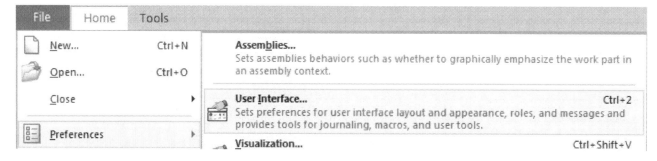

The Theme Type we will use throughout this book is Light (Recommended).

2.1 Creating New Files

- To begin, open NX 10 and select the New File command from the far-left side of the ribbon.

- The New dialog box shown below will then appear. Select the Model template, and click OK. Make a note of the variety of model templates available – NX is extremely robust CAD software, with applications for every stage of the product life cycle, from concept to analysis to manufacturing. There are even industry-specific tools available.

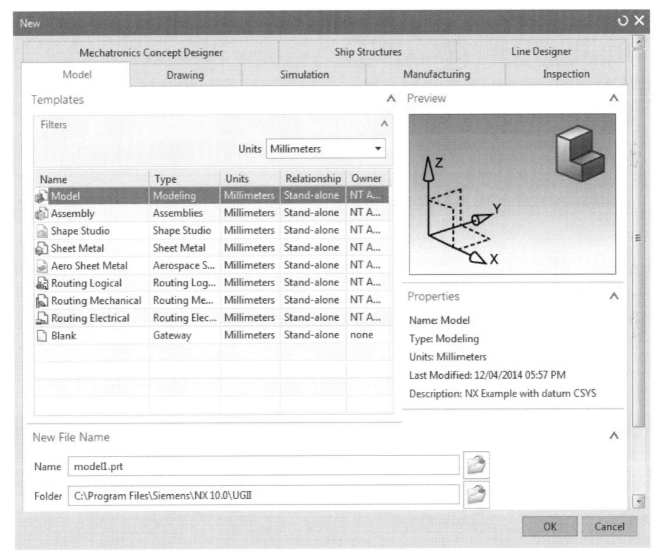

2.2 The Ribbon

When a brand new installation of NX 10 is accessed with no customizations, the user interface comes up in "ribbon mode." The ribbon is very customizable so you can easily display the commands that you use the most. All of the functionality is organized into *tabs* on the *ribbon*. Within each tab, there are *groups*, within each group there are *commands*, and within certain groups there are *galleries* and *drop-down menus* with further commands. Each group also has a *customization drop-down menu* indicated by a down arrow ▾. The examples below illustrate these concepts.

- This is the Home tab.

- On the Home tab, this is the Feature group.

- Within the Feature group, this is the Design Feature drop-down menu.

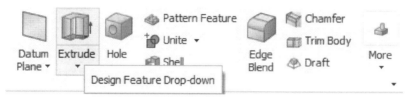

- Within the Design Feature drop-down menu, this is the Revolve command.

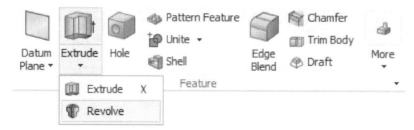

- Galleries come in two forms. For example, this is the More gallery on the Feature group.

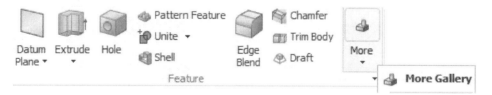

- This is the Sketch Curve gallery on the Direct Sketch group.

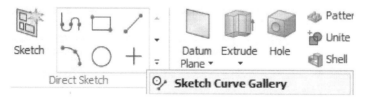

- You can expand the Sketch Curve gallery by clicking the bottom right button.

- This is what the Sketch Curve gallery looks like when fully expanded.

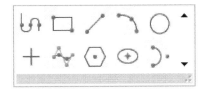

- The customization drop-down menu for the Feature group determines which galleries, drop-down menus, and commands appear in that group.

2.3 Your First Solid Model

The Extrude command is fundamental to solid modeling. This command requires a *planar* section curve as input, and then (by default) sweeps it along one of the plane's two normal vectors to produce a sheet or solid body. The Extrude command is located in the Feature group on the Home tab.

- Select the Extrude tool. The Extrude dialog box will then appear.

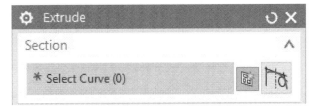

- The red asterisk in the Section field indicates that NX wants you to specify a curve. To get a better idea of what the prompt means precisely, read the Cue Display in the bottom left corner of the software – in this case, it says "*Select planar face to sketch or select section geometry*." The Cue Display is a great place to look when you're not sure what NX wants you to do next – it's usually spelled out right there!

Select planar face to sketch or select section geometry

- The Cue Display is asking us to create a sketch. Note that as you hover your cursor over the X-Y plane in the model, it highlights. Go ahead and click on it to see what happens!

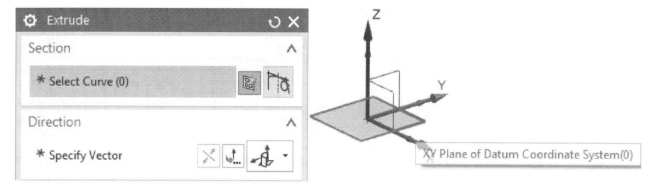

- This brings you into the **Sketch Task Environment**. Note that the tools on the ribbon have changed!

- Your view is oriented to the sketch plane. The coordinate system shown below is an important reference for your sketch features.

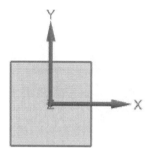

- By default, when you enter the sketcher, the **Profile** tool is enabled. The profile tool has two modes – line and arc. As you can see in the **Object Type** section below, the line icon is shaded, so that mode is enabled.

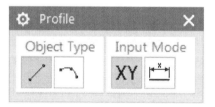

- To create a line segment using the profile tool, <u>two clicks</u> are required – one for the start point and one for the end point. <u>Click once</u> at the sketch origin. Note that as you move your cursor vertically, NX previews your line segment and shows the length in a dialog box. Drag to a **Length** of **25** and **Angle** of **90**, as shown below.

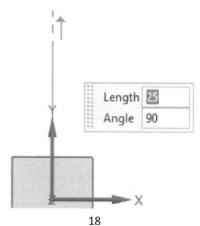

- <u>Click again</u> to complete the line segment. Note that the appearance has changed, and your line has a name.

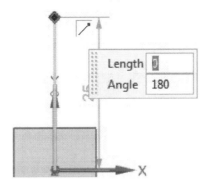

- Move your cursor to the location shown below, and click again. This time it only took one click to produce a line segment! The **Profile** tool uses each endpoint as the start point for the next line or arc, depending on mode. This allows you to sketch complicated contours quickly!

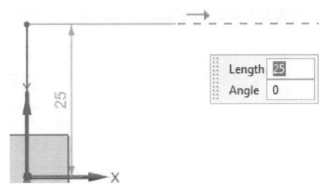

- Type **25** into the **Length** field, and move your cursor down and to the right until a dotted horizontal line appears, joining the cursor location to the end of your first (vertical) line segment. Click when your cursor is locked to the dotted line. *Guide lines* like this appear as you sketch to help you align your clicks with existing features of the sketches. It is worthwhile to learn to use these efficiently, as they can dramatically improve the speed with which you produce accurate sketches on the fly.

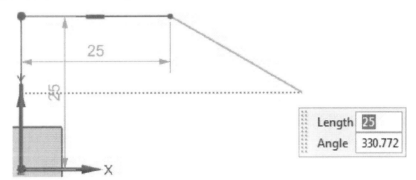

- Move your cursor straight down until another horizontal guide line appears. Click once your cursor has locked to the guide line.

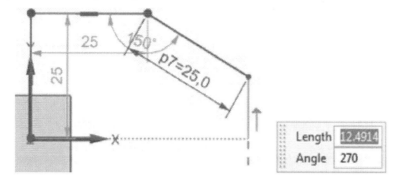

- Finally, move your cursor back to the sketch origin to complete a closed contour.

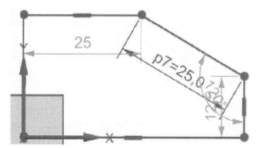

- Congratulations on completing your first sketch! Before we can get back to the Extrude function, you need to click the Finish Sketch icon on the far left side of the ribbon.

- When you return to the Extrude menu, NX will reorient your camera angle to its original state, and *automatically* specify a Direction Vector for the Extrude command. The Start limit is the distance along the Direction Vector at which you would like to begin the extrusion, and the End limit is the distance where the extrusion should stop. Enter the values shown below.

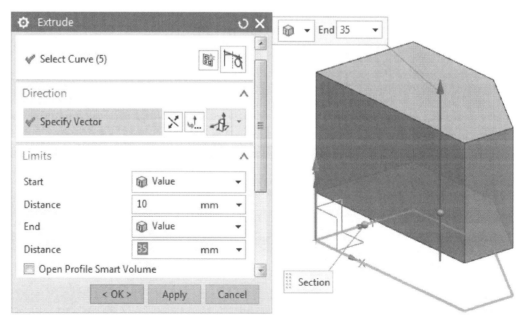

- Click OK, and marvel at your first creation in NX 10! Congratulations!

2.4 Saving Files

All the hard work that you put into using NX 10 won't be worth anything if you can't save your files!

- Select File / Save / Save, as shown below.

- NX will prompt you to give your file a name – although it already has the name *model1.prt*, nothing has been recorded yet, so you can overwrite the directory and name in the Name Part dialog box shown below. Create a new directory on your C drive called "My NX 10 Files" and save your model there!

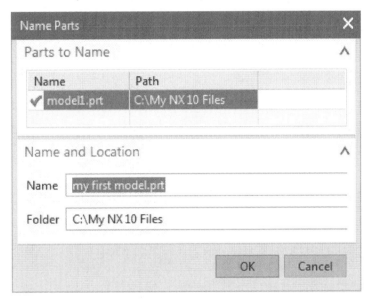

3   The NX 10 Interface

The look and feel of NX 10 is similar to that of many Windows™ based products. Commands are arranged at the top of the screen in a menu bar, and selections are made primarily with the left mouse button. Using the menu bar, different tool palettes can be activated. These tool palettes contain the icons from which most geometry is created.

You will find that NX 10 file management functions are very similar to most typical Windows-based products, such as Microsoft Word™. Files are created, saved, and closed using pull-down menus and dialog boxes.

3.1   The NX 10 User Interface

In NX 10, the tools you need to work through the various stages of the mechanical design process are organized throughout five distinct portals: the quick access toolbar, the ribbon, the top border bar, the resource bar, and the graphics window. Every menu in NX 10 can be customized by right-clicking on empty space within that menu.

3.1.1   The Resource Bar

The Resource Bar is by default found on the left of NX, and it contains tabs arranged vertically, each of which give access to different navigation and organization tools in the window attached to the right of the Resource Bar.

The NX 10 graphics window display, toolbars, and menu options all depend on what role you select. You can change your role on the Roles tab. We will be using the Advanced role throughout this book.

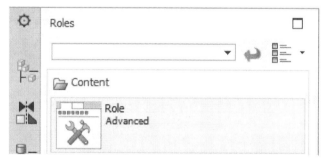

Our recommendation: the Advanced role

As you become familiar with the NX 10 interface, you may wish to customize it to better serve your workflow. To save your preferences in a role, right-click the background in the roles palette, select New User Role and customize it for your needs.

The tabs on the resource bar may be rearranged vertically or horizontally using drag-and-drop techniques. You can also undock the tabs on the resource bar and move them around on the screen. Right-click on a tab, and select Undock Tab, and the tab will appear in its own window.

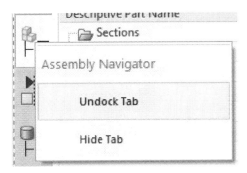

Each of the tabs in the resource bar serves a different important purpose, but the most important within the scope of this book are: the Assembly Navigator, the Constraint Navigator, and the Part Navigator. The Part Navigator will be of particular importance as we begin solid modeling because it contains the Model History – a sequential summary of all the parametric operations performed to produce a model.

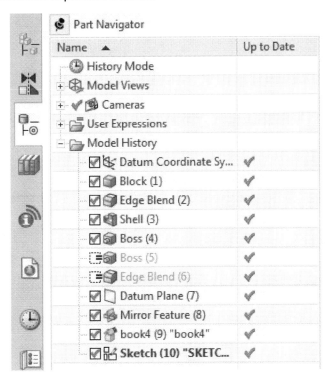

3.1.2 The Quick Access Toolbar

The Quick Access Toolbar shows icons for many commonly-used file management commands. By default, it includes icons for Save, Undo/Redo, Cut/Copy/Paste, Touch Mode, the Repeat Command drop-down menu, and the Window drop-down menu. The customization drop-down includes options for additional file management operations, such as New and Open.

The *File Name* section of the screen displays the active part, i.e. the part that you are currently working on. If you are working with assemblies, it shows both a *Displayed Part* and a *Work Part*. You will learn more about this concept later.

3.1.3 The Top Border Bar

The top border bar is located just beneath the ribbon, and by default it comes with three groups: the Menu, Selection group, and View group.

IMPORTANT: Nearly any command that can be accessed on the ribbon can also be accessed via Menu.

For example, the Extrude command is found via the menu at Menu / Insert / Design Feature / Extrude.

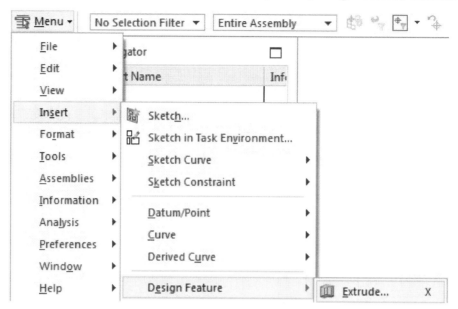

The Selection group is extremely important, as it sets the rules for how your cursor will interact with geometry in the graphics window. You will learn about the Selection group in detail later.

The View group contains commands that control the presentation of geometry within the graphics window.

Model Views can be accessed via the fifth drop-down on the View group, or from within the Part Navigator.

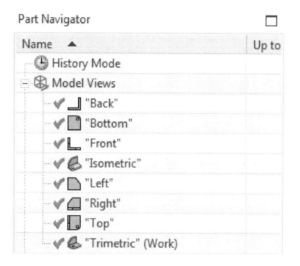

3.1.4 Pop-Up Toolbars & Menus

All geometry is displayed in the main Graphics Window.

The Cue Display contains important information about what NX is expecting from you. If you are performing an operation and are uncertain what to do next, *read the cue*! (Most of the time it is actually helpful!) The Cue Display is located in the bottom left corner of the graphics window.

The Status Display often gives a dialog of what operations are being done. This display is sometimes a good supplement to the cue, and it can be particularly helpful when picking geometry in the graphics window. If you are ever uncertain about what geometry you just picked, look at the status. The Status Display is only visible when a selection is made or an operation is underway, and it can be found in the bottom center of the graphics window.

The Shortcut Toolbar is a useful feature which was added in NX 8.5. This toolbar shows a variety of viewing, editing, and geometry management options, and becomes visible with a single left-click.

The shortcut toolbar looks like this when you left-click on a piece of geometry...

And like this when you left-click on empty space.

The View Pop-Up menu appears upon right-clicking empty space in the graphics window, and includes the Selection Group for quick access.

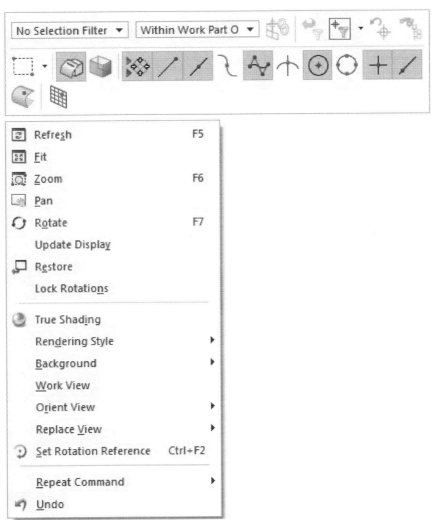

The following is a list of the most commonly used View Pop-Up menu functions:

- **Refresh:** Cleans up any out-of-date items displayed in the Graphics Window.
- **Fit:** Resizes the model to fill the entire Graphics Window.
- **Zoom:** Turns the cursor into a magnifying glass. Click and drag to define a rectangular zoom region. To exit zoom mode or leave any of the following modes where the cursor changes appearance, click the middle mouse button.
- **Orient View:** Allows you to reorient the model to another standard view, such as Top, Front, or Right, but does not replace the current work view.
- **Replace View:** Displays a submenu that allows you to replace the current work view with another standard view, such as Top, Front, or Right. By default, NX 10 starts with the model oriented in the Top view.
- **Set Rotate Point:** Allows you to set a point that acts as the center of rotation.
- **Note:** When rotating an object after setting a rotate point, NX 10 displays the rotate point with a green cross that is visible during the object's rotation. To remove the user-defined point, choose CLEAR ROTATE POINT.

*Note: When rotating an object after setting a rotate point, NX 10 displays the rotate point with a green cross that is visible during the object's rotation. To remove the user-defined point, choose **CLEAR ROTATE POINT**.*

- **Undo:** Undoes the previous operation.

Note: NX 10 saves a 'snapshot' of the model prior to performing an operation - such as creating a curve or deleting an entity. The Undo command essentially returns the model to the saved snapshot. Several actions, such as saving a model or invoking another Application will purge the Undo List, making the Undo command no longer available.

- **[F4]:** Re-does the last command.

Right-clicking on a piece of geometry combines the shortcut toolbar with a popup menu with the usual editing operations.

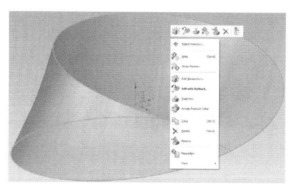

There is also a View Styles pop-up radial toolbar that appears when you click and hold the right mouse button. This allows you to switch between *Wireframe* and *Shaded With Edges* very easily.

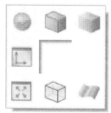

Finally, it is worth mentioning that there are three Application Radial menus available to you with shortcuts for your favorite commands. These are accessed by holding [Ctrl] + [Shift] and clicking a mouse button. These menus can be customized by right-clicking on the ribbon, and selecting the Shortcuts tab within the Customization dialog box.

Application Radial 1: [Ctrl]+[Shift]+left-click

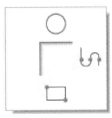

Application Radial 2: [Ctrl]+[Shift]+middle-click

Application Radial 3: [Ctrl]+[Shift]+right-click

Mastery of the application radial menus can be a real time-saver when modeling. We highly recommend that you practice using them!

3.1.5 Customizing the Ribbon

The tabs in the ribbon mode are fairly self-explanatory, although there are some commands available in multiple tabs. For example, the WAVE Geometry Linker command can be found via both of the paths below.

- Home / Feature / More / Associative Copy / WAVE Geometry Linker
- Assemblies / General / WAVE Geometry Linker

The ribbon in NX 10 is extremely customizable. The white arrow shown below minimizes the ribbon. When the ribbon is minimized, left-click on any tab to temporarily expand it. Clicking the white arrow again expands the ribbon permanently.

Right-clicking on a tab gives you the option to undock that tab. Right-click on the Home tab and choose to undock it.

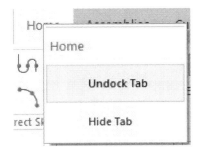

The Home tab will then float down to the graphics window, where you can move and reshape it to your heart's content. Some of you will surely find this to be a major boon to your workflow!

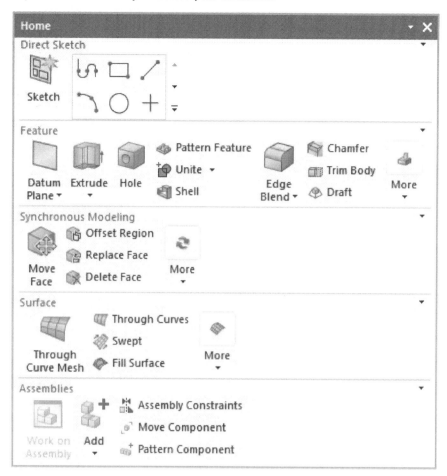

Besides minimizing/expanding the ribbon and docking/undocking tabs, you can customize which icons appear where within each group. For example, within the Feature group on the Home tab, click on the customization drop-down menu (▼) and uncheck the Shell command.

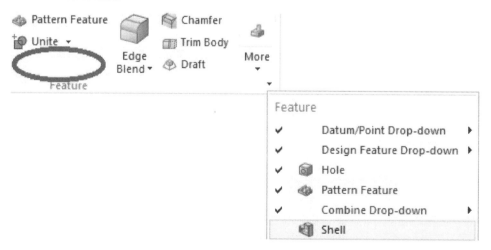

Suddenly the Shell command is no longer appears on the ribbon, and only becomes visible again upon re-checking Shell in the customization drop-down menu!

For further customization options, right-click on any empty space on the ribbon and select Customize from the drop-down menu that appears. The following dialog box will appear. Play around with it to see what's possible!

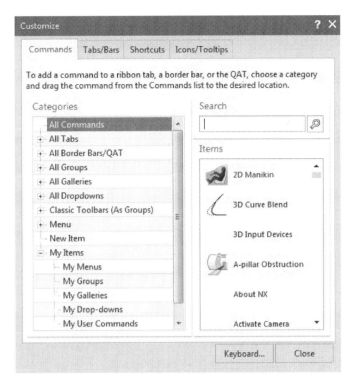

In addition to the usual file management tasks, the File tab contains the very useful Preferences and Start groups.

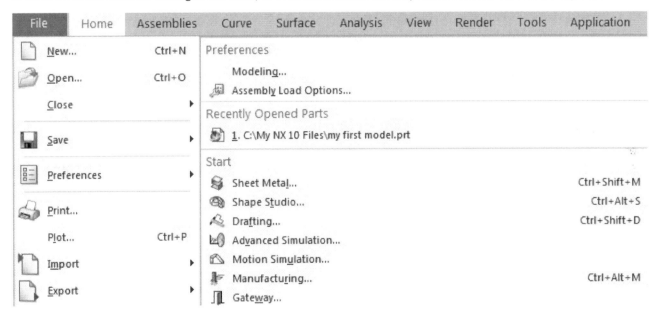

Lastly, if you would rather work in the classical layout of NX 10, we have good news for you. There is an option to switch to classic mode found at Menu / Preferences / User Interface. Just select the Classic Toolbars radio button and click OK!

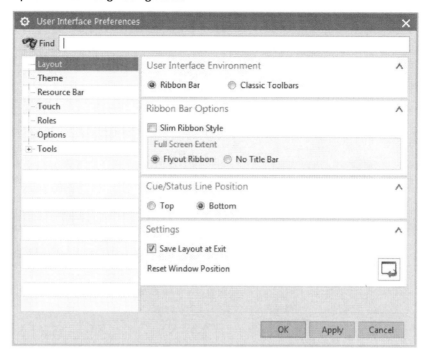

That said, we will work in the Ribbon Bar environment throughout this text.

3.2 Navigating Three-Dimensional Space

The NX 10 user interface is primarily icon-based. Most commands are made by using the mouse to navigate between menus and to pick geometry. *NX 10 requires the use of a three-button mouse to maximize productivity, especially for navigation*. The primary functions of the mouse buttons are illustrated below.

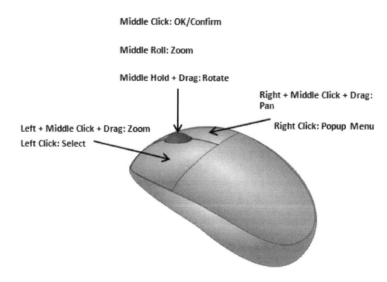

Note: NX 10 may refer to left-click, middle-click, and right-click as MB1, MB2, MB3, respectively.

3.2.1 The Mouse Button Functions

Rotate:

- Press and hold the middle mouse button and move the cursor. The rotate icon ↻ will appear. Drag in the direction of the rotation you want.

- To rotate the model around a single axis, put the cursor near the screen edge. Assuming that the screen is oriented with the x-y plane and the z-axis is facing towards you (as in top view):
- Place along the right/left edge and move up/down for x-axis rotation.
- Place along the bottom edge and move right/left for y-axis rotation.
- Place along the top edge and move right/left for z-axis rotation.

Pan:

- Drag while pressing and holding the middle and right mouse buttons simultaneously.

    OR

- Press and hold [Shift] and drag using the middle mouse button.

Zoom:

- Drag while pressing and holding the left and middle mouse buttons simultaneously.

    OR

- Press and hold [Ctrl] and drag using the middle mouse button.
- In Windows, if you have a wheel mouse, each click will zoom in or out by 25%.

3.2.2 Orient & Refresh

Orient:

To orient the view, press [F8]. This moves the model to the closest pre-defined view (top, front, isometric, etc.) to what you have on screen.

Refresh:

NX 10 will often leave traces of previous modeling operations in the graphics window. To avoid confusion, you can either press [F5] or select View / Orientation / More / View Operation / Refresh to remove extraneous display items.

Note: *This functionality is identical to the navigation menus that are available from the toolbar and view popup menus except that you do not need to enter a special mode.*

3.3 Selecting Geometry

In NX, all menus and commands are selected with the left mouse button. In general, the left mouse button is used to select geometry, either in the graphics window or when using one of the NX navigators.

3.3.1 Selection Filters

In NX 10, the Selection Group is a toolbar that remains on the ribbon, regardless of which tab is selected.

The Selection Filter and Selection Scope drop-down menus are of particular importance – pay attention to the setting of the selection filter to ensure that you are able to choose appropriate items.

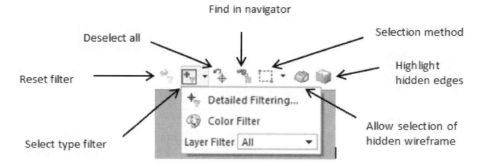

You can unselect items that have already been selected by holding down the [Shift] key and selecting the item again.

3.3.2 The Selection Ball

When selecting geometry, the cursor display will change into a "selection ball" as it is moved into the graphics window, as shown below. Any geometry that falls within the selection ball is a candidate for selection, assuming that it is a valid entity for the active dialog box.

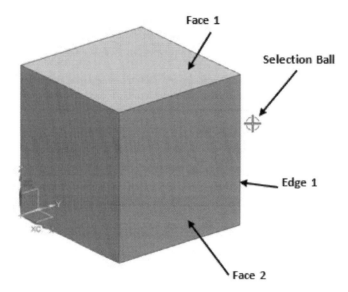

You can adjust the size and behavior of the selection ball using the options found in the Menu / Preferences / Selection dialog box.

3.3.3 QuickPick

Sometimes it is not possible to position the selection ball such that the geometric entity you are trying to select is unambiguous. If you hold the cursor still for a few seconds and then left-click, the QuickPick dialog box will. This allows you to choose among multiple entities within the selection ball as shown in the figure below. You can control the delay time for quick pick from the Menu / Preferences / Selection menu.

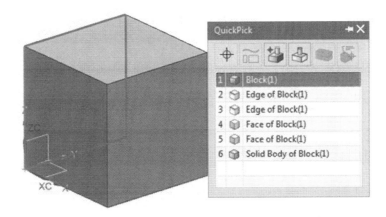

How is the selection order determined in NX 10? The simplest answer is to visualize a light beam of the same diameter as the selection ball shot directly into the computer screen. The first item that this light beam pierces is the first item that NX 10 highlights, the next item pierced is the next item highlighted, and so on. If there is still ambiguity, edges typically are highlighted before faces, and faces before solid bodies. If the thing that you are trying to select is the first thing on the list in the QuickPick menu, just left click again and it will be accepted.

3.4 Command Finder

The Command Finder is a godsend: use it to find commands that you cannot locate in the menus or toolbars. Unfortunately, there is no finder for the command finder so you will have to look for it yourself!

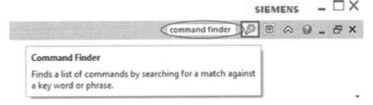

Hint: Command Finder is in the top right corner of the program!

You can even type in commands that exist in other CAD programs and NX will find them for you. For example, type "hollow" into the command finder (a command from some other program), and Command Finder will locate the NX equivalent, Shell.

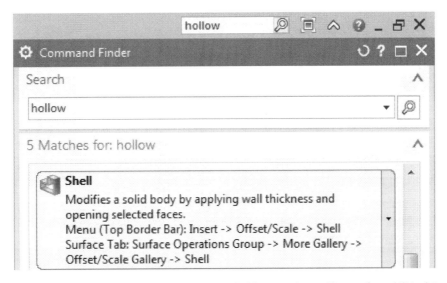

Again - this is a fantastic tool for quickly finding features that are hidden in NX's vast library of capabilities! So no more excuses!

After the search results come back, hover the cursor over the correct result and it will show you exactly where it is located, as shown in the following figure. If it is not in a toolbar, it will show you the path. To use the tool instantly, you can just click on it in the command finder and it will give you the tool operation window.

In the early chapters of this book, we will tell you explicitly where commands are on the ribbon, but as the material progresses and becomes more advanced, we will assume more of you, the reader. If we ask you to use a command that we haven't mentioned yet – use the command finder!

Sometimes a feature you are looking for may not be displayed. Instead of spending forever trying to get around a tool you wish was there, try customizing a menu too see if the tool you want is just hiding from you!

3.5   The WCS

The *WCS* (*Work Coordinate System*) is an important part of NX 10. The WCS is a local coordinate system that you can reposition into convenient locations while performing modeling operations. NX 10 performs many operations with respect to the XC-YC plane of the WCS, which is sometimes referred to as the *work plane*.

3.5.1   The Absolute Coordinate System

By default, the WCS is positioned at the *absolute coordinate system* origin when you create a new part. The absolute coordinate system is positioned at the origin of the model, with (x, y, z) coordinates (0, 0, 0).

When working with assemblies, it is often convenient to create all components such that they share a common absolute coordinate system. The WCS may be placed at the absolute coordinate system origin at any time by choosing: Menu / Format / WCS / Set WCS to Absolute.

3.5.2   The Dynamic WCS

The WCS may be moved using the Menu / Format / WCS / Dynamics tool. This allows you to move the WCS interactively by dragging it to new locations in the graphics window. The dynamic WCS has seven handles, as shown below.

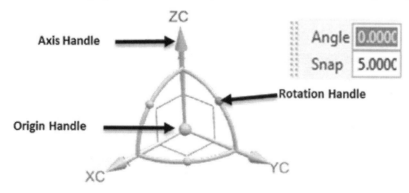

The origin handle allows you to drag the WCS to a new location. The axis handles constrain the WCS motion along the corresponding axis, and the rotation handles constrain the WCS rotation about the corresponding axis. The dynamic dialog box allows you to enter specific offset values. To exit dynamic WCS mode, you can hit the [Esc] key or click the middle mouse button.

Additional tools for controlling the position and orientation of the WCS are found in the Utilities group on the Tools tab, as shown below.

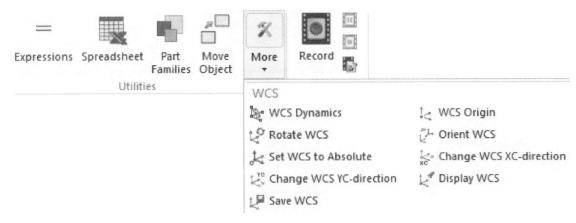

3.6 Object-Action Menus

In NX 10, the *object-action paradigm* has been implemented for many functions. What this means is that you can often select an object in the graphics window and click the right mouse button to access a group of operations associated to the object.

For example, when you select a feature and click the right mouse button, a pop-up menu appears, as shown below.

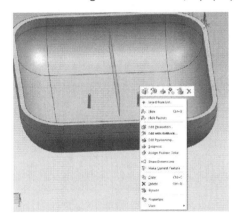

3.7 File Management

File management operations are accessed through the File heading on the menu bar. This is where you can create new files, save files, open existing files, and close files. The file manipulation functions work in a familiar fashion to anyone with experience in Windows-based applications.

3.7.1 Opening Existing Files

Select File / Open to open existing part files.

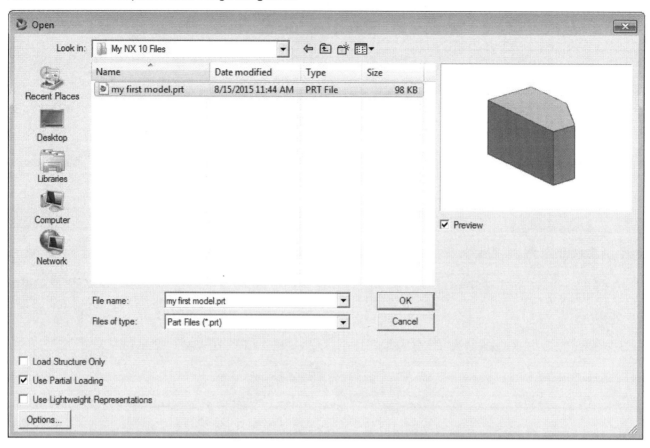

To open a file, either double-click on the file name or single click on the file name and then click on OK. Before opening the file you can also select the load options as shown above. You can also specify if you do not want to load the components of an assembly by checking the Do Not Load Component check box.

3.7.2   Working with Multiple Parts

NX 10 allows you to simultaneously work on many parts. The name of the active part is always displayed at the top of the graphics window. To change to another already opened part, select Window / other_part (located above the tabs), and that part becomes active. If the part name is not displayed in the Window menu, you can select Window/ More... to get a full listing of open parts.

3.7.3   Closing Files and Exiting NX 10

The File/ Close commands can be used to close individual files or all the files that are currently loaded in a session. Selecting File / Close / Selected Parts will display a Close Part window that lists all the loaded parts which you can select individually to close. Selecting File / Close / All Parts will close all loaded parts. You will be given the opportunity to abort the close operation if you are closing a modified part that has not been saved.

The File menu also allows you to exit an NX 10 session using File / Exit. If you do this, NX 10 will prompt you for confirmation to exit if there are any open files that have been modified.

4 Sketching

4.1 Introduction

Sketching is arguably one of the more difficult techniques to master in NX, but it is well-worth the effort. A single sketch can capture a tremendous amount of design intent, and inform the sequencing of subsequent solid modeling tools so that the design process becomes fluid and effortless.

NX has two sketch environments – which is a point of confusion for new users. The Direct Sketch environment is accessible via the Sketch icon on the far left side of the Home tab.

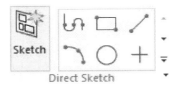

When you enter the Direct Sketch environment, the Direct Sketch group on the left side of the Home tab expands and appears as below.

The other sketch environment is accessible via Menu / Insert / Sketch in Task Environment.

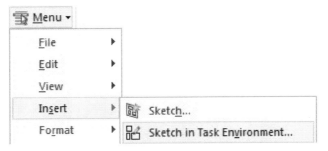

When sketching in the Task Environment, the ribbon changes completely – most tabs disappear, and File becomes Task. Additionally, the entire Home tab is populated with sketch-specific tools. Their names are displayed, too!

In either sketch mode, the sketch tools and Finish Sketch icon are always on the Home tab. For most of this chapter, we will be using Sketch in Task Environment. In order to make sure that you don't inadvertently select the wrong sketch tool, customize the ribbon as follows. On the Home tab, use the customization drop-down arrow on the far right side of the ribbon to uncheck Direct Sketch Group. This will remove the Direct Sketch group from the Home tab. Likewise, on the Curve tab, use the customization drop-down arrow (▾) on the far right to uncheck Direct Sketch Group, and to check Sketch in Task Environment. This removes the Direct Sketch group and adds the Sketch in task Environment icon.

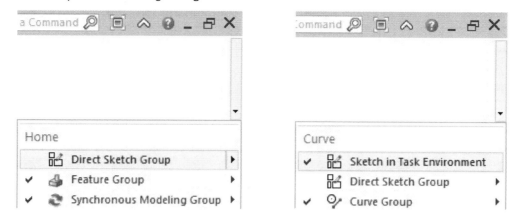

After you have completed these customizations, the Home and Curve tabs should appear as below.

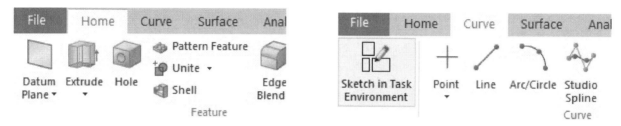

Our preference for Sketch in Task Environment at this stage is purely pedagogical – in our extensive training experience, Direct Sketch causes more confusion for new users than it is worth, so we ask that you follow along and use Sketch in Task Environment for the duration of this chapter. Here is a quick summary of the pros and cons of each:

Direct Sketch

- Is faster for simple sketches (less clicks to reach basic sketch tools)
- Does not require you to click Finish Sketch before selecting a non-sketch modeling tool

Task Environment

- Is better for complex sketches (less clicks for many advanced sketch tools)
- Has a better layout on the ribbon
- Changes the Application Radials ([Ctrl]+[Shift]+click)

4.1.1 Continuous Auto Dimensioning

When you first begin sketching, you will likely encounter Continuous Auto Dimensioning. This option automatically places dimensions for you as you sketch and ensures that your sketch is fully constrained. The figure below shows two versions of the same sketch – on the left, Continuous Auto Dimensioning is enabled, and on the right, it is disabled.

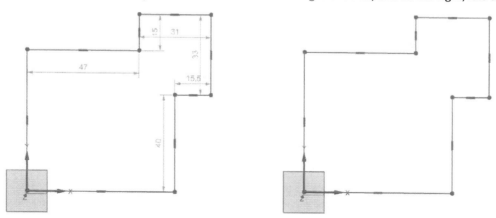

The dimensions placed when Continuous Auto Dimensioning is enabled are "weak" or *driven* dimensions, rather than *driving* dimensions – they can be overwritten by other constraints and dimensions and will not conflict with those other constraints. However, they are sometimes more difficult to edit, and tend to give sketches a cluttered appearance.

From within the Sketch Task Environment, you can disable Continuous Auto Dimensioning by toggling the switch at the bottom of the Constraint Tools drop-down menu on the far right of the Constraints group. Note that this will not affect dimensions already placed within the active sketch, and will not disable Continuous Auto Dimensioning for the next sketch you create.

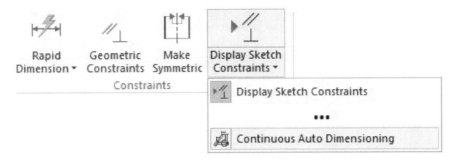

You enable or disable Continuous Auto Dimensioning for all future sketches on the Sketch Preferences menu, found at File / Preferences / Sketch. At this time, please UNCHECK the Continuous Auto Dimensioning checkbox.

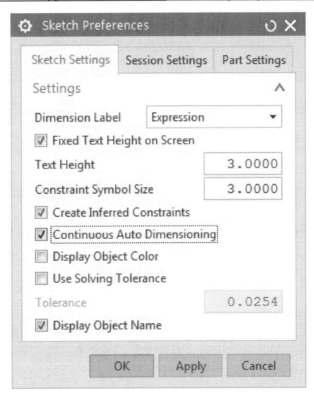

Once you are comfortable with the software, you can decide whether to use it or not, but while you are learning, we recommend that you DISABLE Continuous Auto Dimensioning in the Sketch Preferences menu.

4.1.2 Sketch Strategy

Before beginning a sketch, you will be better equipped to produce it efficiently if your sketching strategy is sound!

1. If you are working in a part file that contains no solid geometry, NX 10 will automatically create a datum CSYS that defines the sketch plane. By default, a sketch is created on the XC-YC plane of the WCS (Working Coordinate System). The datum axes are infinitely long lines that are coincident with the X and Y axes. The datum entities are displayed as shown below.

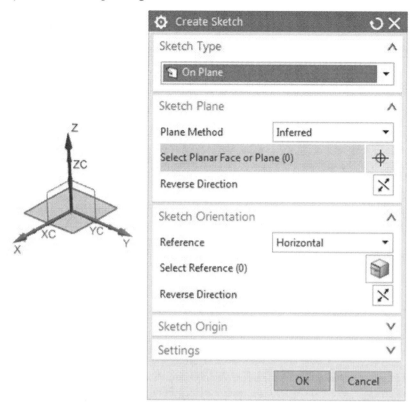

2. Orient your sketch the way you want it. When the Create Sketch dialog box is open and your cursor hovers over a face, the red-blue-green coordinate system that appears gives a preview of the sketch coordinate system's location and orientation. For example, clicking on the upper right corner of the face shown below will orient the sketch coordinate system as indicated.

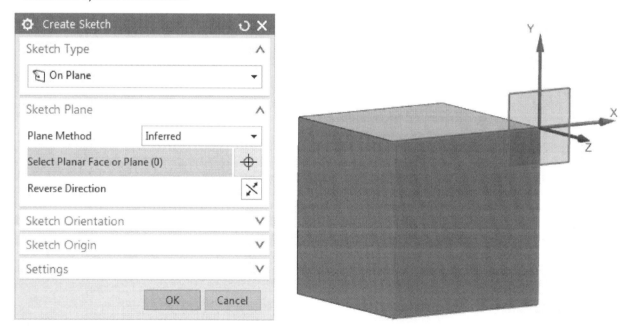

If you prefer your coordinate system in the bottom left corner, you would place your cursor near the bottom left corner before clicking, and the sketch coordinate system would then be placed as indicated below.

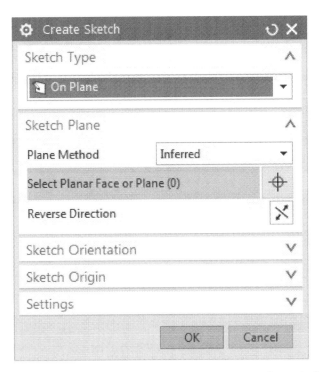

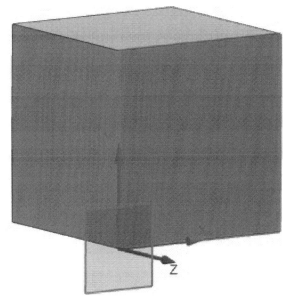

3. Imagine that you want to sketch a pitcher. The figure below illustrates the initial steps of the sketching process. The datum entities and the shape of the desired geometry have been created in three separate sketches. Make a sketch of the contour that resembles the final version. You may want to add a dimension or two at this step, but in general, dimensioning everything each step of the way will slow you down.

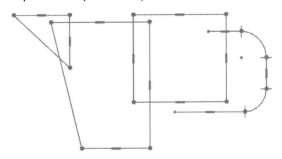

4. Once the basic shape is sketched, add the exact dimensions and constraints. In the next figure, you can see that the pitcher has been sized and all the geometry is ready to create the solid model. It is not necessary to fully constrain your sketch! The sketch below is six constraints away from being fully constrained.

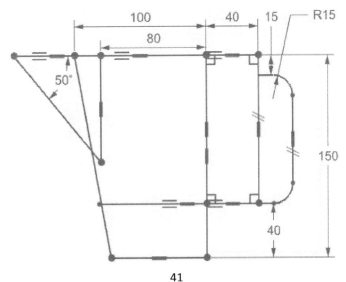

5. The final step in the sketching process is to choose the Finish Sketch icon located in the upper left corner of the Graphics Window when you are in sketch mode. This tells NX that you are finished sketching and are ready for bigger and better things!

Finish

4.1.3 Dynamic Input Boxes

Dynamic input boxes are used to quickly view and modify input data related to a current action or feature. The input fields display labeled values you can change by clicking in the value field and typing a new value.

- To use the dynamic input box associated with a tool, select the tool, then click the first point, once the input box appears, you can enter values into it and press [Enter] to lock the size of the resulting sketch object.
- For certain tools (e.g., Rectangle), once you have entered values, an additional click may be required to determine the orientation. For others, entering the value into the dynamic input box will create the sketch object without an additional click.

4.1.4 Curve Selection

CONTROL POINTS: Every curve has a set of control points that are associated with it, as shown above. Lines have control points at their ends and at the midpoint. Arcs have control points at their ends, midpoint, and center. Circles have a control point at the center and at a 'start' point. In the QuickPick menu, you can see a variety of possible control points available for selection. Make a note of their icons!

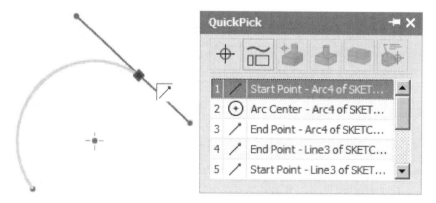

Control points are useful for a variety of tasks, such as building new geometry or making measurements of existing geometry. NX 10 is sensitive to how you pick curve entities and may provide different results based on whether you select the curve itself or its control points.

Important Note: When this book asks you to select a curve, pick anywhere on the curve, but **not** at the control points. When you are asked to select a center point, an end point, or a middle point, you should pick on the control point itself, not the curve. In NX 10, a control point is selected if it is inside the selection ball when you pick. You can also set your snap points to control what you pick as shown below.

Curves can be defined in many ways. They can be placed at screen picks, at *X, Y, Z* coordinates, or they can be connected to another curve at control points. They can also be placed by relations to other curves, such as parallel, perpendicular, tangent, or normal.

4.2 Elementary Sketch Curves

Let's get started by learning how to use some of the basic curve tools available in the sketch environment. Create a new part file and select the Sketch in Task Environment tool. Create a sketch on the X-Y plane.

4.2.1 Line

The Line tool produces a line segment with just two clicks.

- Create a new part file and select the Sketch in Task Environment tool. Select the Line tool. Click once to determine the start point of the line.

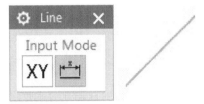

- Click again to finish the line. It's as easy as that!

4.2.2 Arc

The Arc tool has two methods for creating arcs – Arc by 3 Points, and Arc by Center and Endpoints.

- Pan to a different part of the sketch plane, away from the line you created in the last exercise.
- Select the Arc tool and set the Arc Method to Arc by 3 Points. Click once to specify the start point of the arc and move the cursor to the right.

- Click again to specify the end point of the arc, and note that as you move the cursor, the Radius varies in the dynamic input box.

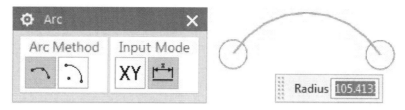

- Click a third time once you are pleased with the radius and the arc will be created.
- Practice making another arc using the Arc by 3 Points method, and this time specify the radius with the dynamic input box.

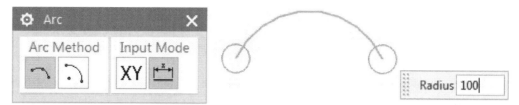

- Pan to a different part of the sketch plane, and change the Arc Method to Arc by Center and Endpoints. Click once to specify the arc center, and then again to specify the start point of the arc.

- As you move the cursor, the Radius and Sweep Angle will vary dynamically, and your third click will determine the arc end point.

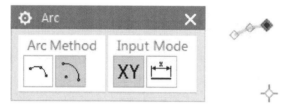

4.2.3 Profile

You will notice, that upon entering the sketch environment, the ribbon shows the Profile tool highlighted, and the Profile tool dialog box is open in the graphics window.

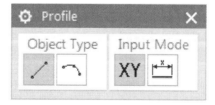

The Profile tool combines the essential functionality of the Line tool with that of the Arc tool. You can choose whether you would like a line segment or an arc by clicking on the corresponding icon in the Object Type section of the Profile dialog box, or you can switch back and forth between arcs and lines more fluidly as follows:

- A single click initiates a line segment. To start an arc, click and hold and then drag before releasing and clicking again. Practice this step by step as follows. Click once to start a line segment and then move the cursor vertically.

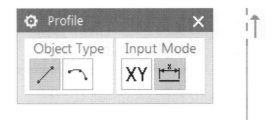

- Click again to end the line segment. With the cursor at the endpoint of the newly-created line segment, click and hold the left mouse button and drag the cursor – first vertically, then slowly to the right. You will notice that the arc comes out tangent to the line segment. Also note that the Arc icon is highlighted in the Object Type section of the Profile dialog box.

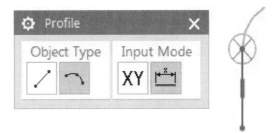

- Move the cursor further right and eventually down until the arc is a perfect half-circle. You will know when to stop with the help of the horizontal guide line.

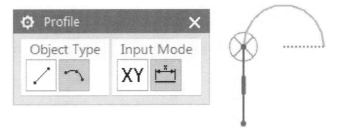

- Click again to end the arc. Note that the Profile Object Type immediately switches back to Line. Move your cursor down vertically until the dotted horizontal guide line appears to indicate that it has the same length as the first line segment.

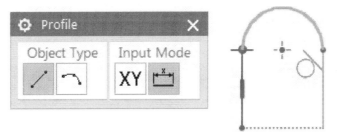

- Click to end the line segment. Let your cursor remain at the end point, and again click and hold the left mouse button. This time, move the cursor to the right, and then move it slightly down. Notice that the arc created in this way is perpendicular to the last line segment!

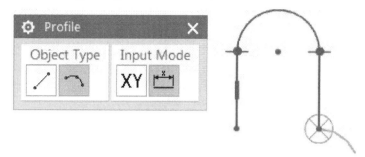

- This is an important point about creating arcs with the Profile tool – the arcs created by the Profile tool in this fashion are always either tangent or perpendicular to the previous object. The direction in which you move the cursor away from the last endpoint determines whether the arc will be tangent or perpendicular. If you make a mistake, you can always move the cursor back to the endpoint and sweep it out carefully in the desired direction. Move the cursor back to the start point of the arc, and this time, move the cursor straight down before moving it slightly to the right. Sweep it out until the arc is a perfect half circle, and click to end it. Move the cursor vertically and click to create another line segment of equal length to the last.

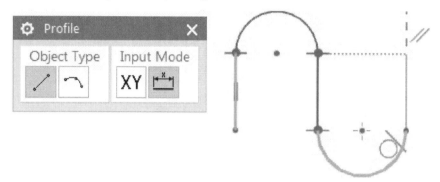

- Continue in this fashion until you've got the hang of alternating between line segments and arcs!

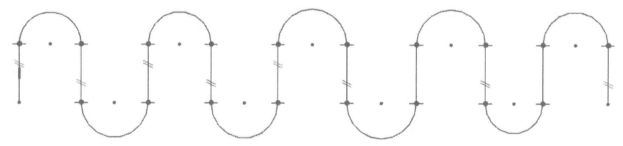

- Once you are satisfied with your progress, you can exit the Profile tool by clicking the middle mouse button twice, or by pressing [Esc].
- Pan to a different (empty) part of the sketch plane, and select the Profile tool again. Now, let's sketch a contour beginning with an Arc. You can of course click the Arc icon under Object Type in the Profile dialog box, but you can also switch to Arc mode with a click-and-drag technique. Simply left-click and drag a short distance in the empty space in the graphics window, and you will note that the Object Type switches to Arc mode! To create your first arc will require three subsequent clicks. This works exactly in the same way as the Arc by 3 Points method of the Arc tool, as you practiced earlier.

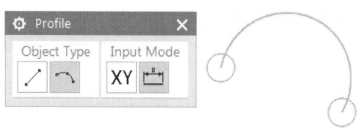

4.2.4 Circle

The Circle sketch tool has two methods for creating circles – Circle by Center and Diameter, and Circle by 3 Points.

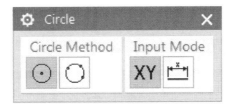

- Circle by Center and Diameter requires two clicks – the first click indicates the center, and the second click specifies a point on the circle.
- Circle by 3 Points requires three clicks – the behavior is similar to the Arc by 3 Points method in the Arc tool.
- Practice both modes. Get comfortable using them with clicks alone, as well as with the help of the dynamic input boxes!

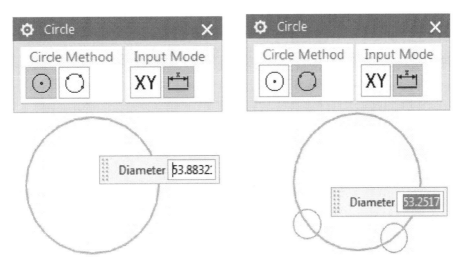

4.2.5 Point

The Point tool is completely self-explanatory. Select the tool and click anywhere in the graphics window to place a point on the sketch plane!

4.3 Geometric Constraints

Constraints are a set of rules that sketch geometry must follow, such as forcing the radii of all circles to be equal or making two lines parallel. Constraints are applied using the Geometric Constraints tool, accessed from the Constraints group on the Home tab in the Sketch Task Environment.

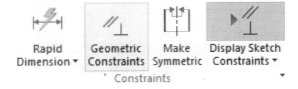

The Geometric Constraints dialog box behaves differently from most other dialog boxes in NX – there is no OK button and no Apply button. You simply select the constraint you wish to apply, then click on the object(s) you wish to constrain. Once you have specified at least one Object to Constrain, and one Object to Constrain to, the constraint is applied and the menu resets.

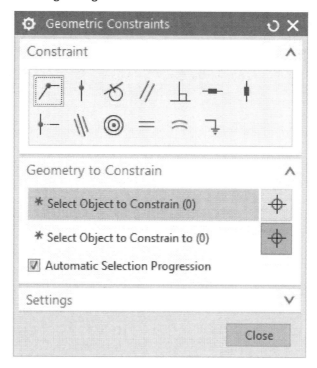

4.3.1 Degree Of Freedom Indicators

When applying dimensions or constraints, you will notice arrows are displayed on some of the vertices of sketched lines, or perhaps at the middle of sketched arcs. These are the *degree of freedom indicators* indicating which entities and vertices have not been fully constrained. As you place more and more dimensions and geometric constraints on a sketch, the degree of freedom indicators disappear one by one. To constrain a sketch fully, you must apply enough dimensions and geometric constraints to remove all of the degree of freedom indicators. You will also need to fix the sketch with respect to previously existing geometry. The figure below shows two lines meeting at a point, and the degree of freedom indicators at that point.

Note: It is not always necessary to fully constrain each sketch, but doing so makes a sketch behave more predictably.

4.3.2 Moving and Deforming Sketches

- Create a new file, select Sketch in Task Environment. Place your sketch on the X-Y plane. Using the Profile tool, sketch the contour shown below.

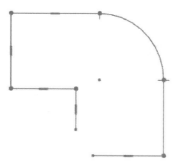

- Note the status display.

Sketch needs 10 constraints

- First, we will practice applying a rigid motion to an entire line segment. Left-click and hold on the vertical line segment shown below. Be sure to click on the body of the line itself – away from the endpoints, and away from the constraint icon at the center.

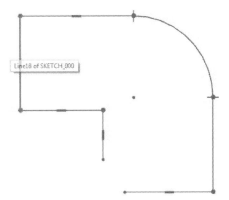

- Continue holding the left-mouse button and move your cursor out to the right. The sketch will deform as shown below. Note that the line retains its length and the vertical constraint no matter how you try to move it.

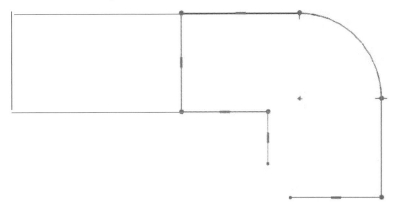

- Press [Ctrl]+[Z] to undo the change applied in the last step. Next, you will resize the arc subject to the existing constraints in the sketch. Left-click and hold on the bottom right endpoint of the arc, as shown below.

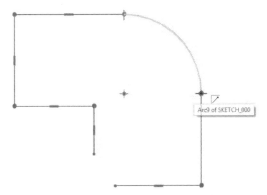

- Continue holding and drag your cursor to the right. Notice that since the bottom right vertical line segment does not have a vertical constraint, as you resize the arc, that line becomes diagonal in the preview.

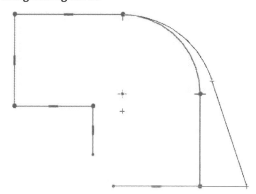

- [Ctrl]+[Z] to undo the change.

4.3.3   Fixed

The simplest of sketch constraints is the Fixed constraint. It is used to anchor one point or line on the sketch. To ensure that it has a "zero point," the Fixed constraint does not fix a point in space – it fixes a point with respect to all other geometry in the sketch. The Fixed constraint allows for a single sketch object as input.

- Select the Geometric Constraints tool, and select the Fixed constraint. Choose the arc center, as shown below.

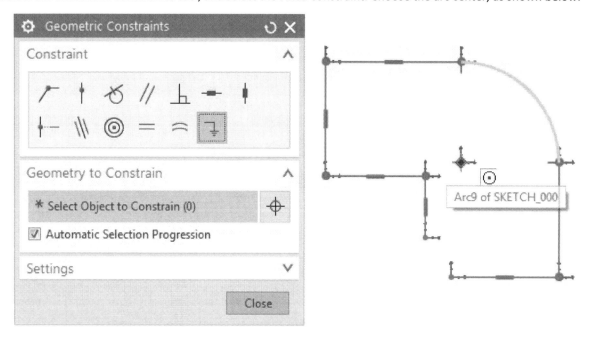

- Note that the degree of freedom indicators at that point have now been replaced by a Fixed constraint icon!

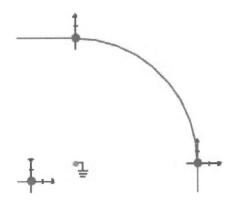

4.3.4 Coincident

The Coincident constraint forces two existing points in a sketch to coincide. A typical use case for this constraint is to make the endpoint of one curve coincide with the start point of another. The Coincident constraint requires two (or more) points as input.

You will use the Coincident constraint to close the gap created in the sketch from the previous exercise.

- Select the Geometric Constraints tool and choose the Coincident constraint. Select the endpoint of the vertical line segment as the Object to Constrain, and the start point of the horizontal line segment as the Object to Constrain to, as shown below.

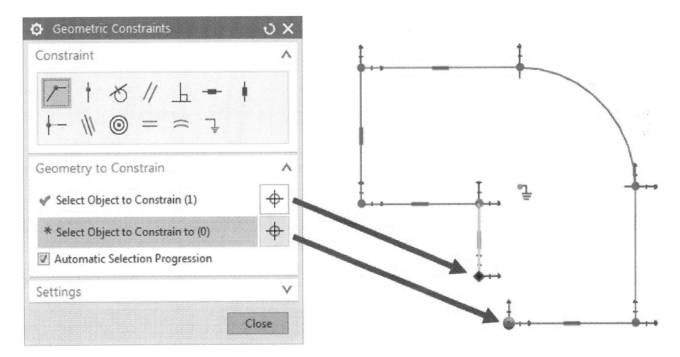

- Once the constraint is applied, the contour forms a closed loop!

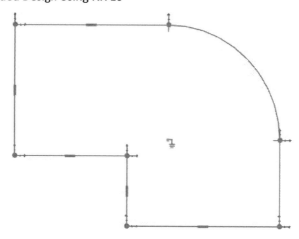

4.3.5 Point on Curve

Point on Curve is a very powerful constraint option. The name is a bit misleading– it should really be thought of as a point constrained to be on an infinite extension of a curve. It may be used to align points, endpoints of curves, or arc center points to lines or other curves. The Point on Curve constraint requires a single curve and a single point as input.

- Continuing with the previous sketch, select the Geometric Constraints tool and select the Point on Curve constraint. Select the horizontal line segment nearest to the arc center as the Object to Constrain, and the arc center as the Object to Constrain to, as shown below.

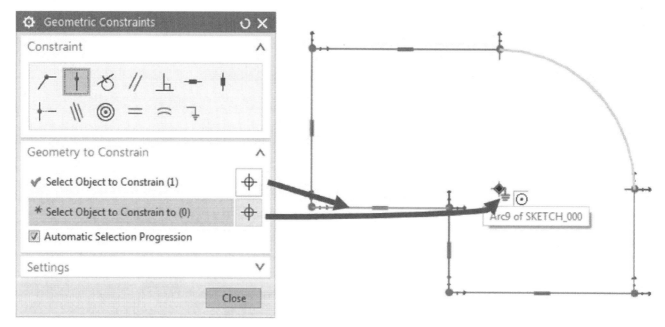

- Once the constraint is applied, a consequence is that the leftmost vertical line segment will have length equal to the radius of the arc on the top right. Try deforming the sketch to see for yourself!

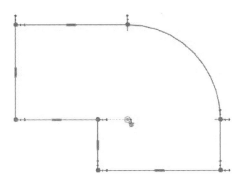

4.3.6 Midpoint

If you are accustomed to other CAD software, you may be surprised by the functionality of the Midpoint constraint. The Midpoint constraint is extremely useful for centering sketch objects relative to others. The Midpoint constraint requires a single line and a single point as input.

The graphic below illustrates the effect of the Midpoint constraint. Prior to the application of the constraint (right), the point (B) bears no obvious relation to the line (A). Upon application of the constraint (left), the point moves along a line parallel to (A) until the line segment joining it to the midpoint of (A) is perpendicular to (A).

- Continuing with the previous sketch, select the Geometric Constraints tool and choose the Midpoint constraint. Select the arc center as the Object to Constrain, and the lowest horizontal line as the Object to Constrain to, as shown below.

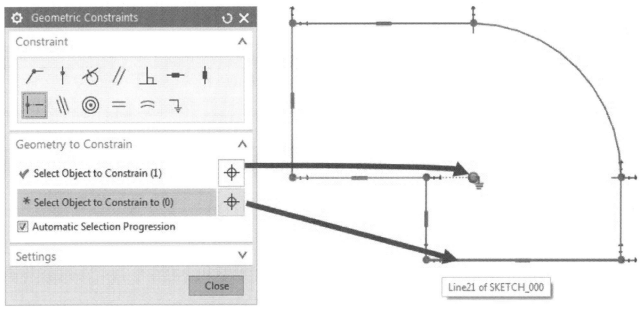

- After applying the constraint, the length of the lowest horizontal line will always necessarily be twice the radius of the arc. Try deforming the sketch to see for yourself!

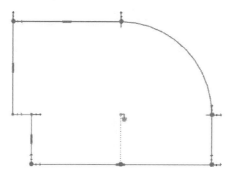

4.3.7   Equal Length

The Equal Length constraint is straightforward – it simply forces two lines to have the same length. Note that it only works on lines, and not arcs or any other kind of sketch curves. The Equal Length constraint requires (at least) two line segments as input.

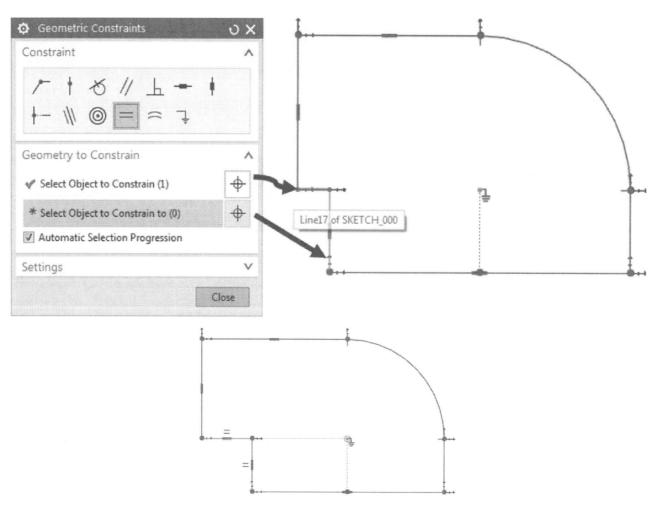

4.3.8   Concentric

The Concentric constraint is used to force the arc centers of circles or arcs to coincide – it offers no additional functionality over the Coincident constraint. The Concentric constraint requires two (or more) arcs or circles as input.

- Continuing with the previous sketch, use the Circle tool to add a circle above the contour sketched so far.

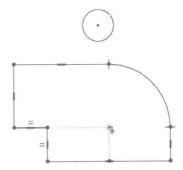

- Select the Geometric Constraints tool and select the Concentric constraint. Choose the newly-sketched circle as the Object to Constrain, and the pre-existing arc as the Object to Constrain to.

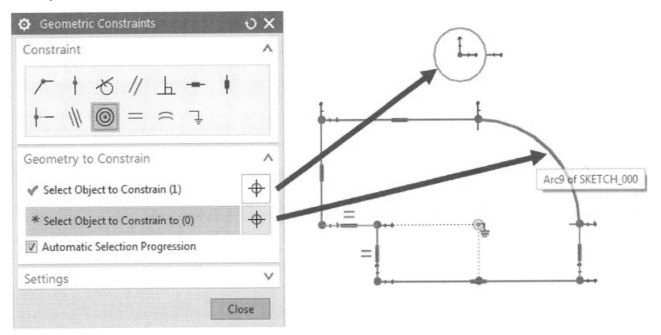

- After applying the constraint, the circle and arc are concentric!

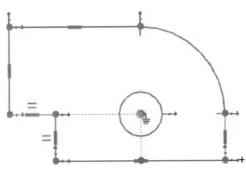

4.3.9   Horizontal and Vertical

The Horizontal and Vertical constraints are used to force line segments to be parallel to the X and Y axes of the sketch coordinate system, respectively.

When you sketch a line that is nearly horizontal or vertical, NX 10 will often automatically apply a horizontal or vertical geometric constraint to them. You may also place these constraints manually if this does not occur.

For example, when using the Profile tool, if you see a horizontal dotted guide line, this is an indication that the software will infer and place a Horizontal constraint on the resulting line segment.

The thickened bar in the middle of the line segment is the Horizontal constraint.

4.3.10 Automatic Selection Progression

Automatic Selection Progression advances the menu automatically after you specify the Object to Constrain, so that your next click specifies the Object to Constrain to. In the next few exercises, we will illustrate some cases in which you might want to disable Automatic Selection Progression.

- Pan to a different part of the sketch plane, away from the sketch objects you have placed so far, and sketch the contour shown below using the Profile tool.

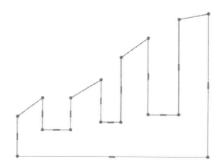

- Select the Geometric Constraints tool and uncheck the Automatic Selection Progression checkbox. Select the Equal Length constraint, and select the two lines indicated below as Object to Constrain. Since Automatic Selection Progression is disabled, you will have to manually click Select Object to Constrain to before selecting the third line.

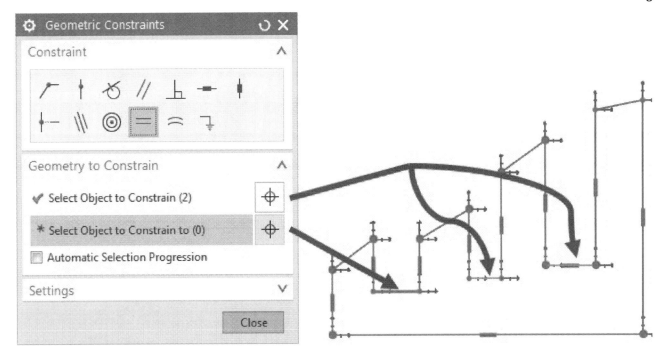

4.3.11 Collinear

The Collinear geometric constraint is similar to the Point on Curve constraint. The Collinear constraint aligns two or more lines with each other, as suggested by the icon. The Collinear constraint requires two (or more) lines as input.

- Select Geometric Constraints and choose the Collinear constraint. Select the three rightmost diagonal line segments as the Object to Constrain, and the leftmost as the Object to Constrain to.

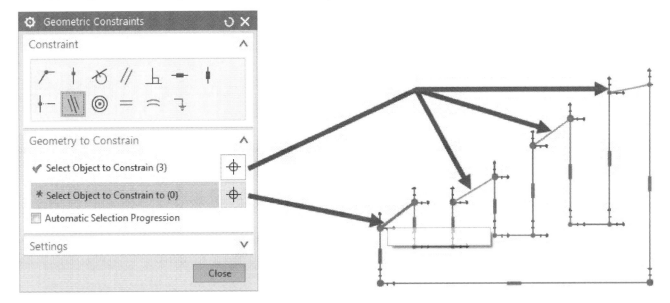

- Use the Collinear constraint to align the three horizontal line segments of equal length. Feel free to either enable or disable Automatic Selection Progression. Your sketch should appear as below when you are done.

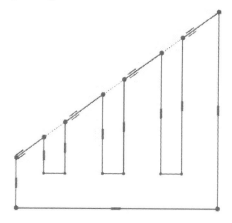

4.3.12 Parallel

The Parallel constraint forces two (or more) lines to be parallel.

- Continue with the previous sketch, and select the Geometric Constraints tool. Select the Parallel constraint. Choose the leftmost diagonal line as the Object to Constrain, and the leftmost horizontal line as the Object to Constrain to, as shown below.

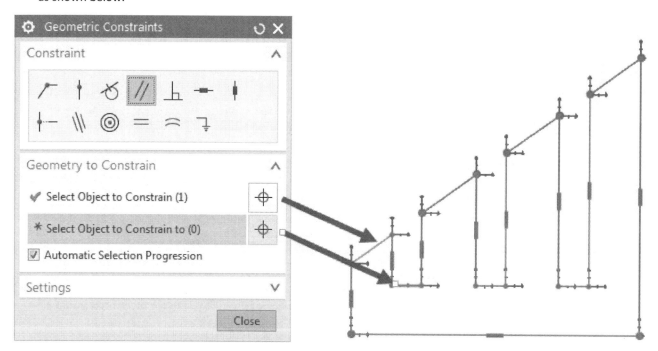

- The Horizontal constraint on the short line segment forces the diagonal line to become horizontal, and the Collinear constraint force the other diagonal lines to become horizontal as well!

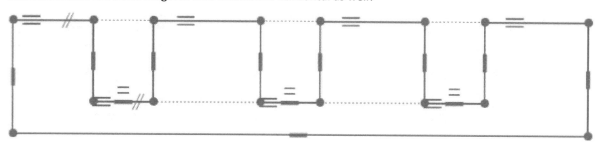

4.3.13 Tangent

The Tangent constraint forces tangency between two curves at a point. The appearance of the constraint in the graphics window is slightly unusual – it is a line passing through the coincident point at a 90° angle to the tangent line!

- Sketch a trapezoidal shape with rounded corners as shown below. Do a really bad job so that there will be plenty to clean up with the tangency constraint! Apply the tangency constraint to each coincident point joining an arc and a line.

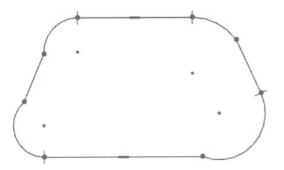 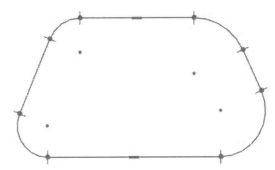

4.3.14 Equal Radius

The Equal Radius constraint is similar to the Equal Length constraint, but it can only be applied to arcs and circles. The Equal Radius constraint requires two (or more) arcs or circles as input.

Be sure not to confuse the icon when you use the tool – the Equal Length constraint will not allow you to select arcs! The appearance of the constraint in the graphics window is an equals sign, just like that of Equal Length.

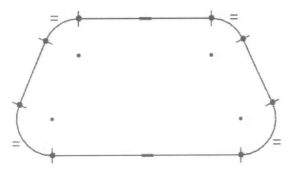

4.3.15 Perpendicular

The Perpendicular constraint forces two (or more) line segments to be perpendicular to each other.

- Explicit use of the Geometric Constraints tool is not the only way to apply sketch constraints. Consecutively left-clicking on curves and points in a sketch will result in relevant constraints appearing on the pop-up shortcut toolbar. Left-click on the bottom horizontal line segment of the previous sketch, and the right diagonal line. The pop-up shortcut toolbar will then appear with a summary of the constraints that are applicable to those two line segments. Find the Perpendicular icon and click to apply the constraint.

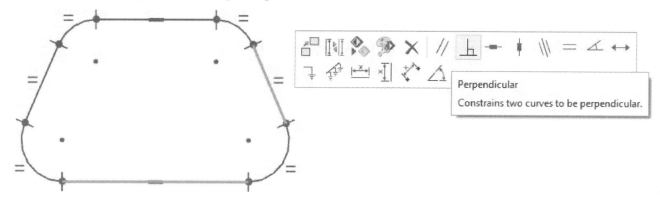

- This technique spares you the hassle of selecting the Geometric Constraints tool and finding the appropriate constraint each time you wish to constrain part of a sketch. There is also no issue with Automatic Selection Progression. We strongly recommend mastering this shortcut!

4.4   Dimensions

The dimension tools in the Sketch Task Environment can be found on the Dimension drop-down menu, found in the Constraints group on the Home tab.

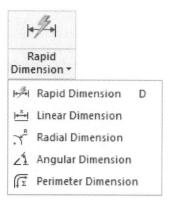

4.4.1   Rapid Dimension

By default, NX 10 uses the Rapid Dimension tool. This tool is incredibly powerful because it is able to place whichever type of dimension you want based on your selections. In fact, it is so smart that you won't even need any of the other dimensioning tools for a while! To use this option, click on the Rapid Dimension tool and select the entity or entities that you want to dimension. At the most basic level, you can open this tool and feed it two objects and it will produce a dimension!

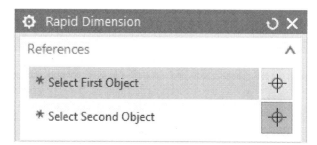

By default, the Measurement Method is set to Inferred, which is good enough for most practical purposes. The tool is smart, and depending on how you click it will figure out whatever you want, whether it be a linear dimension, an angular dimension, a perpendicular dimension, a radius or diameter, or anything in between!

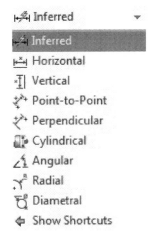

- To begin, create a new file, and select the Sketch in Task Environment tool. Place your sketch on the X-Y plane.
- Using the Profile tool, create the sketch shown below.

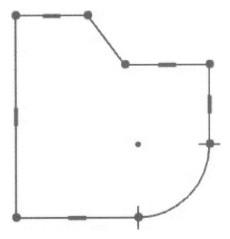

- If your view becomes misaligned, use the Orient to Sketch button to reposition the camera!

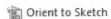

In the following sections you will learn how to use all of the rapid dimensioning capabilities.

4.4.2 Linear Dimension

The Rapid Dimension tool can produce linear dimensions in several ways. This exercise will walk you through three different techniques!

- Select the Rapid Dimension tool, and when prompted for the First Object, click on the line shown below. Click on the line itself, away from the endpoints, and away from the vertical constraint.

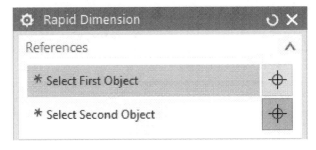

- Although the Select Second Object prompt had a red asterisk previously, it is now a green checkmark, despite the fact that you have only selected one object so far! The Inferred Measurement Method assumes that when you click on a line segment, you intend for the First Object to be the start point of that line, and the Second Object to be the end point of that line. When the Specify Location section of the menu highlights in orange, NX is prompting you to place the dimension on the sketch, so click to place it. Enter a value of 100 into the dynamic input box.

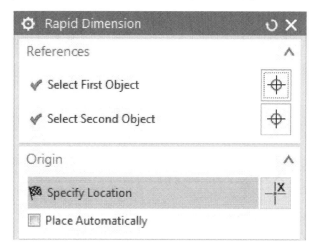 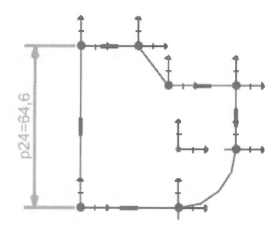

- For the next linear dimension, select the two vertical line segments as shown below. After selecting the First Object, the tool will appear as though it is ready to place, but your second click will redefine the Second Object to produce a different sort of linear dimension. Again, make sure to click on the lines themselves and not any constraints or control points. Enter a value of 100 mm into the dynamic input box.

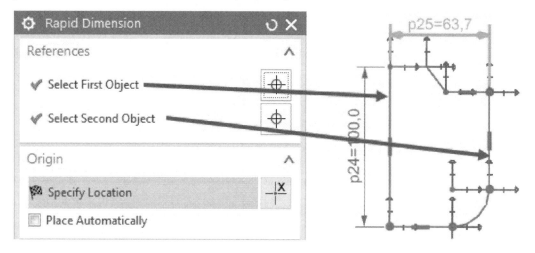

- For the third linear dimension, select the point shown below as the First Object – use the QuickPick menu to be sure you've got the endpoint of the line!

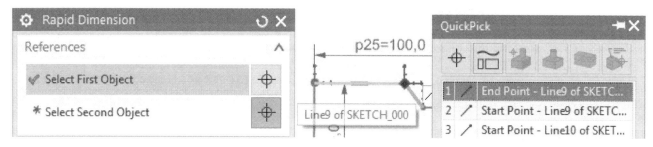

- For the Second Object, click the point shown below. Again, feel free to use QuickPick if it helps!

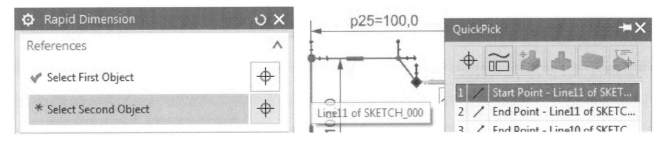

- After clicking the second point, drag your cursor upward and to the right. Note that if you move too far right or too far vertically, the dimension will come out vertically or horizontally, respectively. Dragging perfectly diagonally ensures that the resulting linear dimension is placed perpendicularly to the objects in question.

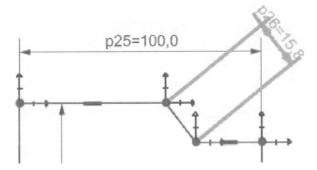

4.4.3 Angular Dimension

Placing angular dimensions with the Rapid Dimension tool is easy and fun!

- Click on the line segments as shown below, and as usual, select the lines themselves and not their control points or constraints. As you drag the cursor vertically and to the left, you will see an angular dimension appear as shown below! If you drag diagonally in a different direction, you will see the complementary angle.

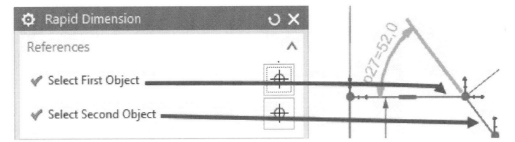

4.4.4 Radial Dimension

You can also use the Rapid Dimensioning tool for Radial Dimensions by simply selecting a radius while in the Rapid Dimensioning menu.

- To apply a radial dimension to the rounded corner on the bottom right of the sketch, place your cursor on the arc – with the tip of the cursor *ever so slightly* on the interior of the arc. You will see the "bullseye" Arc Center icon. Make sure that you see this icon before you click.

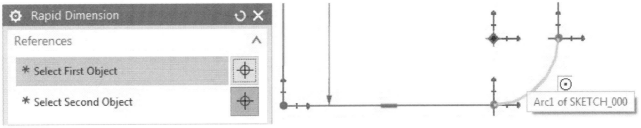

Upon clicking, the Rapid Dimension tool will not require a Second Object, and will preview a radial dimension. Click to place it and enter a value of 25 mm.

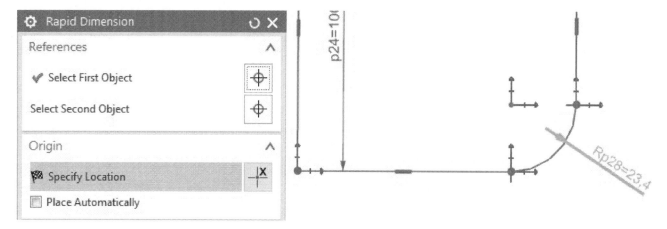

- Experiment on your own placing additional dimensions on the sketch. Try corner-to-corner, and other variations to get a feel for how the Rapid Dimension tool reacts to your mouse movements, and what the resulting dimensions will be!

4.4.5 Removing Dimensions From a Sketch

Menu / Edit / Delete may be used when you have placed a dimension on a sketch that is not required, or you can right click on the dimension and click on the X.

You may also use the Menu / Edit / Undo command; however, in some cases NX may undo more than you bargained for. *Be careful, the Redo command is limited.*

4.4.6 Moving a Previously Placed Dimension

Moving sketch dimensions is just like moving any other sketch object – click and hold and drag!

4.5 Additional Sketch Curves

4.5.1 Rectangle

The Rectangle tool has three modes of operation.

- The icons on the Rectangle tool illustrate the three modes - By 2 Points, By 3 Points, and From Center.

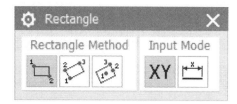

- Select the From Center method and click the sketch origin. Sketch a rectangle as shown below.

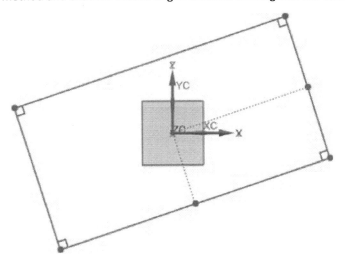

- Notice that the rectangle comes with two Midpoint constraints!
- Select the Rapid Dimension tool.
- Apply a dimension of 120 mm as shown below.

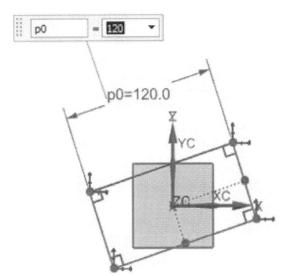

4.5.2   Polygon

The polygon tool can be used to create any n-sided polygon.

- When you click on the Polygon icon, it brings you to a window where you can select the Center Point, Number of Sides, and Size of your polygon.

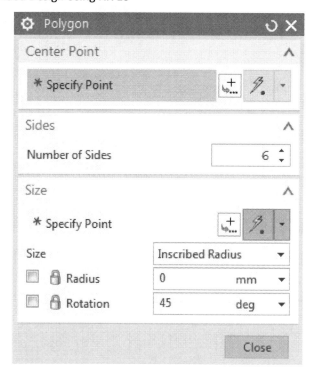

- Change the **Number of Sides** to **6** and click where you want the center of your hexagon to be.
- You can then move your mouse to adjust the size and rotation, or you can lock in a **Radius** and **Rotation** by typing in your values to the right of where it says **Radius** and **Rotation**.
- Give your hexagon a radius of **25mm** and a rotation of **15 degrees**.

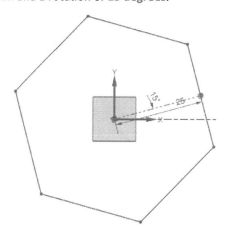

4.5.3   Studio Spline

Use a studio spline to model a shape you cannot represent with simple arcs and lines. The studio spline is an amazing tool because you get to define the points that control the shape, and as you continue, you will see the effect that each of the points has on the overall spline. You can then begin to drag the points around to get the exact shape you desire. It is great for defining shapes that must be artistic in nature.

- Begin by selecting the **Studio Spline** icon from the ribbon.

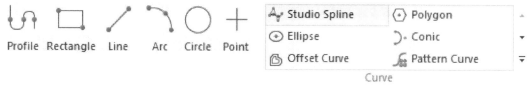

- The menu shown below will appear and you can begin clicking point locations for your spline.

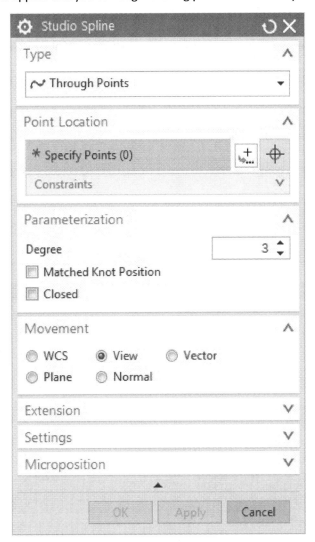

You will notice the overall shape of the spline will change as each point is added. See a completed spline in the following figure.

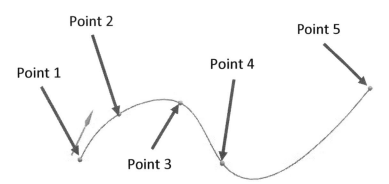

To change the shape of the spline, left click and drag any of the existing points. In the following figure this is done to point 4.

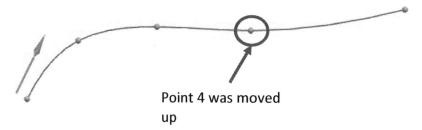

Point 4 was moved
up

To make a continuous closed shape, use the Closed button choice in the studio spline menu.

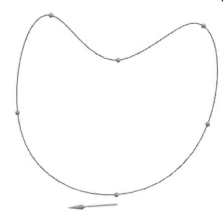

4.5.4   Offset Curve

Use the Offset Curve tool when you want to make a curve larger or smaller while keeping its same shape.

- Using the Rectangle tool, create a rectangle.
- Select the Offset Curve tool.

- While in the Offset Curve menu, select the curve that you wish to offset, and change the distance to 5mm. You can reverse the direction of the offset by clicking the button with two arrows underneath the distance input.

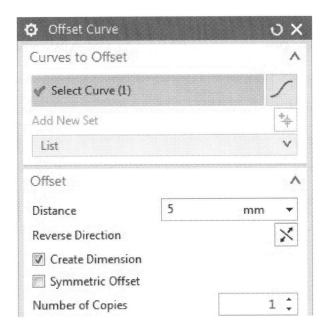

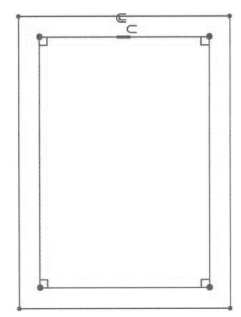

4.5.5 Pattern Curve

- Create the following sketch

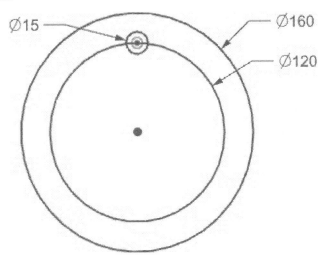

- Select the Pattern Curve tool.

- Choose the 15 mm circle as the Curve to Pattern, and set the Pattern Definition Layout to Circular.

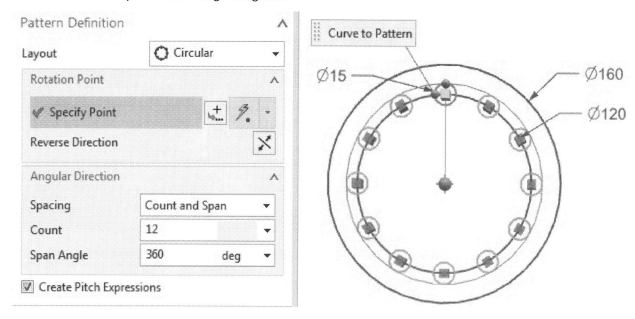

- Add the curves shown below to the sketch.

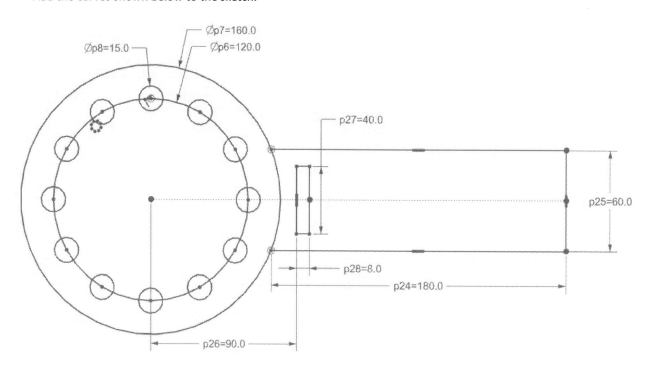

- Use Pattern Curve feature to create a linear pattern of the 40mm x 8mm rectangle across the larger rectangle as shown in the following figure.

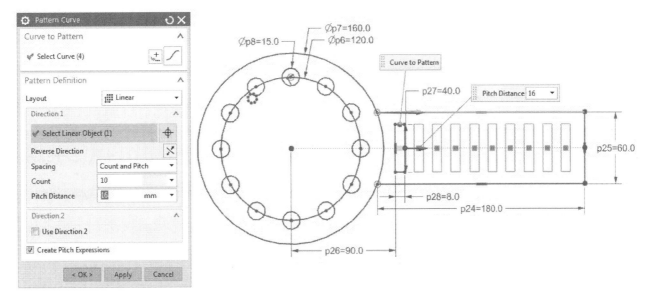

- **Extrude** the sketch.

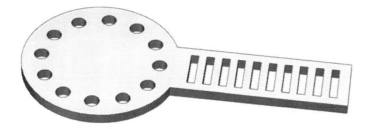

4.5.6 Mirror Curve

Sketching surfaces often requires several identical features to be placed on the same sketch plane. NX 10 offers a mirror curve operation that allows you to replicate your drawing. The resulting sketch has the same properties as the original, and if either the original or mirrored sketch is modified, the entire sketch updates accordingly.

- Draw a curve as shown next.

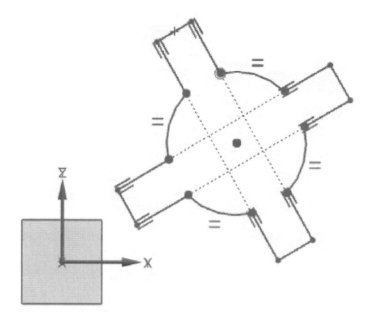

- Select the Mirror Curve tool.

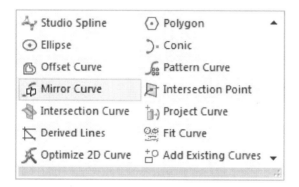

Read the cue line – it is asking you to select the pattern of objects to mirror.

- Select all the lines and arcs in your first quadrant sketch. Select them individually or left click in a blank portion of the sketch and create a large selection box to include all lines and arcs.
- Middle click.

Read the cue line – it is asking you to select the centerline.

- Select the Y-axis. Note: NX 10 automatically lets you select any axis lines as mirror lines.
- Select Apply. The mirrored geometry will appear to the left of the Y-axis.
- Select your original sketch again as well as the mirrored geometry.
- Select the X-axis as your centerline about which to mirror.
- Select OK.
- The following figure illustrates the result.

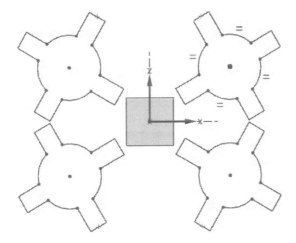

Note: After the mirror command is complete, the mirror line is automatically converted into a Reference line as shown next. You do not need to create a reference line to use for the mirror function.

4.6 Edit Curve Tools

4.6.1 Quick Trim

The Quick Trim tool is helpful for more complicated sketches by combining rudimentary sketch operations and deleting the excess curves.

- Create the following sketch using only the Rectangle tool and the Circle tool.

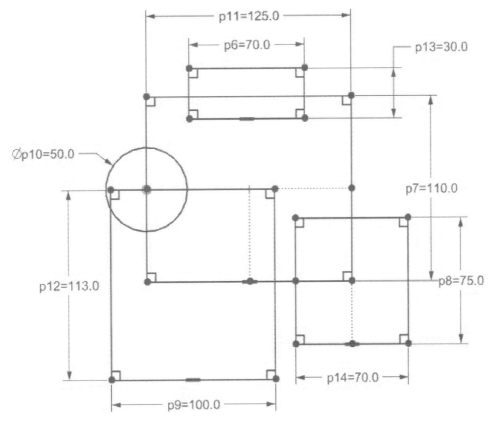

- Use the Quick Trim command to remove the interior curves from the sketch.

73

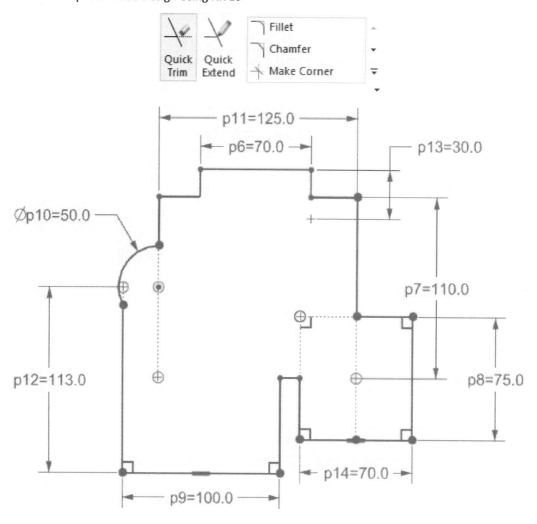

- Finish Sketch and Extrude to create the geometry shown below.

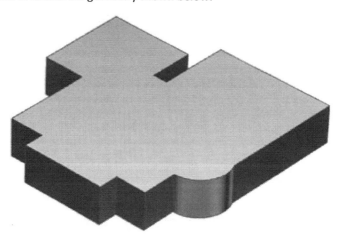

4.6.2 Fillet

The Fillet tool is used to round sharp corners on sketches (much like an actual fillet rounds sharp edges on an object). There are two modes of operation for the Fillet tool.

- Sketch a rectangle and open the Fillet tool. By clicking and holding and dragging, the cursor will become a pencil which you can use to draw through the lines you would like to join with an arc. Click and hold and drag as shown below.

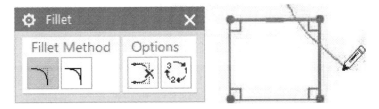

- The other way to use the Fillet tool is to sequentially click the edges you wish to blend. Click the vertical line segment and then the horizontal one, and then click again to finalize the arc!

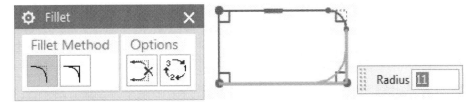

4.7 Additional Constraint Tools

4.7.1 Convert To/From Reference

The Convert To/From Reference sketch tool allows the creation of reference curves within a sketch. Reference curves show up as dotted lines in your sketch. They can be constrained and dimensioned just as regular sketch curves, but cannot be used for extrusions, sweeps or other operations that produce solid-geometry.

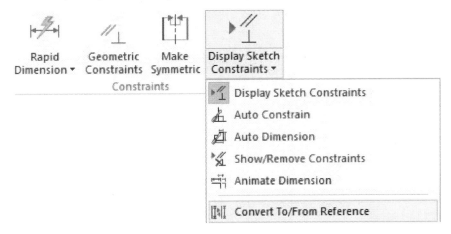

- Create a Sketch in Task Environment on the X-Y plane. Use the Line tool, the Rapid Dimension tool, and the Geometric Constraints tool to produce the sketch shown below.

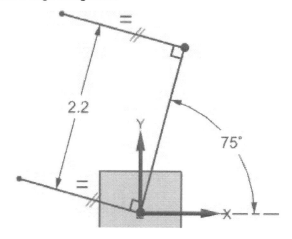

- Although Convert To/From Reference is on the ribbon, there is a much more efficient way to access the tool! Simply left-click on the sketch curve of interest – in this case, the line segment at a 75° angle to the X-axis – and wait for the popup toolbar to appear. Look for the Convert To/From Reference icon!

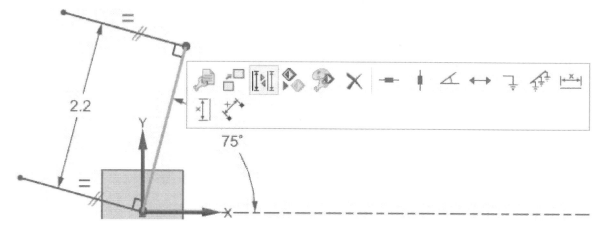

- The popup toolbars are generally a very efficient way to work – no right-clicking and hunting on the drop-down menu, no navigating through the ribbon. Once you become comfortable with the icons, the toolbars will speed up your workflow dramatically!

4.7.2   Perimeter Dimension

When you need to model a molding or some kind of belt that has a constant length, use the Perimeter Dimension constraint. The perimeter constraint allows you to assign a total length value to all the entities of a contour together. The Perimeter Dimension tool is found on the Dimensions drop-down in the Constraints group.

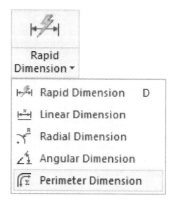

- Sketch the figure shown below. Ensure that the arcs and lines are tangent to each other at each intersection. (Constraints are hidden in the screenshot below)

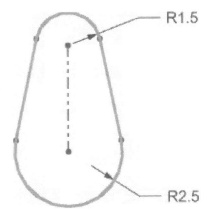

- The shape just sketched is unconstrained because the reference line joining the arc centers has no dimension. Applying a perimeter constraint will fully constrain the shape.
- Select the Perimeter Dimension tool, and choose the curves of the contour. Enter a Distance of 20 mm.

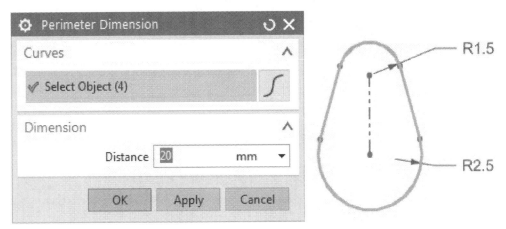

Note: Perimeter Dimension only works on contours consisting of arcs and lines – it will not work on studio splines!

4.7.3   Removing Unwanted Constraints

Selecting and removing constraints one-by-one can be difficult and tedious. Fortunately, the Show/Remove Constraints command can simplify this process!

- Create the following sketch.

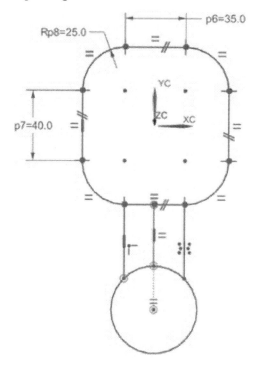

- Select the Show/Remove Constraints feature.

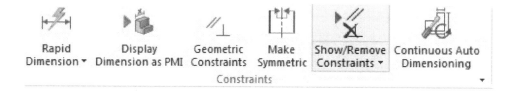

- By default the Show/Remove Constraints window will show *all* of the constraints used in the sketch.

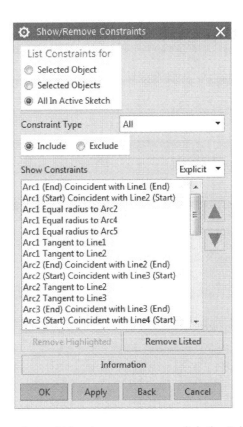

- To make it easier to find the constraint to hide, show or remove, click the Selected Objects radio button under the heading List Constraints for.
- Upon selecting an object, the list of constraints will be filtered down to only those that involve the selected object.

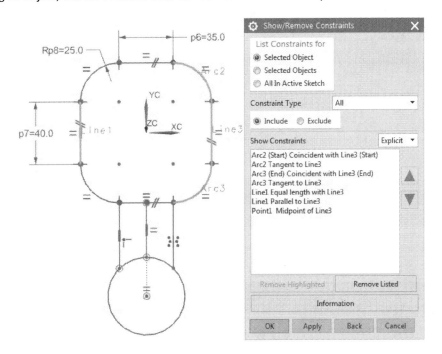

- If you are looking for a single constraint type (e.g., Equal Radius), the constraints can be filtered further by choosing the drop-down box labeled Constraint Type.
- Choose Equal Radius, and see how the list reduces to only a single constraint used on the selected object!

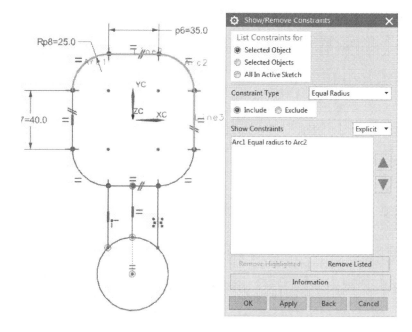

- To remove the constraint simply highlight it and click Remove Highlighted.

4.8 Sketch on Path

For many types of geometry the best construction method is to sweep a section curve along a drive curve. Good examples are moldings, railings, and bezels. In cases like these it will be best to use the "On Path" choice in the sketch command dialogue.

- Create a new sketch, and select the On Path choice by clicking on the dropdown button as shown below. Select OK, and then select a curve.

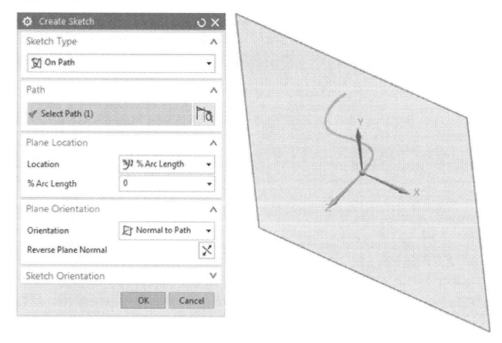

- When the curve is selected, drag the plane that appears by its center point to the end of the curve until the % Arc Length box reads 0. The plane will move to the end with a point at the intersection of the sketch plane and the curve. A datum axis for both the horizontal and vertical directions will also be created.

- Now select OK.
- Create your sketch geometry in the plane and dimension to the center point.

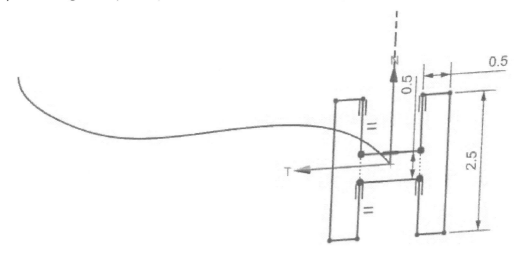

- Notice the center point of the plane is the end of the drive curve.
- Use Home Tab / Surface Section / More / Sweep along Guide, select the section, select the guide, leave the offsets 0, and click OK.

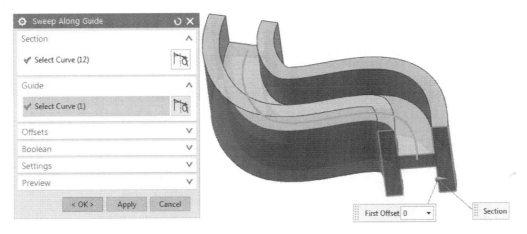

4.9 Sketching on a Solid Face

This exercise will show you how sketches can be placed upon solid faces. When sketches are put upon faces, they are linked to that face and therefore move when the face moves. When you place a sketch on a solid face, you have to be careful with way the model is facing and what vectors you choose as you place it.

- Begin by creating the model shown below: it is 90 mm thick.

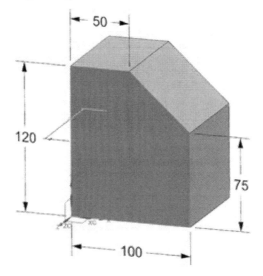

- Next open a Sketch in Task Environment, and select the slanted face.

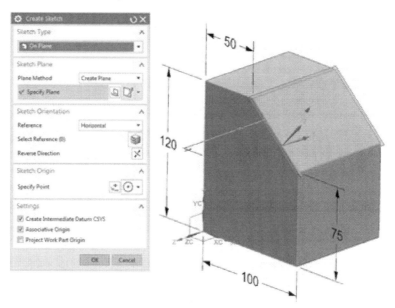

- Notice how the new coordinate system is oriented. Select a better Horizontal Reference.

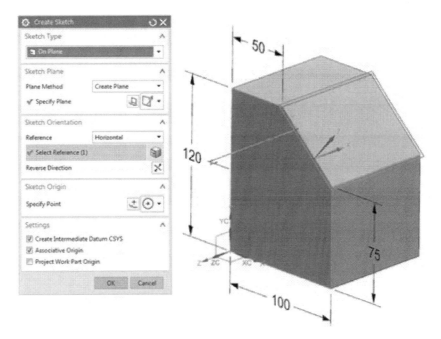

- Once you select OK, the model will take on an advantageous orientation.

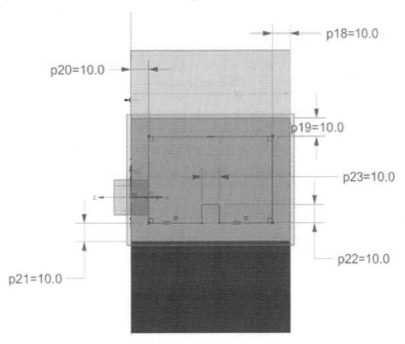

- Extrude the sketch starting at -10mm and extending forward with the Boolean set to Subtract.

- Modify the original sketch so that the vertical dimension (formerly 75 mm) becomes 20 mm.

4.10 **Direct Sketch**

We conclude this chapter with a brief lesson on the Direct Sketch environment. So far we have been using the Sketch in Task Environment command rather than Sketch, for the following reasons.

Direct Sketch tends to confuse new users because:

- The appearance of the ribbon doesn't change – you can be *in* a sketch and not realize it if you navigate away from the Home tab.
- The Direct Sketch group contains tools that look almost identical to those in the Curve group on the Curve tab – it is easy to mistakenly grab the 3D Line tool instead of the sketch Line tool.
- Certain basic tools, such as the Geometric Constraints tool, are buried in the More gallery in Direct Sketch mode – thus requiring more clicks to make a precise sketch.

All that said, Direct Sketch is fantastic if you need to make a quick sketch and don't want to wait for the system to enter the Task Environment. It allows advanced users to work much more efficiently to build a model from scratch, placing sketches and using them to Extrude, without even clicking the Finish Sketch icon!

- Create a new part file.
- Next, make sure the Direct Sketch group appears on your Home tab – recall that we removed it earlier. To add it back, use the customization down-arrow (▼) on the far right side of the ribbon and make sure the Direct Sketch group box is checked!

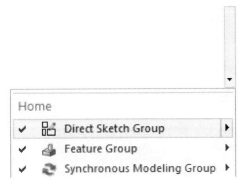

Home

✓   Direct Sketch Group   ▶

✓   Feature Group   ▶

✓   Synchronous Modeling Group   ▶

- Click on the **Profile** tool in the Direct Sketch group.

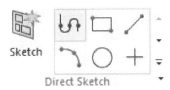

- Note that when the Profile tool dialog box appears, a preview of a sketch plane is generated. If your Datum CSYS is enabled, you can begin a sketch on any of the three standard coordinate planes by clicking when they highlight. We will sketch on the YZ plane.

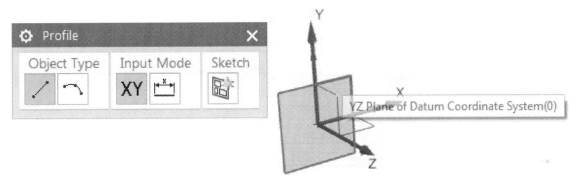

- Click on the YZ plane and click at the origin to begin using the Profile tool. Sketch the racetrack shape shown below.

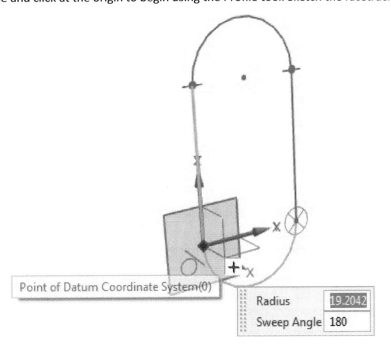

- Notice that, when you click the plane to sketch on, the view is NOT oriented to view the sketch plane that you selected. Orienting the screen to the 'Sketch View' tends to give the user a better perspective of the profile they are sketching and an easier ability to sketch horizontal, vertical and perpendicular lines – but for the advanced user, is not strictly necessary.
- Note that the left side of the Home tab has expanded into Direct Sketch mode – but it is not necessary to click the Finish Sketch icon before selecting another tool!

- Select the Extrude command and click on your sketch – it will automatically finish for you and create a solid!

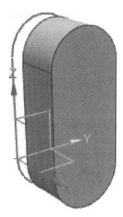

5 Design Features

5.1 Introduction

Design features are essential for creating solid geometry. Unlike sketches and curves, design features allow you to create solid geometry directly. Using design features, you can create holes, slots, and other geometry that results from manufacturing and machining operations.

Design features are found in the Feature group of the Home tab or via Menu / Insert / Design Feature.

Many of the Design Feature commands are found in the More gallery.

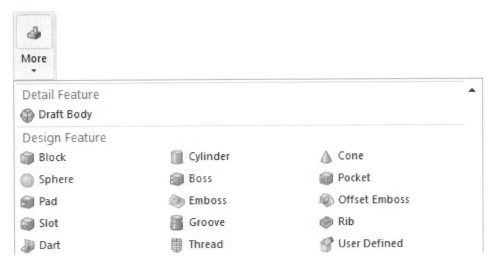

5.2 Extrude

The Extrude function takes a set of coplanar curves and sweeps them along a vector to create a 3D body (*assuming that you have body type* Solid *selected*). If you extrude a string of curves that is not closed, the result will be a sheet body (*see below*). Before continuing with the exercises below, <u>please make sure you have completed the exercise in Chapter 2</u>.

5.2.1 Start & End Limits

Extruding a closed string of curves is one of the simplest ways to create a solid.

- Using the sketcher, create the geometry shown in the figure below.

> *Reminder: To exit the sketch mode, click the* Finish *icon on the leftmost end of the ribbon!*

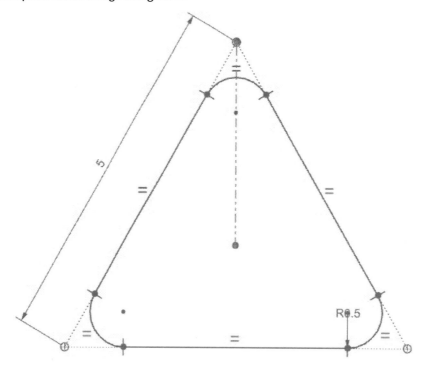

- Select Extrude. When performing operations on a sketch, the entire sketch will be selected if Feature Curves or Infer Curves is selected in the Selection Intent menu for curves. See in the following figure.

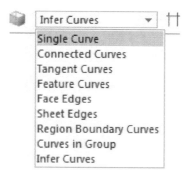

- NX 10 will shade the body to be extruded and provide an End dialog box for distance of extrusion, as shown in the previous figure.

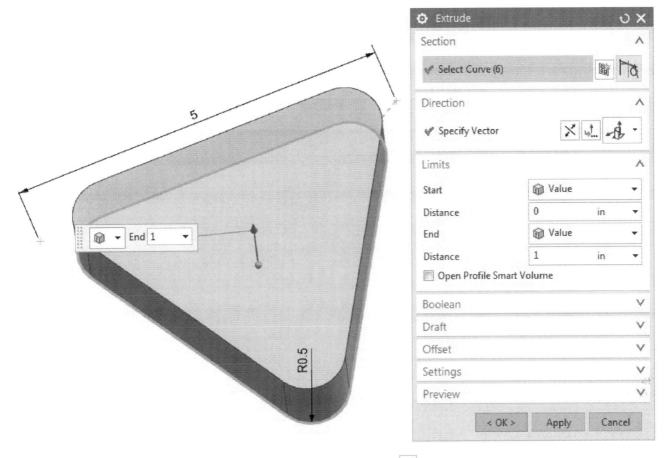

- Accept the default direction, or use the Reverse Direction button ✕ to flip the direction in order to get the solid body preview in the +Z axis direction.

- If you choose the Direction ↳… button, NX will open the Vector construction dialog as follows. The default extrude direction is normal to the sketch plane. You can also use this menu to define extrusion directions that are not normal to the plane of the section string! For this exercise, leave the Type set to Face/Plane Normal and click OK.

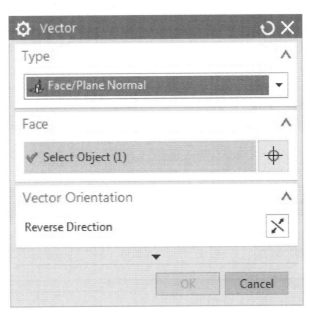

- In the Extrude dialog box, enter a Start Value of 1 and an End Value of 3, and click OK.

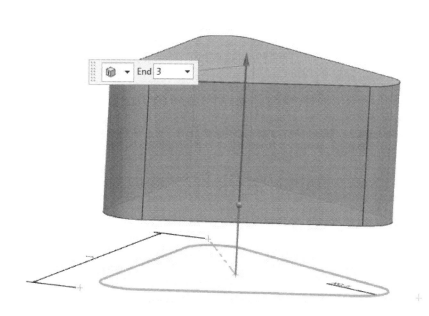

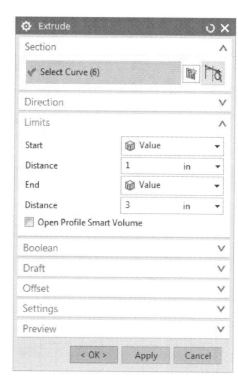

Note: You can also enter negative values for the Start and End Limits of the extrusion.

- NX 10 also has the option to create a sketch if you do not have any predefined curves. You can use the Sketch Section icon to start a new sketch and use it for extrude.

Note: *Rather than enter numerical values for the Start Limit and End Limit, you can simply click and drag the blue direction arrow to the specified extrusion value, both in the positive and negative direction. This is an easy way to create a quick extrusion. Changing your view to trimetric or isometric may make this easier to see.*

5.2.2 Offset

By using the offset parameters in the Extrude dialog box, you can create a solid with sidewalls. Taking advantage of this feature often allows you to make simpler sketches.

- Remove, by using Undo (*or delete*) the Extrude feature that you performed in the last project.
- Create another Extrude feature. This time, click on the Offset dropdown and select Two-Sided. Then, enter 0.5 for the Start and 0.75 for the End as shown below.

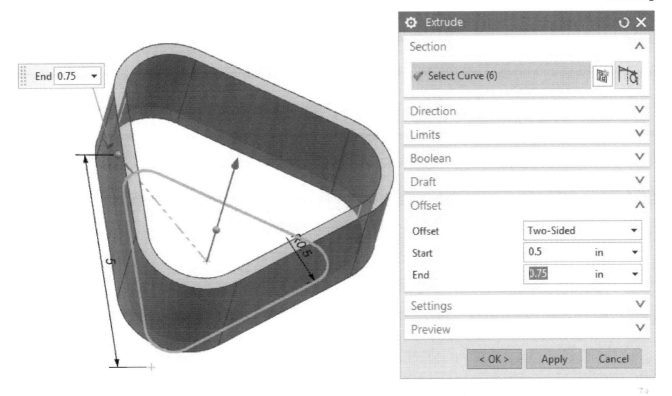

Note: The offset direction vector always points toward the outside of a closed curve!

- As seen from a top view, this model will look like the figure below. The inner face of the solid is offset 0.5 in from the section string in the direction of the offset arrow. The outer surface of the solid is 0.75 in from the section string. This gives a total solid thickness of .25in. You can enter these offset values in either order – i.e. 0.75 could have been entered for the first offset or for the second offset, and the results would have been the same.

5.2.3 Draft

You can also specify a *draft* angle to be applied to an extrusion – the angle can be defined either from the start limit or from the defining section curve.

- Undo (*or* delete) the Extrude feature that you created in the last project.
- Extrude the original sketch again. This time, however, extrude from 0 to 1, leave the offsets 0, and click on the Draft dropdown (From Start Limit) and type in a value of 20 degrees. You should see the geometry shown in the following figure.

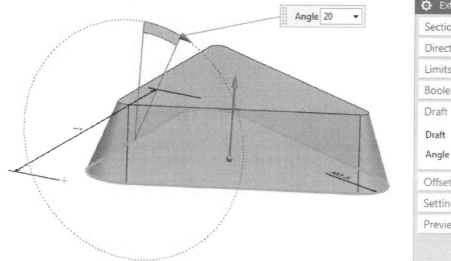

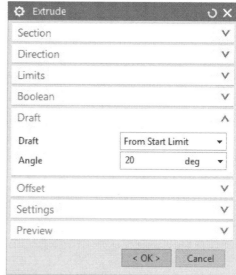

In this model, the solid faces are angled inward **20** degrees. If a negative value were entered for the draft, the faces would angle outward.

Note: The top radii at the triangle's corners get smaller or larger when the part is drafted, depending on the angle.

5.2.4 Sheet Bodies

The Extrude command can produce sheet bodies as well. Whenever you select an open section curve, the result will be a sheet body, and if you wish to produce a sheet body from a closed section curve, you can do so by changing the Body Type to Sheet.

- Undo or delete the extrusion from the last exercise.
- Select the Extrude command, and choose the same section curve as before. Enter a Start Limit of 0 and an End Limit of **1 mm**. No offset, no draft. Under Settings, change the Body Type to Sheet.
- The end result should appear as below.

5.3 Revolve

Revolving curves about a centerline is the second basic way to create solid geometry, since many common parts are bodies of revolution. The Revolve command is found just beneath Extrude on the Design Feature drop-down menu, in the Feature group, on the Home tab.

For example, the wheel shown in the figure below could be created very easily by sketching a section and revolving that section about the wheel's center. Just as with the **Extrude** function, you can create either sheet bodies or solids by revolving, depending upon whether the section string is open or closed.

- Create the following sketch.

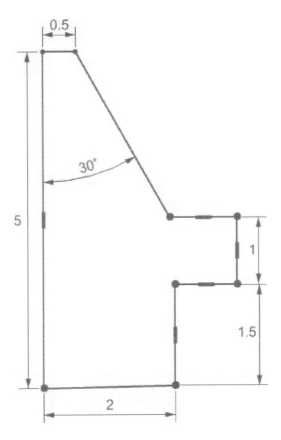

- Select the **Revolve** command, and choose your sketch as the **Section Curve**.
- Select the **5in** vertical line as shown in the previous figure as the **Axis**.
- Enter a **Start Angle** of **0** and an **End Angle** of **270** in the **Limits** menu, as shown in below.

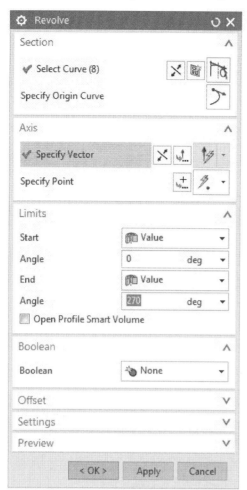

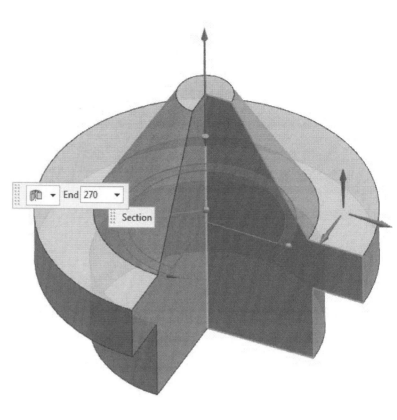

- Choose OK to create the geometry. The figure below illustrates the resultant model for End Angle = 360 degrees.

5.4 Primitives

To create elementary solid shapes, you may define Primitives. The four primitive commands are found in the More gallery in the Feature group on the Home tab. They are used to create solid blocks, cylinders, cones, or spheres.

The dimensions of a primitive are parametric; however, the position is not parametric. Because of this, some users avoid primitives completely. Primitive features are placed and sized according to the location of the WCS.

5.4.1 Block

In this project, you will create two blocks, both 2 in by 3 in by 6 in in size.

- Select the Block tool and click on the Point Dialog icon found in the Origin section of the menu.
- Fill out the Point dialog box as shown below, and click OK.

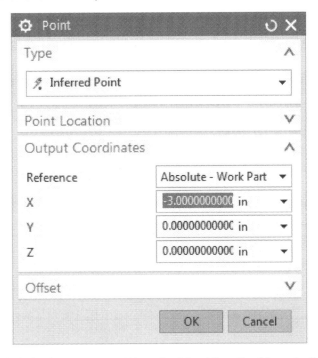

- Upon returning to the Block dialog box, enter an X length of 2, a Y length of 3, and a Z length of 6, and click Apply.
- For the second block, change the Type to Two Points and Height.

- In the Origin section of the menu, click the Point Dialog icon and specify coordinates (3, 0, 0).
- In the Point XC, YC from Origin section of the menu, click the Point Dialog icon and specify coordinates (5, 3, 0).
- Input a Height of 6, and choose OK. Your model should resemble the figure below.

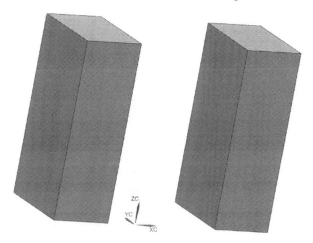

Note: By Default, NX 10 will always create a new solid body, but you can choose a Boolean operation such as Unite, Subtract or Intersect depending on your project need. This is located at the bottom right corner of the block menu, as previously shown.

5.4.2 **Cylinder**

In this project, you will create a Cylinder of Diameter 0.88 in and Height 2.5in.

- Select the Cylinder tool, and set the Type to Axis, Diameter and Height.
- Select the +ZC axis. *This defines the center axis of the cylinder.* Enter a diameter of 0.88in and a height of 2.5in.
- Compare your results to the cylinder shown in the following figure. If your part file contains solid geometry, NX 10 will display the Boolean menu.

5.5 **Project – The Pool Rack**

Building the solid geometry of a basic pool rack shown below requires two extruded body features. Both are defined using a single sketch, and will then be united together. <u>This model will be used in a later chapter</u>, so save the part file as *pool_rack_<your initials>.prt*.

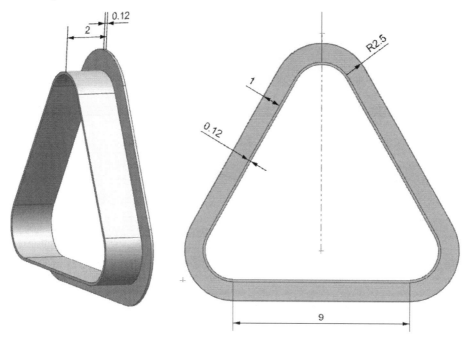

- Sketch a triangle as shown in the following figure. If you'd like, you can use the sketch made in *5.2.1* and modify the dimensions to match the diagram.

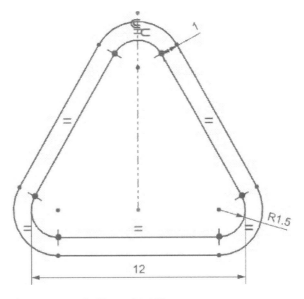

- Insert a **2in** thick extrusion with an outward offset of **0.12in**.
- Insert a **0.12in** thick extrusion with an outward offset of **1** with the **Unite Boolean** operation selected.
- Your part should look like this.

5.6 Hole

Although you can create a hole simply by subtracting a cylinder from a solid, use of the **Hole** tool allows you to create parametric counterbored, countersunk, threaded, and clearance holes. The **Hole** tool is found in the **Feature** group on the **Home** tab.

5.6.1 General

- Start with a **Block** that is **100 mm x 80 mm x 10 mm.**
- Select the **Hole** tool, and set the **Type** to **General Hole.** Enter a **Diameter** of **10mm.**
- Click on the top **100 mm x 80 mm** face of the block. NX will throw you into the **Sketch Task Environment.** Note that when you enter the sketcher, the **Sketch Point** tool is loaded, and a point has been placed at the exact position you clicked on the top face of the block.

- Position your hole using the Rapid Dimension tool in the sketcher, as shown below.
- The point is positioned **30 mm** from both edges.

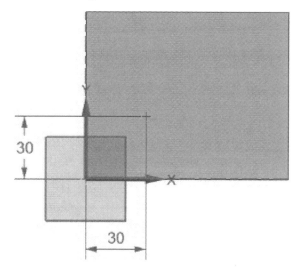

Note: You can create more than one point at a time, making it possible to create multiple holes with a single application of the Hole tool.

- Once you have positioned your point, click Finish. This will take you back to specifying your hole.
- Make sure the Form is Simple and set the Depth Limit to Through Body. Click Apply when you are done.

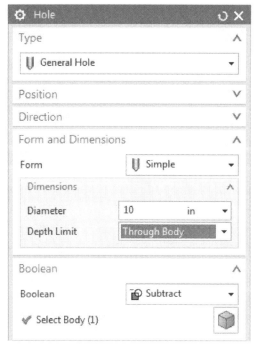

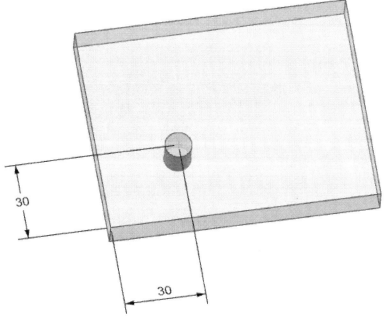

5.6.2 **Threaded**

- Change the Type to Threaded Hole, and click on the top face again to enter the Sketch Task Environment. Position the resulting point anywhere you like on the face.
- Specify a Thread Size of M10 x 1.5 and a Depth Limit of Through Body, as shown in the following figure. Be careful not to confuse Thread Depth and Depth Limit – this is a common error!

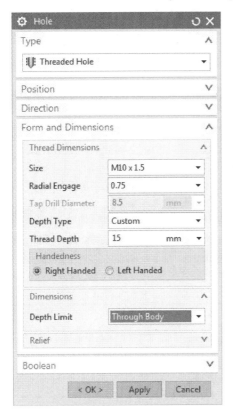
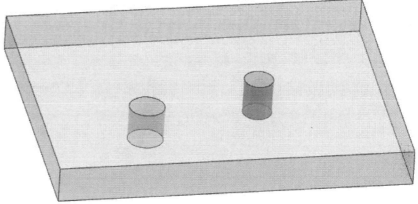

- Click OK to create the threaded hole. You will notice that the threaded hole is only symbolic. Not showing the threads saves memory and loading time.

5.6.3 **Screw Clearance**

- Select the Hole tool, change the Type to Screw Clearance Hole, set the Form to Countersunk, and the Screw Size to M10. Position the hole anywhere you'd like on the top face of the block. Your model should appear as below!

5.6.4 Tapered

This option is very useful for creating holes for self-tapping screws.

- Start with a Block and create use the Hole tool to place a General Hole with Form set to Tapered. Enter any parameters you wish.

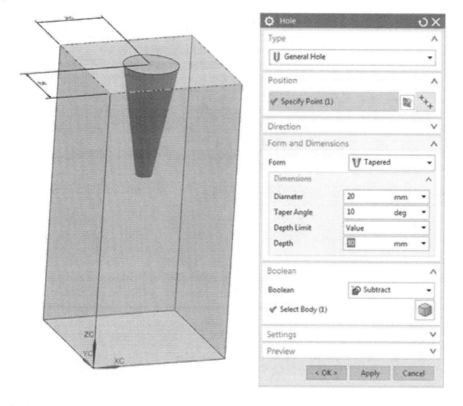

5.6.5 Depth Limits

Depth Limits are a parametric feature used to control your Boolean operations. We will walk through the different Depth Limit options in this exercise.

- Make a 100 mm x 50 mm x 30 mm Block and Shell the top face out with a Thickness of 3 mm.

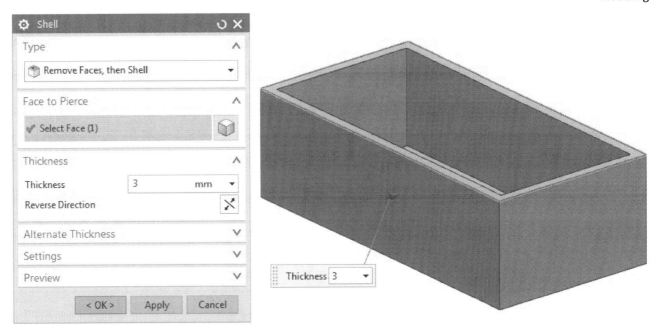

- Select the Hole tool, and set the Type to General Hole. Begin by setting the Depth Limit to Value and entering a Depth of 50 mm. Your preview should appear as below.

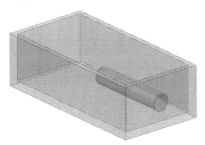

- Now change the Depth Limit to Until Selected. Select the inner face of the shell and then you will see that the hole goes to that face as in the following figure.

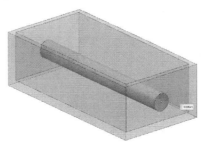

- Finally, try Until Next. This will extend the hole to the next face it reaches, as shown in the following figure.

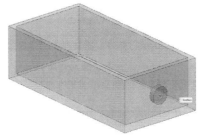

- You have already seen the Through Body setting in action (and it is self-explanatory), so we'll skip it!

5.7 Pocket

The Pocket tool allows you to easily create rectangular, circular, or custom-shaped cuts in a solid body (shown below). Like holes, they require a placement plane. The Slot and Pad tools are very similar to the Pocket tool – if you understand how to use one, you should be able to employ them all.

- Create a Block with dimensions 4 in x 7 in x 2 in, select the Pocket tool, and choose Rectangular. When the next menu appears, click the top face of the block as shown below.

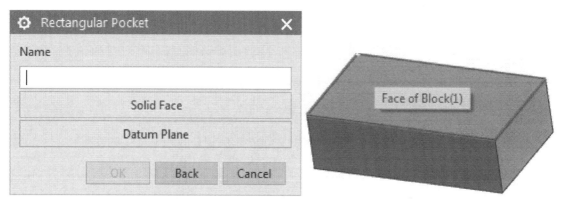

- When the Horizontal Reference menu appears, select one of the 7 inch edges of the selected face. On the Rectangular Pocket dialog, enter the parameters shown below.

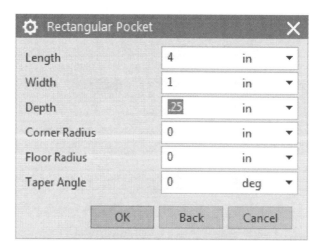

- Choose OK. A preview will be generated, centered where you clicked on the face. The next step is to position the pocket on the face. We will do so by first specifying perpendicular dimensions from the edges of the top face to the edges of the pocket. From the Positioning menu, select Perpendicular, as shown below.

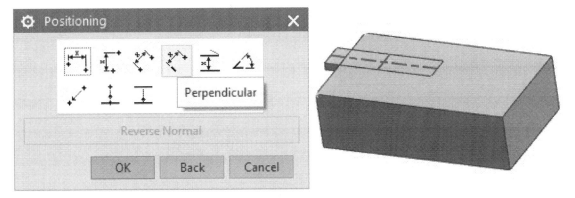

- This brings up a rather cryptic dialog box named Perpendicular.

- Remember, if at any time, you are unsure what to do, read the Cue Display!

Select target edge/datum

- Many tools in NX feature a target/tool paradigm. For these tools, the target is the object being acted upon, and the tool is the object performing the action. In this case, the block is the target and the pocket is the tool – so the Cue Display is telling you to select an edge on the block! Choose one of the 7 inch edges of the top face.
- The Perpendicular dialog box now appears different, and the Cue Display reads "Select tool edge." Now select the nearest edge of the pocket to the edge you selected in the last step. The Create Expression dialog box will appear in the graphics window, as shown below. Enter a value of 1 in.

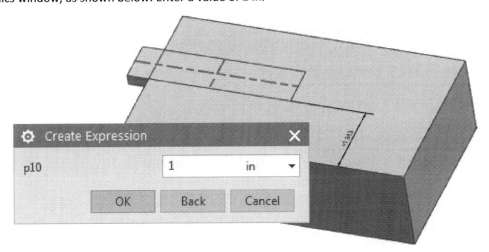

- Repeat the last few steps to create a perpendicular dimension of 1.5 inches between the 4 inch edge of the top face and the 1 inch edge of the pocket nearest to it. Note: if your pocket was initially positioned as in the images above, it will be necessary to enter a value of -1.5 in. You will now see two dimensions in the graphics window.
- From the Positioning dialog box, select the Angular method. This will be used to rotate the pocket relative to the 7 inch edge selected for the first perpendicular dimension.

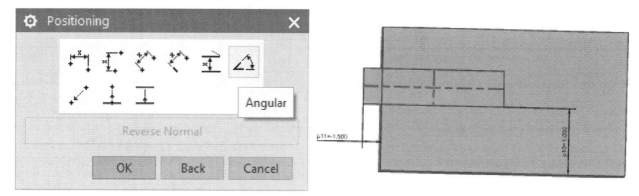

- As with the perpendicular dimensions just created, you must specify an edge of the target body and then an edge of the tool body. What is not obvious from the menu is that *where* you click on the edges determines the orientation of the angle. Click on the right side (+X direction) of the 7 inch edge of the target above, and then click on the right side (+X direction) of the nearest 4 inch edge of the tool. Give the resulting angular dimension a value of 20.0 degrees.

While creating angular dimensions, it is important to pay attention to which end of the target and tool edges are selected. Angles are constructed by two vectors whose directions are defined by the "positive" direction of the selected edges. If you find that you often wind up with dimensions that don't seem to be placed sensibly, re-try the angular dimension while paying close attention to how you are picking the edges.

Another common mistake is canceling from the Positioning menu. Selecting Cancel in this menu at any time will throw you completely out of the 'Form Feature' menus. Select OK when you are satisfied with the position of a form feature and the feature will be inserted with the dimensions you have applied.

Note: Pad command is very similar to the Pocket feature, but rather than removing material, it adds it. To create a Pad, follow the instructions provided for the Slot, including selection of a Horizontal Reference. A Corner Radius and Taper Angle may also be specified for a Rectangular Pad.

5.8 Boss and Groove

The Groove tool automates the procedure of subtracting an annulus of material from a solid body. The tool may only be used on cylindrical or conical faces. A typical application is to apply it to the cylindrical face of a Boss. The figure below shows the finished model for this project.

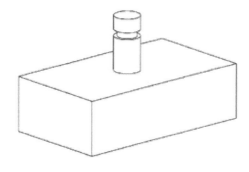

- Delete the pocket from the last exercise. You can do this by left-clicking on Rectangular Pocket (2) in the Model History, and selecting the "X" icon from the pop-up toolbar.

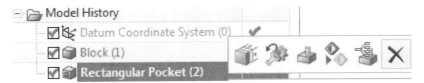

- Select the Boss tool.

- Use the creation parameters shown in the following figure.

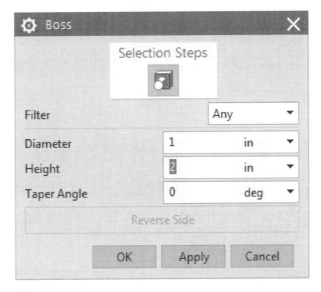

- Use two perpendicular dimensions to position the boss in the center of the top face of the block – 2 inches and 3.5 inches will suffice. Click Apply on the Positioning dialog box rather than OK so that you can apply multiple dimensions.
- Select the Groove tool, and choose Rectangular.

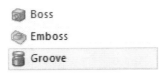

- Pick the cylindrical face of the boss. Enter the values shown below into the Rectangular Groove dialog box. The Groove Diameter is the inner diameter of the subtraction annulus. The width is the thickness of this annulus.

- Choose OK. The subtraction annulus will appear as shown below.

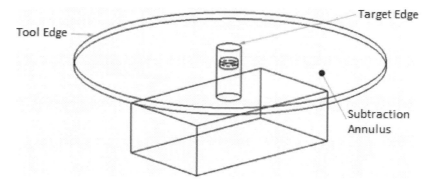

- The only meaningful dimension here is along the axis of the cylinder. Therefore, the Positioning menu is not displayed, and you are instead prompted for a target and tool edge. Select them as shown above.
- Enter a dimension value of 0.5 and click OK. The end result is shown below!

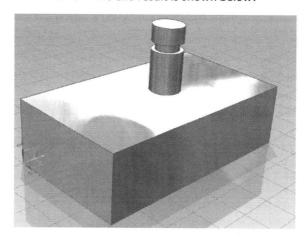

5.9 Project – The Hinge

The following figure shows the geometry of a basic hinge. Building the solid model will require knowledge of the extruded body and hole features. This model will also be used in a later chapter, so please save the part file as hinge1_<your initials>.prt.

Open a new part in NX 10. Make sure to set the Units to Inches.

- Sketch a rectangle and a circle as shown below.

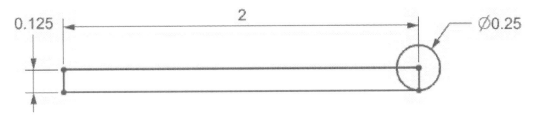

- Select the Extrude tool and set your Selection Intent to Connected Curves. Choose the rectangle as your Section Curve and enter Start and End Limits of 0 in and 5 in. When you finish, click Apply.
- Change your Selection Intent to Single Curve, and choose the circle as the Section Curve for your second Extrude operation. Leave the Start and End Limits set to 0 and 5. Set the Boolean drop-down to Unite, and click Apply.
- Change the Boolean drop-down to Subtract, and Extrude the circle from 1 to 2. Click Apply.
- Extrude the circle from 3 to 4, again with the Boolean set to Subtract. Your model should appear as below.

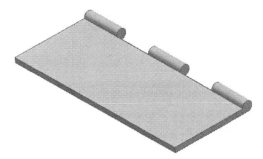

- Select the Hole tool and position three counter bored holes on the top face of the hinge with the parameters specified below. Click Apply when you are done.

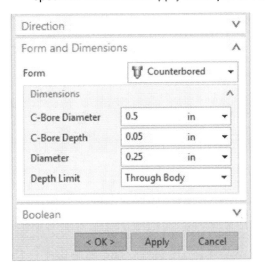

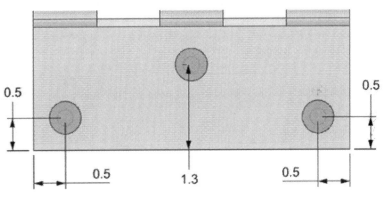

- Change the Form of the hole to Simple, and enter a Diameter of 0.125. Leave the Depth Limit set to Through Body. As for the position, click on the edge of the cylinder as shown below. Make sure that the Arc Center icon appears, so that you are guaranteed to get the arc center and not a point on the edge!

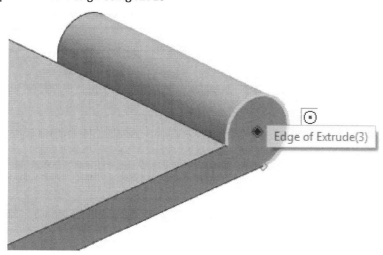

- Click **OK** and your model should now appear as below!

- Save your file in *C:\My NX 10 Files* as *hinge1_<your_initials>*. After you save, make a note of the file name at the top of the application.

NX 10 - Modeling - [hinge1_ss.prt]

6 Modifications to Parts

6.1 Introduction

The Part Navigator is a powerful, easy-access organization tool for many common NX 10 commands. It is located in the Resource Bar on the left side of the NX 10 interface. By default, the features are displayed in the order that they were created (Right Mouse Button / Timestamp Order).

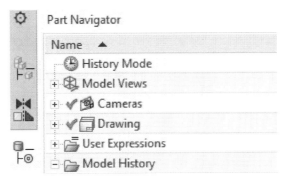

Next to the name of each feature in the Part Navigator, there should be sections which provide information about the part (Timestamp, Layer, etc). You can add these columns and configure new user-defined attributes by right-clicking the header of the Name column and selecting Columns / Configure.

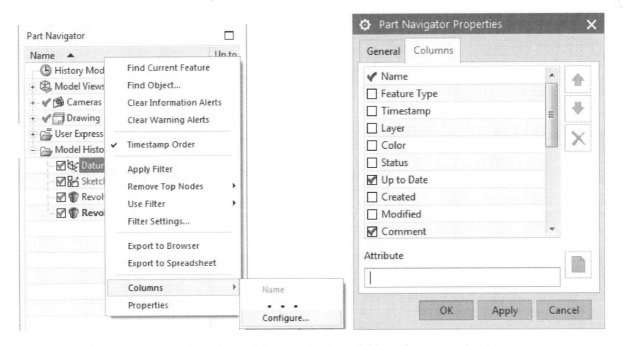

Throughout this chapter, we will explore the model-editing tools available in the Part Navigator.

6.2 Project – The Hinge, Part II

To illustrate the use of the tools in this chapter, we will make a second copy of the hinge created in the last chapter, and modify it.

- To begin, open the part file *hinge1* that you created previously.
- Next, select File / Save / Save As, and save a copy of the file as *hinge2_<your_initials>*. Note that the name at the top of the application has changed! This means that you are now working on *hinge2*.

The Model History for your part *hinge2* should appear as below.

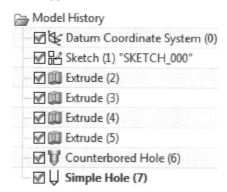

6.3 Dependencies

Parent/Child Relationships are the dependencies created when building up a CAD model. The skill of creating (and controlling) well-behaved parent/child relationships is what separates the expert-level user from the novice.

When you add a parametric feature to a model, NX 10 stores all of its information, including any pre-existing geometry that is referenced by the feature. If this geometry is modified, the feature must be updated.

In a geometrically complex model, it is often helpful to learn more about the Parent/Child relationship structure. This can be accomplished by selecting the feature in the Part Navigator and by expanding the Dependencies and Detail windows at the bottom of the Part Navigator. Once you understand the intricacies of a model's construction techniques, you can use the Edit Feature functionality to change the Parent/Child Relationship of features. This, in turn, allows you to perform parametric modifications that would otherwise be impossible.

Dependencies help illustrate how changes to a component or steps in the modeling process impact other parts of the model. Although dependencies are shown in their own panel, NX 10 highlights parent and child dependencies in the main Part Navigator screen using different colors, as shown below.

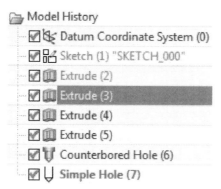

6.3.1 The Dependencies Panel

The parent/child relationships are shown explicitly for any highlighted item in the Model History in the Dependencies Panel, located at the bottom of the Part Navigator.

Dependencies	∨
Details	∨
Preview	∨

Expand the Dependencies Panel and highlight *Extrude (3)* – the parent/child relationships involving *Extrude (3)* are made completely explicit in the panel, as shown below.

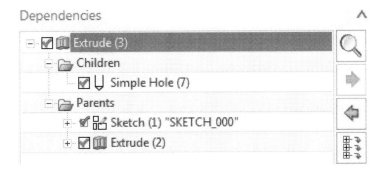

6.3.2 Timestamp Order

There is an alternative to the chronologically-correct Model History in the Part Navigator. You can view a model in terms of the bodies contained therein, and the interrelationships between the operations that gave rise to that body. By default, the Model History is configured in *Timestamp Order*. To turn off Timestamp Order, right-click along any of the headers for the columns in the Part Navigator ("Name", for instance). Uncheck the box that says Timestamp Order.

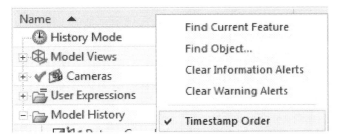

Rather than viewing the Model History chronologically, you are now viewing it genealogically – in terms of dependencies. For example, if you click the "+" sign next to *Extrude (3)*, you will recognize the nested operations from the view in the Dependencies panel.

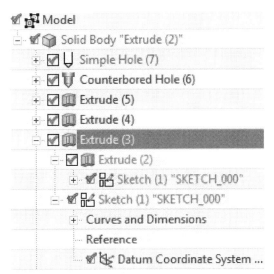

For the rest of this chapter, we will work in Timestamp Order, so please re-enable it at this time!

6.3.3 Reordering Features

When you *reorder* an operation in NX 10, it is moved to a different place in the model's creation history. The geometry of the model is recalculated because of the reorder operation, and the model's topology may or may not change. You can reorder individual features by using Menu / Edit / Feature / Reorder or by using the Part Navigator right-click pop-up menu. Follow the exercise below to see the effects of reordering for yourself!

- Click and drag *Counterbored Hole (6)* to reorder it between *Extrude (3)* and *Extrude (4)*.

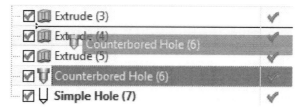

- Note that the Model History is fine like this!

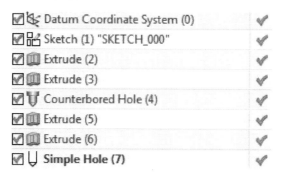

- Click and drag *Simple Hole (7)* to reorder it between *Extrude (2)* and *Extrude (3)*.

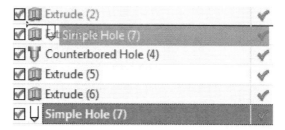

- NX will warn you because it detects a dependency between *Simple Hole (7)* and *Extrude (2)*!

- In fact, the dependency is between *Simple Hole (7)* and *Extrude (3)*, but since *Extrude (3)* unites the cylinder with the box, the software infers an additional dependency.
- Undo ([Ctrl]+[Z]) the first reordering to restore the model to its original state.

6.4 Show & Hide

When models get complicated, it is extremely valuable to be able to show and hide objects at will from the Graphics Window. In this section, you will learn about the basic Show and Hide functions, as well as the Show and Hide menu.

These tools can be found on the View tab on the ribbon, but we *strongly* recommend that you *not* use the ribbon to access them. There are much more efficient ways to access these tools, as you will learn in the exercises below.

6.4.1　The Class Selection Menu

Right now, your model probably looks something like the image below (your Datum CSYS may be in a different location).

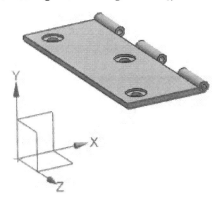

The sketch, and the dsatum CSYS are clearly visible in the Graphics Window. Suppose you want to view only the body, and none of the construction data (like the beautiful screenshots in this book!). For this, you'll want to know how to Hide geometry from the Graphics Window.

- Use the keyboard shortcut [Ctrl]+[B]. (This is the shortcut for the Hide function.) This will bring up the Class Selection menu.

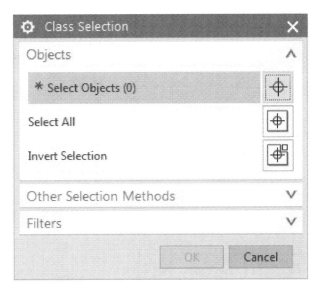

- The Class Selection menu appears when you invoke certain commands that otherwise require their inputs to be specified prior to invocation. Both Show and Hide are examples of such functions.

6.4.2　Show / Hide

- Select the geometry out of the Graphics Window that you wish to hide – in this case, the datum CSYS.

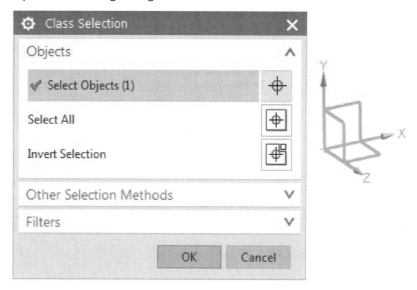

- Next, right-click on *Simple Hole (7)* in the Part Navigator and find the Hide icon on the pop-up toolbar. (You can also find Hide on the pop-up menu).

- Oops! That seems to have made the whole solid body of the model disappear! All that remains is the sketch!

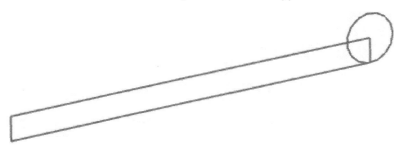

- To bring the solid body back, use the keyboard shortcut [Ctrl]+[Shift]+[K].

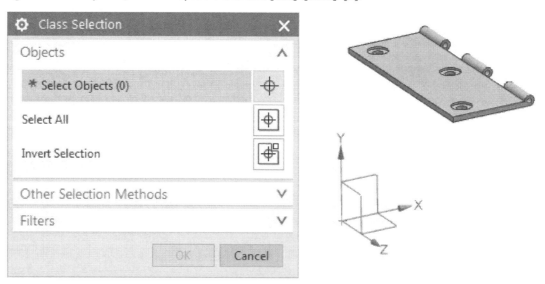

- This again brings up the Class Selection window, but inverts the hidden and shown objects in the Graphics Window. It's like looking into the parallel universe of hidden objects in NX! Select the solid body of the hinge.

- This brings the hinge back into view.

6.4.3 Show and Hide

Another way to show and hide objects systematically is to use the Show and Hide menu. This gives you control over visibility of objects in your model on a class-by-class basis.

- Use the keyboard shortcut [Ctrl]+[W] to access the Show and Hide menu.

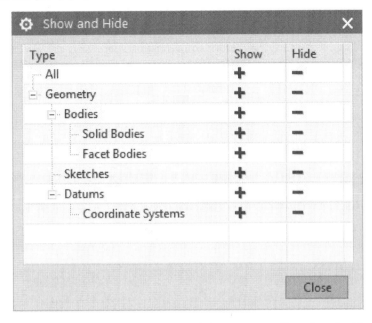

- You can use the +/- buttons to show or hide all objects of the corresponding class. In this case, we wish to hide the sketch from our model, so press the "-" button adjacent to *Sketches*.

6.5 Deleting and Suppressing Features

6.5.1 Deleting Features

When you Delete an individual feature in NX 10 it is permanently removed from the model's creation history. Consequently, the model will revert to a state it would have been in if the feature had never existed. The feature can never be retrieved unless an Undo operation is possible. You can delete a feature using Menu / Edit / Delete, by the keyboard shortcut [Ctrl]+[D], or by right-clicking it in the Part Navigator and selecting Delete from either the toolbar or pop-up menu.

- Right-click on *Extrude (3)* in the Model History and select Delete from the pop-up toolbar.

- Do more Note that *Simple Hole (7)* has vanished from the Model History because of its explicit dependence on *Extrude (3)*!

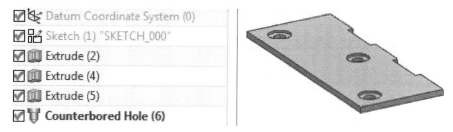

- Undo!
- You can also delete features via the keyboard shortcut [Ctrl]+[D]. This brings up the Class Selection menu if you use the keyboard shortcut before selecting the feature to be deleted. Note: you can click on features out of the Part Navigator when the Class Selection menu is open.

6.5.2 Suppression

When you Suppress an individual feature in NX 10, it is *temporarily* removed from the model's creation history. As with deleted features, the model will revert to the state it would have been in if the feature never existed. The difference is that a suppressed feature can be retrieved using the Unsuppress operation. You can suppress individual features by using Menu / Edit / Feature / Suppress or by using the Part Navigator right-click pop-up menu.

- Left-click on the green checkbox next to *Extrude (3)*.

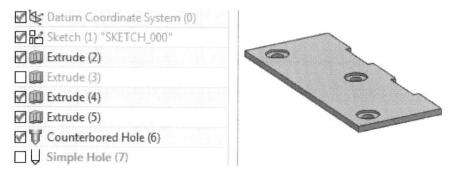

- The appearance of the model in the Graphics Window is the same as though *Extrude (3)* were deleted – but *Simple Hole (7)* has also been suppressed, rather than deleted.
- To unsuppress, you can either left-click on the box next to *Simple Hole (7)*, or right-click and select Unsuppress.

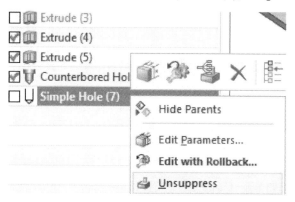

6.6 Editing Features

Rather than create the complementary half of *hinge1* from scratch, we will make edits to certain features in the Model History of the newly saved *hinge2*. We will use Make Current Feature, Edit Parameters and Edit with Rollback in this exercise.

6.6.1 Make Current Feature

Make Current Feature is used to roll back the clock on your model to a specified state. It can be used as a diagnostic tool, to pinpoint the operation that caused a model to go haywire, or to produce a view of a model at an earlier point in time.

- Right-click on *Extrude (3)* in the Model History, and select Make Current Feature from the pop-up menu.

- Note what happens to the sequence of operations in the Model History – the green checkboxes become dotted diamonds, and the names of the operations are grayed out. They have been suppressed, but in a way that new operations will be inserted in between *Extrude (3)* and *Extrude (4)* in the Model History. Moreover, the corresponding features have disappeared from the model in the graphics window!

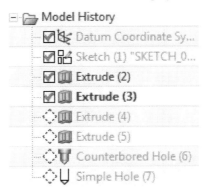

6.6.2 Edit Parameters

The Edit Parameters tool re-opens the dialog box corresponding to the feature selected, and allows you to adjust the parameters and other inputs, rather than deleting the feature and using the tool again.

- Right-click on *Extrude (3)* and select Edit Parameters from the pop-up menu.

- Within the Extrude dialog box, change the Boolean from Unite to Subtract, and click OK. Your model should now look like this.

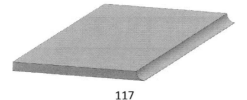

- At this point, we will need to revise later operations in the Model History, so right-click on *Simple Hole (7)*, and select **Make Current Feature** from the pop-up toolbar.

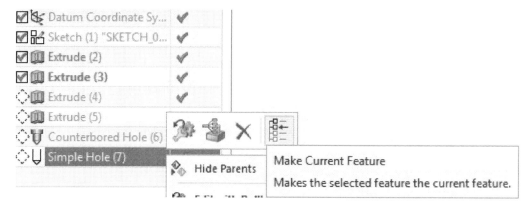

- Uh oh! Our edit seems to have wreaked havoc on the other operations in the Model History. An information window like the one shown below will appear.

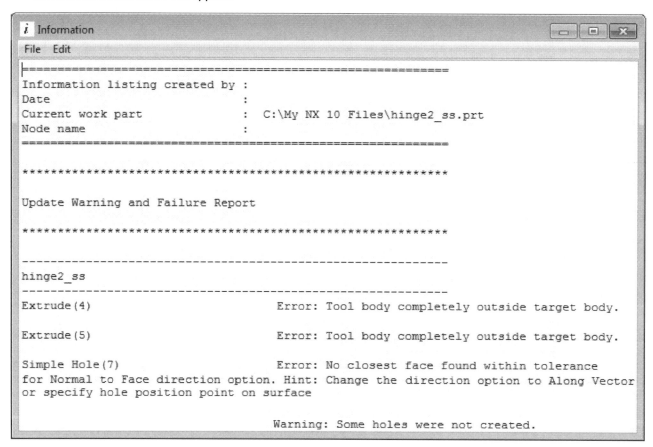

- Next, we'll see what we can do to fix the errors resulting from that change. This is very common in parametric modeling, and the ability to fix errors resulting from changes to the Model History is an extremely valuable asset to a designer, so this will be great practice! The features in the Model History that were compromised by the edit are now indicated by red "X"s.

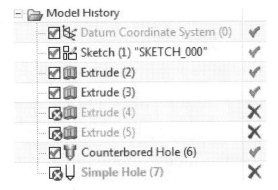

- Right-click on *Extrude (4)*, and select **Edit Parameters** from the pop-up toolbar.

- Change the **Boolean** in the open **Extrude** dialog from **Subtract** to **Unite**. Note that the Model History looks a little better, and that your model looks more like it should!

6.6.3   Edit with Rollback

Succinctly, **Edit with Rollback** = Make Current Feature + Edit Parameters.

- Double-click on *Extrude (5)* in the Model History. This has the same effect as right-clicking and selecting **Edit Parameters**. Again, change the **Boolean** from **Subtract** to Unite. The Model History has improved dramatically – the only operation that remains to be fixed is *Simple Hole (7)*!

- Right-click on *Simple Hole (7)*. Note that the first two icons on the pop-up toolbar are **Edit Parameters** and **Edit with Rollback**. Select either one.

- You will need to deselect the point that previously indicated the position. You can do so by holding shift and left-clicking on it, or by using the **Deselect All** button, found in the **Selection** group on the Top Border Bar (as shown below).

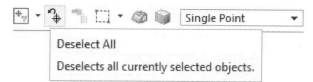

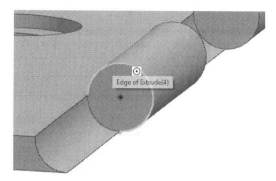

- To specify the new location for the hole, select the point indicated below. Recall that you can select the center of an arc by clicking on the arc itself, so long as the Arc Center ⊙ icon appears.

- Your Model History should now be free of errors and the complementary hinge should appear as below!

- Remember to Save the file!

6.7 Object Display

The Edit Object Display command allows you to control the color, translucency, and more for your solid models. The Edit Object Display command is found on the View tab, but we recommend that you access it via the toolbars, pop-up menus, or the keyboard shortcut [Ctrl]+[J].

6.7.1 Class Selection Filter

When you first invoke the Edit Object Display command, you will again meet the Class Selection menu. Oftentimes, you may wish to modify the appearance of certain bodies in a model or certain faces on a body. You can narrow down your possible selections by using the Selection Filter on the Top Border Bar, or by using the Type Filter found on the Class Selection menu.

Type Filter

This will bring up the Select by Type dialog box. The advantage of specifying your selection intent in this way (rather than by using the Selection Filter drop-down) is that you can filter for multiple types – e.g., points and curves, or facet bodies and solid bodies.

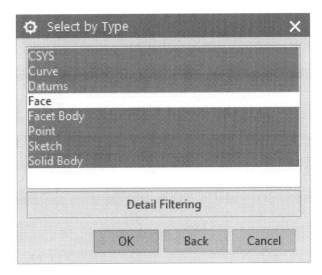

Make sure that solid bodies are selectable, and choose the solid body of *hinge2*.

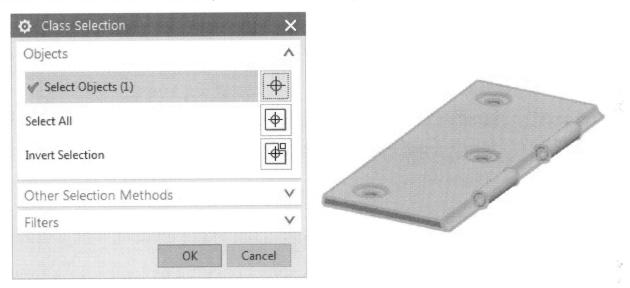

6.7.2 Color

- Once in the Edit Object Display menu, the color is the first most basic attribute you can modify. Click on the Color palette icon (rectangle) shown below.

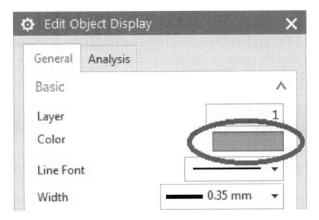

- From within the Color dialog box, pick your favorite color. Ours is Magenta!

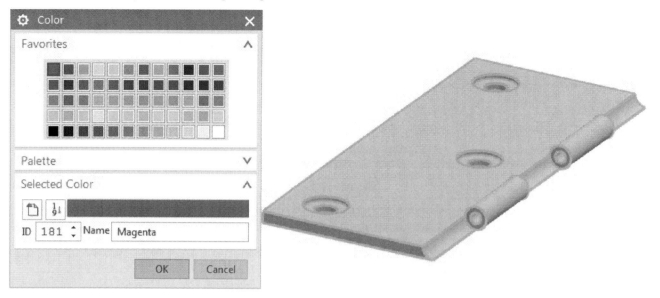

- When you return to the Edit Object Display menu, click OK to confirm the change. Your model will take on a lovely magenta hue!

- Let's change the colors of some faces. Select the Edit Object Display tool again ([Ctrl]+[J]). This time, when the Class Selection menu appears, change the Type Filter to *Face*.

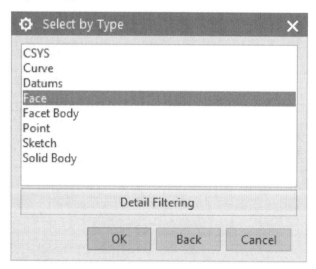

- From the Class Selection menu, choose the ten faces shown below.

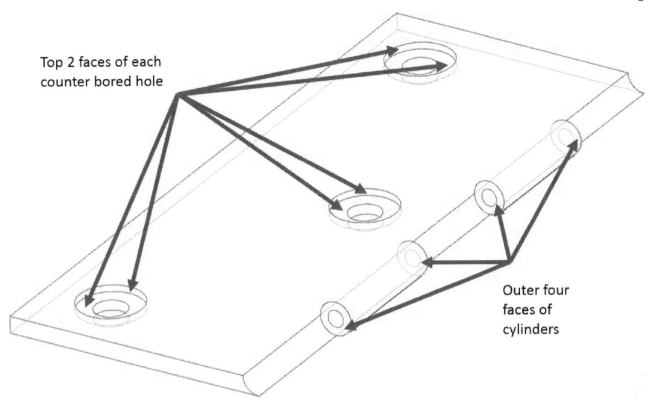

Top 2 faces of each counter bored hole

Outer four faces of cylinders

- Give those faces a nice green hue!

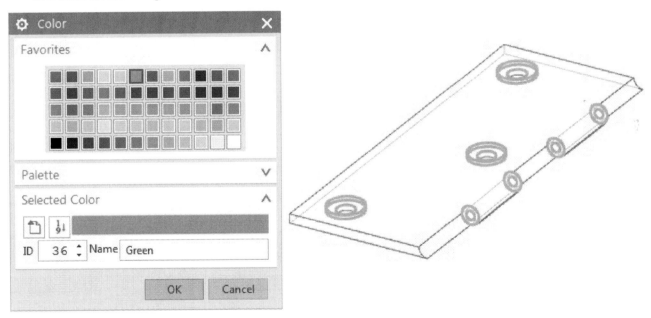

- Your model is even better than before!

6.7.3   **Translucency**

Besides color, you can also modify the translucency of bodies in your model.

- Change your Selection Filter to Solid Body.

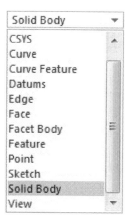

- Left-click on the solid body of *hinge2*. When the pop-up toolbar appears, find the Edit Object Display icon.

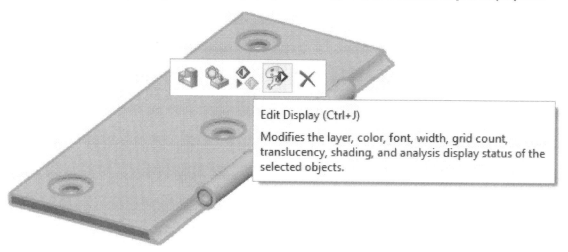

Edit Display (Ctrl+J)

Modifies the layer, color, font, width, grid count, translucency, shading, and analysis display status of the selected objects.

- This brings you directly into the Edit Object Display menu. Drag the slider under Translucency to modify the appearance of your model.

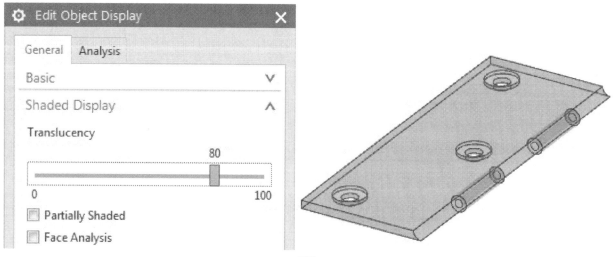

- This is useful for modeling actual transparent parts, and also for temporarily making parts transparent for the purpose of working with them in an assembly. It can be advantageous to modify the translucency of an object while you work on it so that you can see details of other parts behind it in the assembly!
- When you are done exploring the Edit Object Display menu, there is no need to save. (Make sure you saved the changes made throughout 6.6!). We will return to this model in Chapter 16 – Assemblies.

6.8 Pop-Up Toolbars & Menus

It should also be mentioned that most of the operations discussed in this chapter can be applied by either left-clicking on an object in the Graphics Window and waiting for the pop-up toolbar to appear, or by right-clicking on the object and choosing from the pop-up menu.

See if you can remember which commands the icons on this toolbar correspond to – effectively using the toolbars can increase your productivity with NX by orders of magnitude!

7 Combine Bodies

7.1 Introduction

Building complex solid geometry often requires combining multiple entities. In NX 10, a Boolean operation is a feature operation that manipulates solids and sheets. There are three types of Boolean operations – Unite, Subtract, and Intersect. Unite and Subtract can only be used on solid bodies while Intersect can be used on solids and sheets. We will also discuss the Sew operation which works with sheets as well as solids. All of these can be found in the Feature section of the Home Tab.

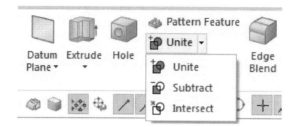

The next figure illustrates the effects of each Boolean operations on solids. You can add geometry to a model by Uniting solids together, or you could create a cavity in a Target model by Subtracting a Tool solid from it. The Intersect Boolean operation is useful when you are modeling a solid based on different shapes in different views.

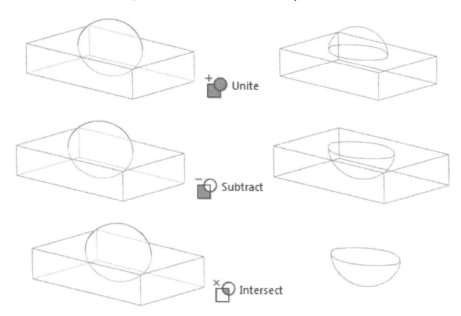

Note: For Unite, Subtract and Intersect, NX 10 allows you to retain the Target and Tool body designations. Even after the Boolean operation has been completed, it is possible to differentiate between the original two parts.

7.2 Unite and Subtract

In this example, you will create three separate solids from a single sketch. You will then combine three bodies into a single solid body using Unite and Subtract operations.

- Sketch the geometry shown in the figure below. Place all three strings in a single sketch. Don't worry about exact dimensions – just make it look roughly like the shape as shown, with a lower length of 6.5in.

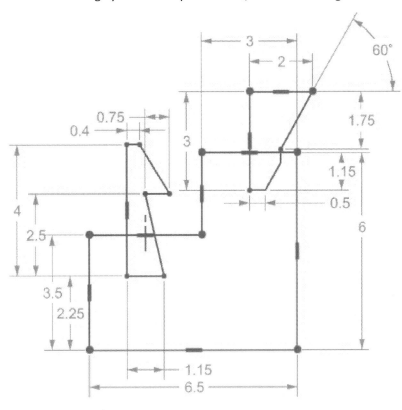

- Click the Extrude command.
- Since we want to extrude the center profile only, you will need to use the Connected Curves selection filter (as indicated below) to avoid selecting the entire sketch.

- Extrude the profile with a Symmetric Value of 1.5in.

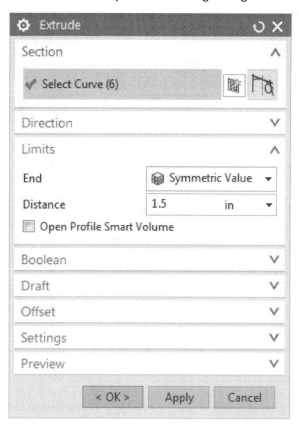

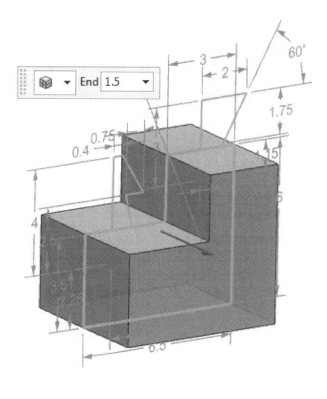

- Revolve the left profile 360 degrees. Make sure Connected Curves is selected in the selection intent menu.
- The Boolean section should be set to None.

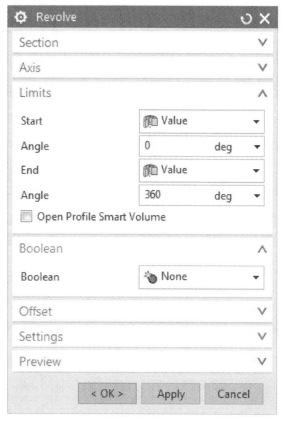

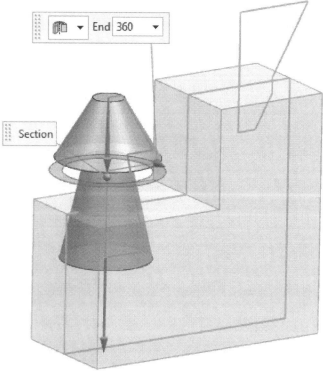

Revolve the Right most profile using the steps outlined above. Again, select None from the Boolean options. Your model will consist of three solids, as seen in the figure below. Move your mouse over each of the solids and notice how NX 10 highlights them individually.

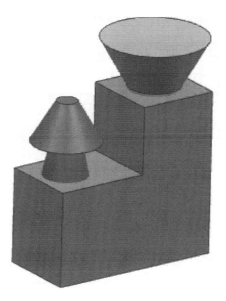

- Select Unite.
- Pick the Red Solid as the Tool shown in the previous figure.

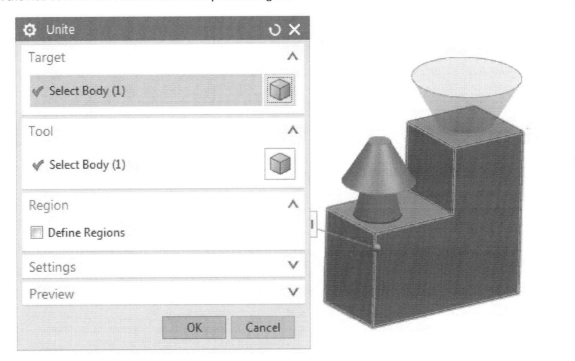

The cue is prompting you for a target solid. The target solid is the entity from which the tool will be subtracted. There can only be one target body.

- Pick the gray block as the Target
- Press OK
- Select Subtract.
- Pick The Gray Solid as the Target.
- Pick The Blue Solid as the Tool.
- Press OK

You should now have one solid body, as shown below. The Subtract operation created a hole in the target solid and consumed the tool solid, while the Unite operation simply added the two solids together.

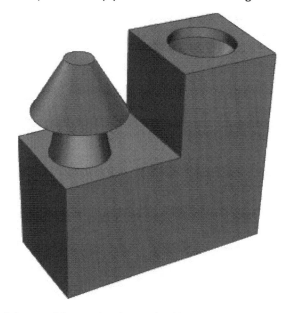

Note: You could have selected Unite or Subtract while creating the revolved body and skipped the last few steps, but we want you to learn both options.

7.3 Intersection

Intersecting two solids is a great way to make complicated shapes. For example, the following figure details a tab that must be curved with a radius in one direction.

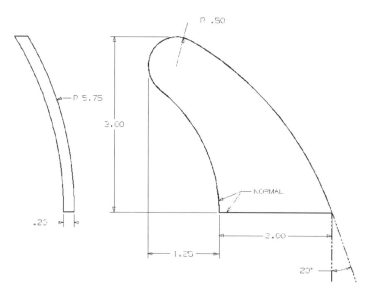

Since this geometry is curved in two planes, it is a good application for construction using the 'Intersect' operation. A very effective approach for this model is to create the two solids shown in the next figure and then perform an Intersect Boolean operation using them as tool solids.

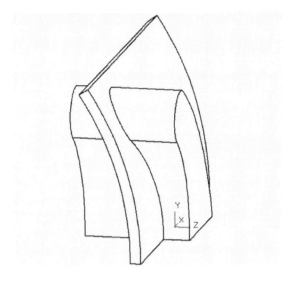

- Sketch the side view of the tab as shown in the figure below.

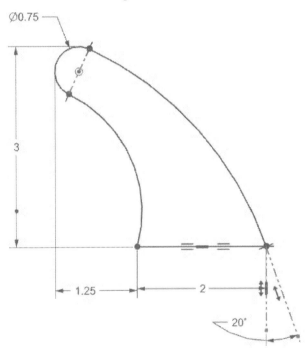

- Extrude your sketch symmetrically by 1.5.
- Sketch the geometry shown in the following figure. Create this sketch on the datum plane that is vertically perpendicular to the plane of the first sketch. It only needs to consist of two entities: an arc and a vertical reference line. The reference line is tangent to the arc and is used to control the orientation of the arc. The height of the arc does not need to be a specific value as long as it is a bit taller than the height of the tab. For this example, the height of the arc is related to the first sketch by setting it equal to the height variable plus an arbitrary 0.25in.

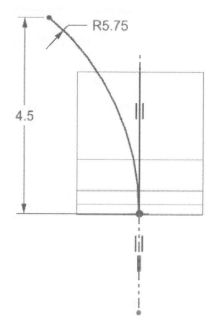

- **Extrude** the arc symmetrically by **4in** with an offset of **0.2** toward the arc's center.
- Observe the offset arrow to determine if you need to enter a positive or negative **0.2** offset dimension. Recall that this offset value can be entered as the first or the second offset.

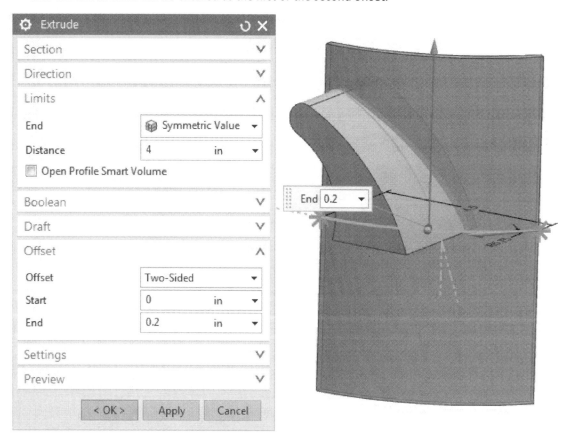

- Select **Intersect** .
- Pick the solid created by the first sketch.
- Pick the solid created by the second sketch.
- You should have the same geometry as shown in the following figure.

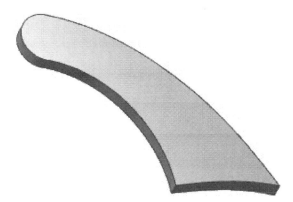

Solid geometry that does not overlap is discarded when an Intersect Boolean operation is performed. Thus, the outer extent of your tool solids is somewhat arbitrary – just make sure that they are large enough to create a complete intersection solid.

In these examples, you first created the solid geometry and then subsequently performed a Boolean operation using them as tool solids. You can also perform the Boolean operation at the same time that you create the new solid by choosing the appropriate selection from the Boolean Operation drop down menu.

7.4 Inferred Boolean

In this project we are going to look at the Inferred Boolean option. If you set your Boolean option to Inferred, NX will predict the Boolean option that you want. For example, if you create an Extrude and there are no other solids in the model, the inferred option will simply create a solid. If you create an Extrude that intersects an existing solid, the Inferred option will choose to subtract the Extrude from the existing solid. Finally, if you create an Extrude that touches face-to-face with an existing solid, the Inferred option will unite the Extrude to the solid.

Now let's try all of these techniques by creating some kind of pipe fixture.

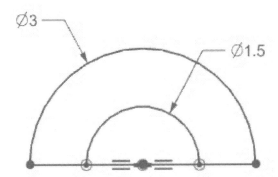

- To begin, create the sketch shown in the previous figure.
- Click Extrude to extrude the outer profile in the –Z direction, shown in the following figure, to a distance of 0.5in and set your Boolean option to Inferred, also shown in the following figure.

Note: It may be helpful to change your selection intent to Single Curve before selection. You will notice that the Inferred Boolean option has decided to create the solid.

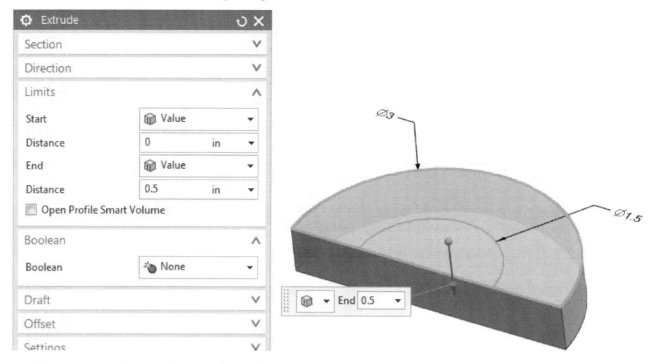

• Now create another extrude using the inside arc and part of the line.

Note: Using Stop at Intersection, highlighted in the following figure, will help your selection by only selecting a length of curve until it recognizes an intersection with another curve.

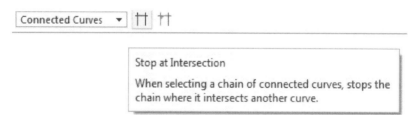

Stop at Intersection

When selecting a chain of connected curves, stops the chain where it intersects another curve.

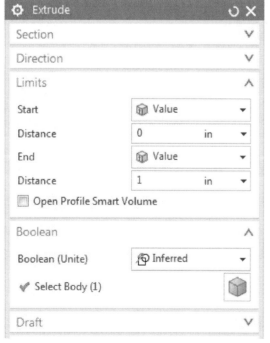

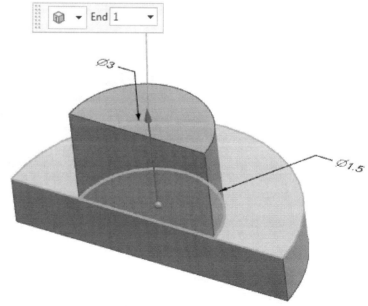

- Set the Extrude to a distance of 1in in the +Z direction, and use the Inferred Boolean option as shown in the previous figure. You will notice that NX inferred a Unite between the Extrude and the existing solid.
- Finally, we are going to use the Inferred Boolean option to create a subtraction.
- Create the following sketch on the top face of the solid.

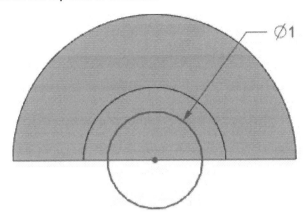

- Now use the Extrude command with the Boolean option set to Inferred and extrude with the Through All option selected as shown in the following figure.

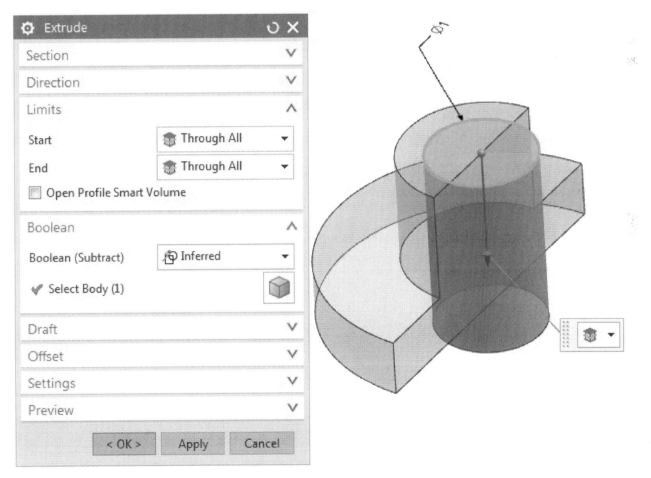

- Use NX Inferred to subtract the Extrude from the solid, as shown in the following figure.

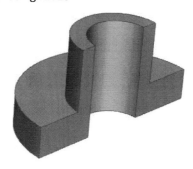

7.5 Sew Command

The Sew option is similar to Unite, but where Unite can only be used to combine solid bodies together, Sew allows you to combine sheet bodies as well as solid bodies. You can only sew solid bodies that have coincident faces.

7.5.1 Sewing Sheets

The most common use of the Sew command is to sew sheets together. This is possible even if there are small gaps between the sheets. To sew any sheet bodies with adjacent edges simply use Sew command as shown in the following figure.

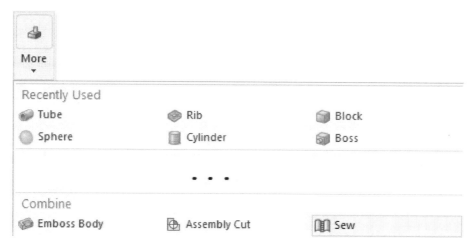

- Sketch a rectangle like the one shown below.

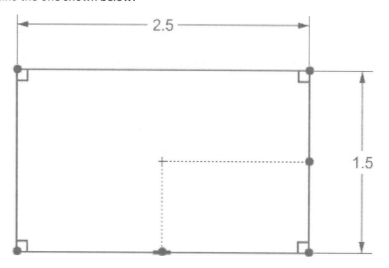

- Select the Offset Curve command from the Curve Tab.

- Select any curve from your sketch.
- Input an Offset Distance of 0.05 inches and choose None for Trim. Be sure the Associative checkbox is NOT checked and Input Curves is set to Keep from the Settings section.
- Your model should look like the following figure.

Note: You may need to Reverse Direction in the Offset Menu to get a similar outcome.

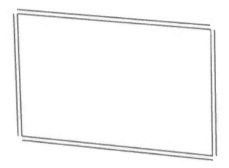

- Extrude the four new curves 1in. Compare your results to the following figure.

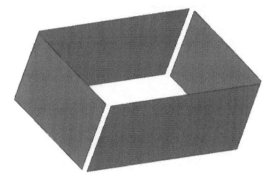

- Select Sew command.
- Enter a Tolerance of 0.10. This value is chosen because it is greater than the offset distance of 0.05 inches. The tolerance must be large enough to capture the seam.
- Select any of the four sheets as the Target sheet.
- Select all three remaining sheets as Tool sheets.
- Compare your results to the following figure.

Note: Sewing sheets is best when sheets do not have gaps. Sewing sheets with gaps is possible by modifying tolerances as shown in example above, but it changes the geometry depending on the size of the gap. When gaps are bigger and surface geometry is critical, it is best to patch it up using a sheet from a new line or from the Through Curves feature.

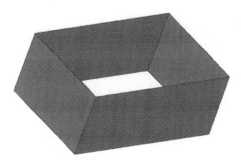

7.6 **Unsew**

The *Unsew* tool does the exact opposite of the Sew command. The basic principle of this tool is that when you select a face of a solid that you wish to Unsew, the rest of your solids turn into sheet bodies as well. You can then separate the unsewn sheet from the other sheets.

- Start by selecting Block and creating a block 1in x 6in x 4in , as shown in the following figure.

- Add an Edge Blend of 0.5in on each corner.

- We want to replace the top face of the block with something more exciting, so click on Unsew command.

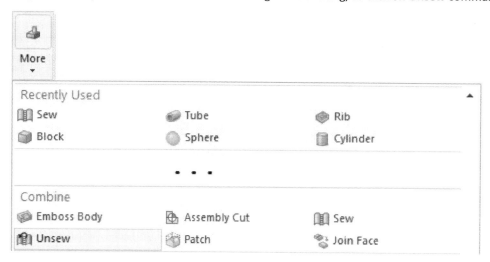

- Select the top face, as shown in the following figure, and Click OK.

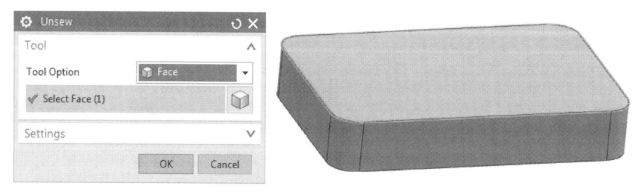

- It looks like nothing happened, but what we've actually turned this solid block into sheet bodies by Unsewing the top face. Select Delete Body command and then choose the top face.

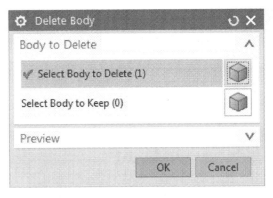

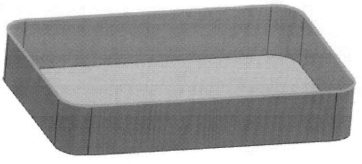

- To create a more exciting top face we need to create an Extrude with a Draft.
- To do this, select Extrude. Pick the outer edges of the open box as shown in the following figure. Extrude downward toward the bottom with a Draft of -60 degrees. Make sure to set the output as Sheet.

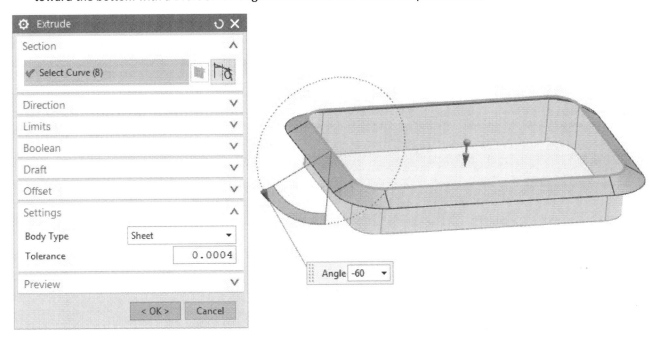

- Next select the N-Sided Surface command from the Surface Tab. Choose the outer edges of the open side of the box as the Outer Loop.
- Next select the drafted Sheet as the Constraint Faces as shown in the following figure.

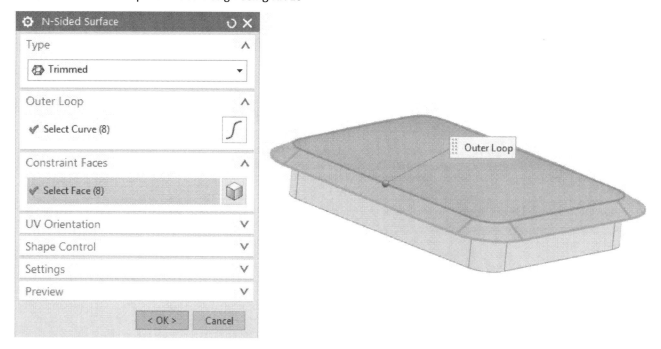

- Select Delete Body to remove the unwanted drafted sheet from the model since it is no longer needed.
- Sew the new top face together with the rest of the sheet body to create a new solid body.
- Another edge blend can even be added to show that the newly created body works as a solid.
- Compare your results to the following figure.

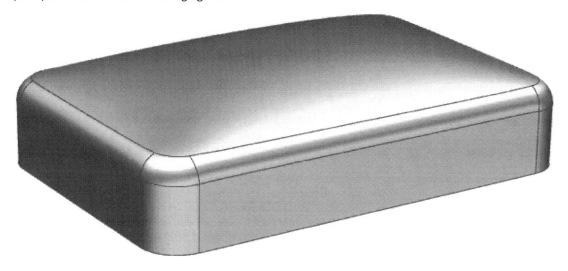

7.7   Emboss Body

The Emboss Body tool works similar to the Subtract command. The basic principle of this tool is that when you select a target solid that you wish to emboss, the tool solid in a sense pushes its shape through the solid to create a cut-out imprint into the target solid.

- Start by selecting the Cylinder command and creating a cylinder 4in high by 2.5in diameter.
- Next sketch an arc and Extrude it through the cylinder with an offset of 0.5in. Make sure the Boolean is set to None.

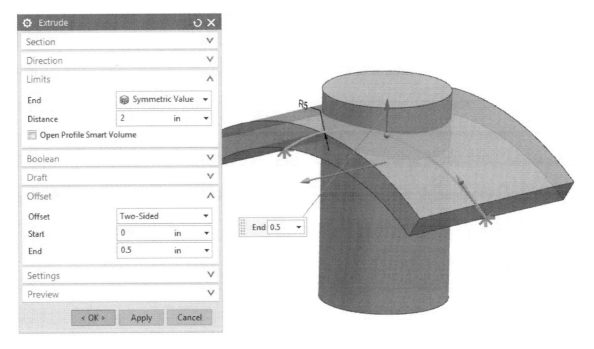

- Now that you have a cylinder and an extruded arc, the next step is to select Emboss Body from the Home tab.

- Select the extruded arc as the Target and the Cylinder as the Tool. You may need to select the outer face of the cylinder as the Region.

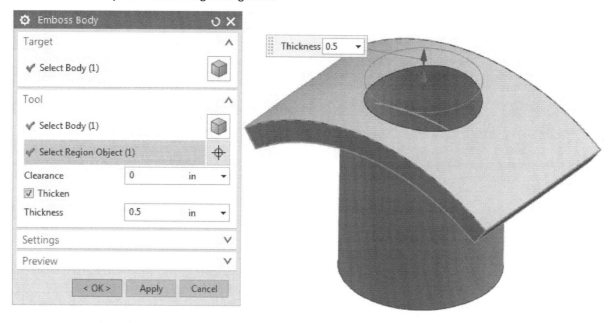

- As you can see the cylinder not only subtracted itself from the extruded arc, it also embossed its lower half as an imprint into the solid.

7.8   The Stepped Plug

The geometry shown below could be constructed by subtracting a number of blocks from a body of revolution. It is much quicker, however, to simply intersect two bodies.

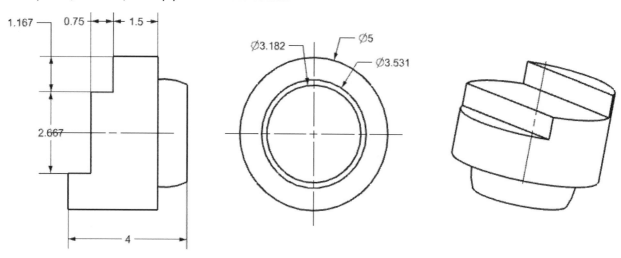

7.8.1 Practice Outline

- First, create the sketch shown in the next figure.
- Notice how the center line of the middle profile passes through the midpoint of top edge line of the larger profile. You can enforce this constraint with the proper set of dimensions; however, there is a better use of geometric constraints.

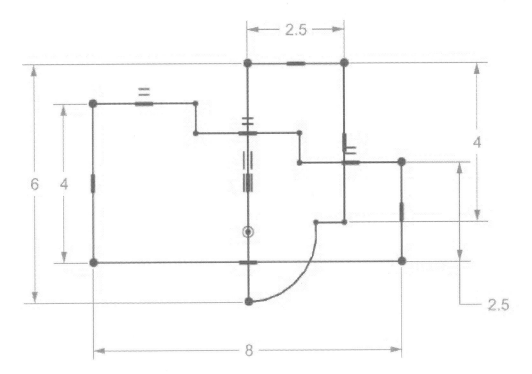

- Next, use the Revolve and Extrude functionality to create two tool solids.
- To complete the model use the Intersect function, selecting the two bodies as Target and Tool solids (the order does not matter).

8 Detail Features

8.1 Introduction

The *Detail Feature* operations can be used to create curvature, smoothness and rounded qualities on existing surfaces and between surfaces and solids. Like Design Features, Detail Features can be parametrically controlled, allowing you to modify values later.

Detail features are found in the Feature group on the Home tab. This chapter discusses the functionality of the Edge Blend, Draft, and Chamfer commands.

Additional blend tools can be found in the Blend gallery in the Surface group on the Surface tab.

Note: You can build many models without using Detail Feature operations; however, using them will greatly improve your modeling proficiency, productivity, and overall model appearance.

8.2 Edge and Face Blends

Edge Blend and Face Blend are extremely powerful and flexible tools in NX 10. Their basic job is effectively the same – to apply fillets to edges of solid bodies. For variable radius blends, blends with tangency constraints, and law controlled radii, specific blend operations may be appropriate.

8.2.1 Edge Blend

The Edge Blend tool creates a smooth curve between two faces that join in a sharp corner. The simplest way to use an edge blend is to specify a radius that will be created in the corner. A good way to predict the result is to think of a ball with the specified radius being rolled across the surfaces, blending the faces as in the figure below. Wherever the ball touches the corner is where the blend surface will be created.

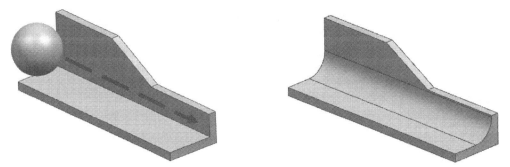

- Create a new part file Units set to Inches, and create the sketch shown below and Extrude it 2in.

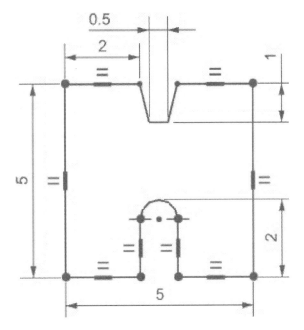

- Select the **Edge Blend** tool, and select the edges shown in the following figure. Set the **Blend Face Continuity** to **G1**, the **Shape** to **Circular**, and specify a **Radius** of **0.5 in**. Expand the **List** subsection of the menu.

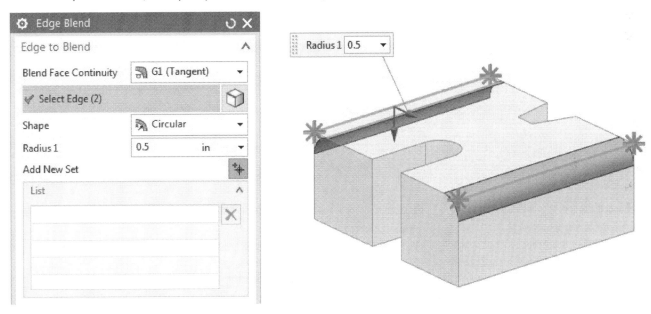

- Click the **Add New Set** button. Select the four edges shown below, and specify a **Radius** of **0.25 in** for this set.

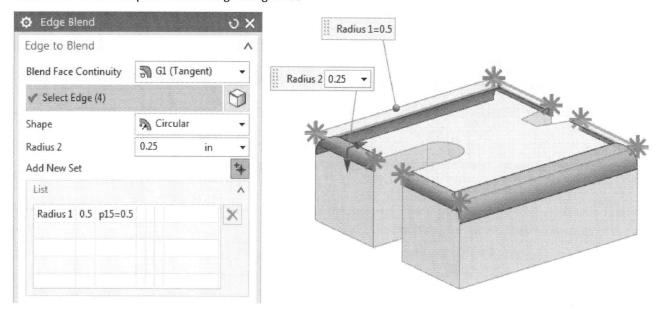

- Click the **Add New Set** button again, and select the edges shown in the following figure. Specify a **Radius** of **0.25** in.

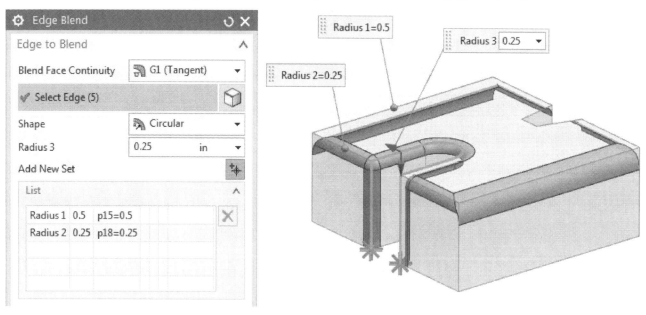

- Finish the blend by clicking **OK**.

Tip: You can work much faster by using the selection intent menu correctly. Try using other options from the Selection Intent Menu like Face Edges and Vertex Edges!

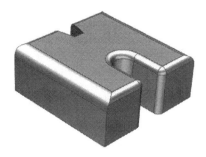

146

8.2.2 Blend Face Continuity

A new option in the Edge Blend menu as of NX 10 is the Blend Face Continuity drop-down menu. In this menu, you can choose between producing a G1 blend, or a G2 blend. The curvature combs of these blends are displayed below.

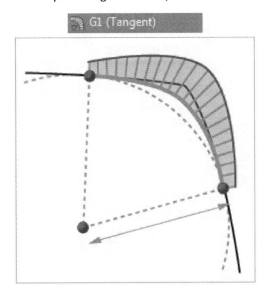
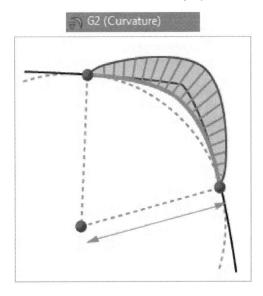

8.2.3 Variable Radius Edge Blend

The Edge Blend function can also be used to vary the radius of the blend as it traverses the distance of the edge. Use the geometry from the previous project.

- Select Edge Blend.
- Select the edge shown below.

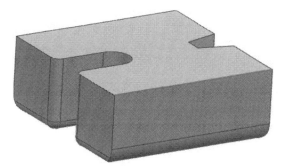

- Under the Variable Radius Points Section, click Specify New Location.
- Select the midpoint of the edge.

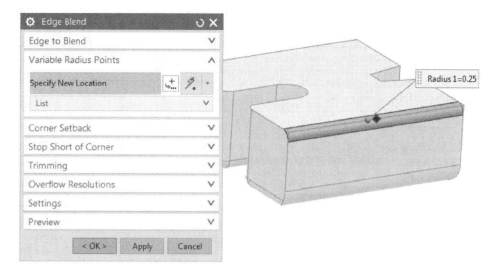

- Enter the value of 0.25.

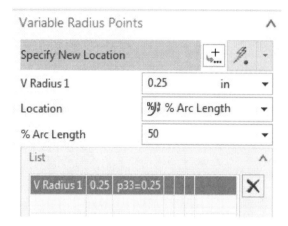

- Select the end points of the edge and enter a V Radius of 0.75 on the start point and 1 for the end point.

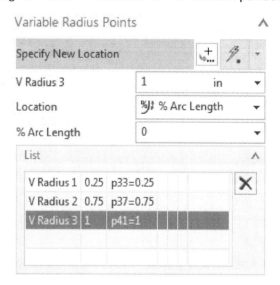

- Compare your results to the following figure.

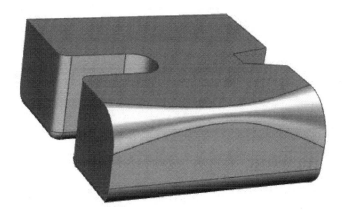

8.2.4   Face Blend

A Face Blend can be created between two sets of faces of solid or sheet bodies that are not necessarily adjacent. There are two main face blends: Rolling Ball and Swept Section. Rolling Ball is the simpler and more commonly used face blend. Swept Section is an advanced face blend in which the blend surface is controlled by a cross section swept along a spine curve.

There are also three different options to define radii: Constant, Law Controlled and Tangency Controlled. We will discuss the Rolling Ball type face blend in this chapter. Swept Section is not discussed in this book.

Use the geometry from the previous project.

- Select Face Blend from the Surface Section of the Surface Tab.

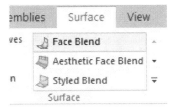

- Specify the Type as Two Defining Face Chains.
- Specify the Section Orientation as Rolling Ball
- Select the First Face Chain as shown in the following figure.

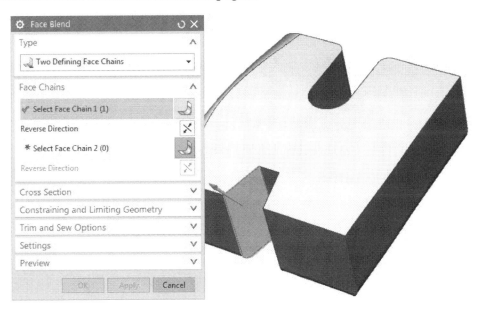

- Enter a radius value of 0.4. Make sure that the arrow is pointing towards the other angled face. If it is not, use the Reverse Normal button to reverse it.

Note: Face Blend even allows you to select multiple faces in a set, if you need it.

- Select the Second Face Chain (opposite face). Again make sure that the arrow is pointing inward.

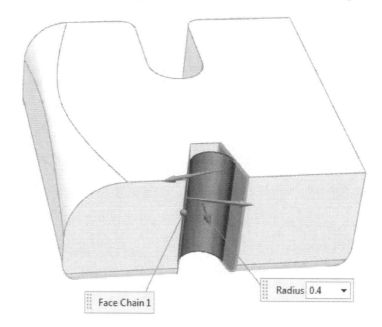

- Compare your results with the following figure.

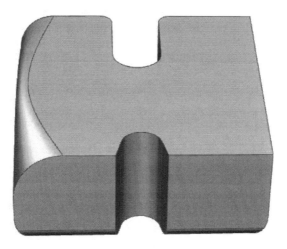

Notice how the blend is created between faces that are not adjacent to each other. This is good functionality in that it lets you skip between surface/surfaces and create clean blended geometry.

8.2.5 Coincident Edge Blends

When you need to create a blend that does not run out tangent to a face, you can use a Coincident Edge blend. This is an option found under the Face Blend command. Typically, the coincident edge blend is needed in situations where one or more faces are not large enough to accommodate the blend. To create this blend, you must select the edge that will not be tangent.

- Create the sketch shown below and extrude it 5in.

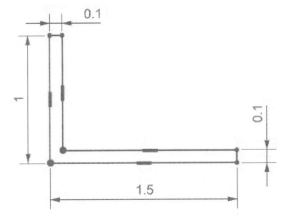

- Select the First and Second Face Chain Sets. Make sure that the arrows are pointing correctly towards the centerpoint.

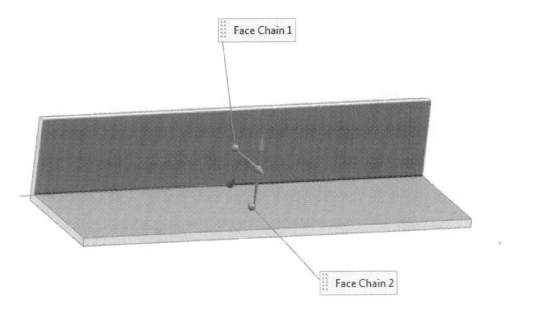

- Select the Coincident Curves as shown below and type in the radius value 2.

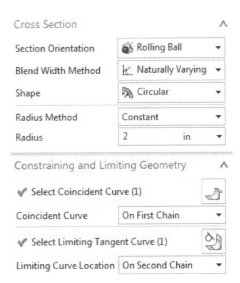

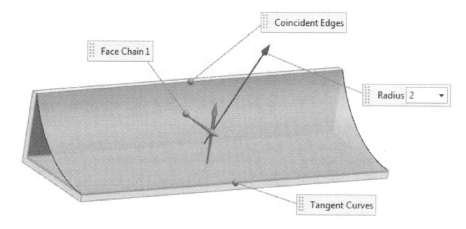

- Compare to the following figure.

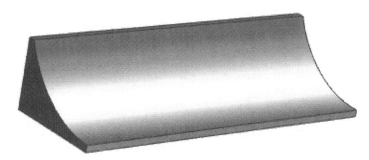

8.2.6   Tangent Curves

The Tangent-Curves are used when you have a blend whose radius is dictated by the length of one of the sides of the object to be blended.

- Use the initial geometry from the previous project or create a new part with the same geometry.
- Create a sketch and cut off the geometry approximately as shown below.

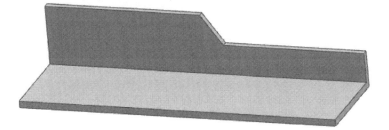

- Select Face Blend.
- Select the first and second face chains as shown below.
- Make sure that the arrows are pointing correctly towards the center point.

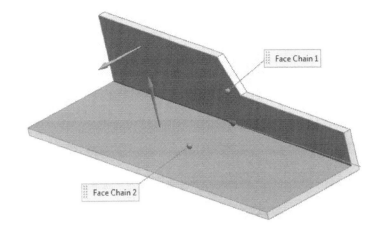

- Set the Radius Method to Tangency Constraint.
- Select the Tangent Curves as shown.

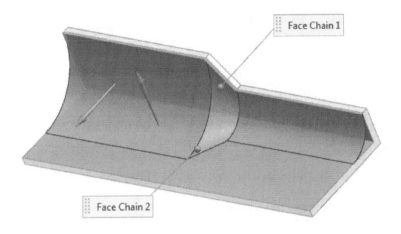

- Compare to the following figure.

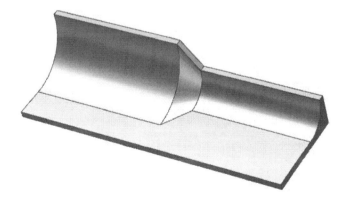

The order in which you apply blends can make a big difference on complicated models that often have intersecting blends. In general, you should apply the largest radius and most critical blends first and move on to the smaller radius and less critical blends last. However, experience teaches that some experimentation is often required to complete the blending of a solid model. Often times it pays off to do the blending after the part design is completed.

Note: If a solid model is used only to create a drawing, you should be cautious about spending too much time blending. Blends do not always show up correctly in a drawing and will sometimes require a "fudged" approach in drawing views - regardless of whether or not they are modeled correctly.

8.3 Draft

Draft is used to apply an angle to the faces of pre-existing solid geometry. You have already learned that a draft angle can be applied to an extruded body at the same time that it is created; however, with this approach, all of the side faces of the extrusion will be drafted. This is often required when creating complex models, such as cast or molded parts. There are four draft features available in NX 10: Draft from Plane, Draft from Edges, Draft Tangent to Faces, and Draft to Parting Edges.

8.3.1 Draft from Stationary Plane

This feature allows you to specify certain faces of a solid to be drafted by a specified amount. The applied draft angle is measured relative to a specified Stationary Plane (the plane where dimensions remain constant). The Stationary Plane is defined by selecting a Reference point and a Draw Direction (Reference Vector Direction).

Consider the simple shape shown below. Suppose that leftmost 2 faces must be drafted inward by 20 degrees and far right face must be drafted inward by 30 degrees.

In this case, suppose that the underside of the solid is defined as the Stationary Plane and the Draw Direction is normal to this plane. Upon the application of the draft features, the lower edges will remain fixed, while the faces will become angled inward.

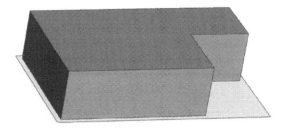

- Sketch the geometry shown below and extrude it 2in.

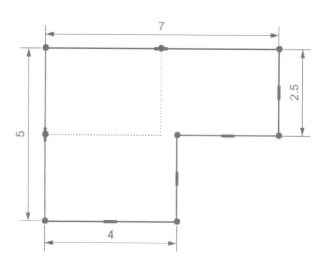

- Select Draft from the Feature section.
- Select From Plane or Surface for the Draft Type.
- Select Draft direction ZC.
- Select the bottom face as the stationary plane.
- Input Angle = 20 degrees.
- Pick the leftmost faces shown in the following figure for Set 1.

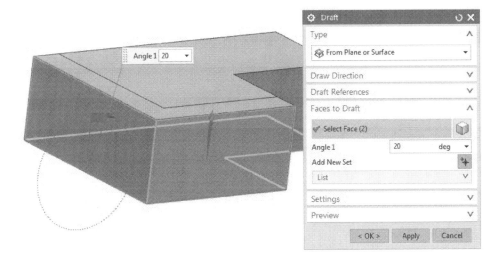

- Click Add New Set and select the rightmost face for Set 2.
- Input Angle = 30 degrees.

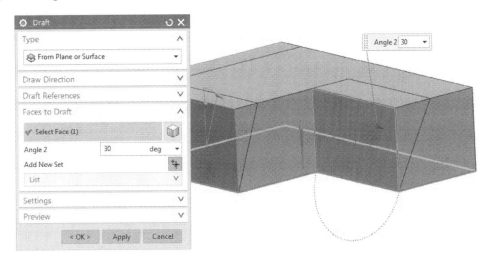

- Compare your results to the following figure.

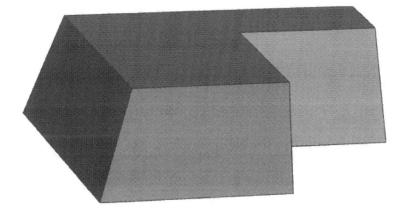

Note: Don't forget to read the cue. Cue reading is the easiest way to find out what NX is expecting from you.

8.3.2 Draft from Stationary Edges

Consider the solid body shown below. This geometry is typical of a cast part with a non-planar parting line, which in this case is the bottom surface. You will need to apply drafts to the left, right, front, and rear surfaces. Applying drafts to the left and right surfaces can be accomplished using the Stationary Plane method. Applying a draft to the front and rear surfaces requires a different technique, since the parting line is not planar.

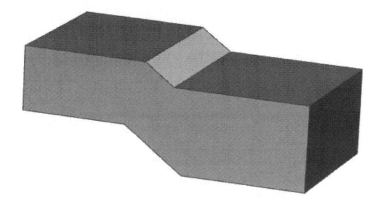

This type of geometry can be created using From Edges. It is similar to the From Plane, but instead of specifying a plane you select edges that remain fixed when the draft is applied.

In this example, a From Edges Draft is applied to the front and rear faces of the solid shown on the previous page.

- Create the sketch shown in the following figure.

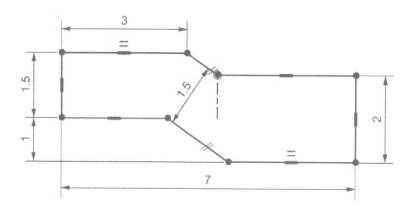

- Extrude it 4in.
- Select Draft from the Home tab.
- Select From Edges for the Draft Type.

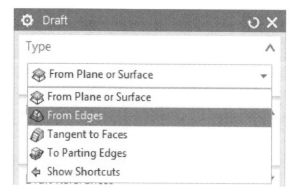

- Pick Z-Axis for draw direction. Just as before, this defines the Draw Direction vector – an orange arrow will appear to indicate its direction. In this case, it should point upwards.

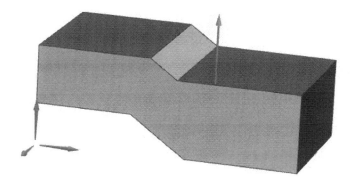

- Pick the 3 bottom as shown below to designate the Stationary Edges.
- Input Angle = 30.

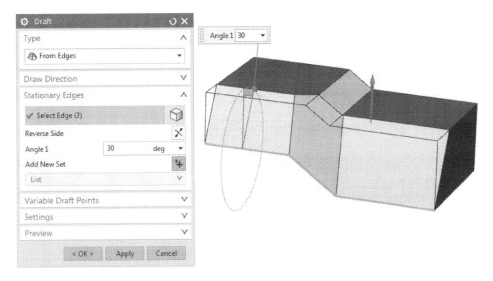

- Click Add New Set and select the stationary edges for the rear face. (You can change the angle or keep it the same.)
- Compare your result to the figure below.

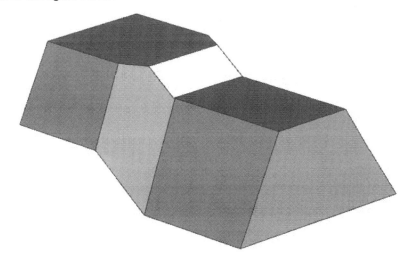

8.4 Chamfer

Chamfer, like the Blend feature, is used to add manufacturing details to solid bodies. They are both typically attached to model edges and may either add or remove material. Because they are parametric, their size is easily modifiable. A chamfer is a flat surface made by cutting off an edge or corner or by adding a flat surface to a corner at an angle.

Consider the solid body shown below. It is tempting to use the sketcher to create the entire top view shape as shown, including the radius and chamfer details. The disadvantage of this approach is that it will result in a more complicated sketch. By using the Blend and Chamfer features to add details (instead of the sketcher) the model will usually be easier to create and will respond to modifications in a more robust fashion.

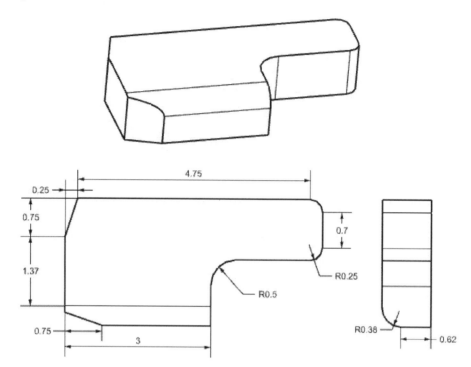

- Create the following sketch.

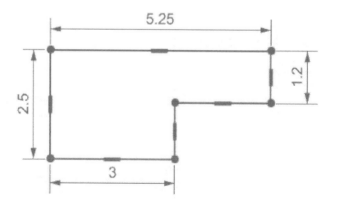

- Extrude by 1in.
- Select Chamfer from the Feature section of Home Tab.
- Select Asymmetric from the Cross Section menu shown below.

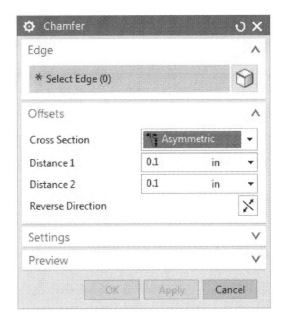

- Pick the Edges as shown in the following figure.

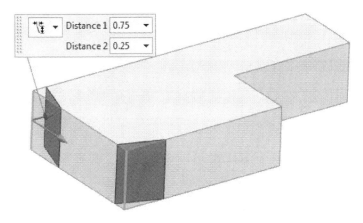

- Enter the values: Distance 1 = 0.75 and Distance 2 = 0.25.
- Select Edge Blend.
- Pick the edge as shown below.
- Enter Radius = 0.5.

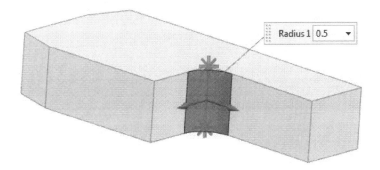

- Click Add New set, then pick the edges shown in the following figure.

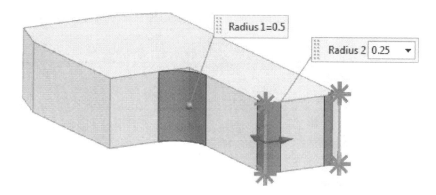

- Enter Radius = 0.25.
- Click Add New Set, pick the edge shown in the following figure.

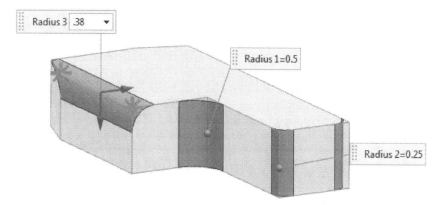

- Enter Radius = 0.38.
- Compare to the following figure.

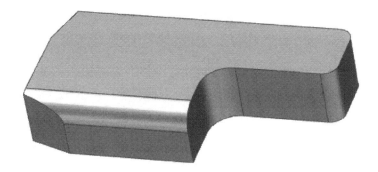

8.5 Bridge

You can create a Bridge between two faces or fill a gap by using the Bridge command. You can choose either the tangent or curvature continuity type between the bridge surface and the faces to be bridged.

Note: The Bridge command applies to surfaces, which is discussed in more detail later in this book. Therefore, the Bridge project detailed below may seem a little advanced to new users. Fear not, and have fun!

- In the sketcher, draw two curves similar in shape and size to those below.

Hint: Use a simple arc for your first curve and a Studio spline with four points for the second.

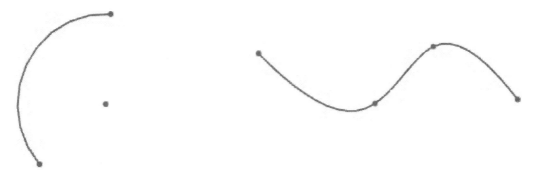

- Extrude the Arc by 4in to create a surface.
- Extrude the Spline 4in with a 5 degree draft as shown next to create the second surface.

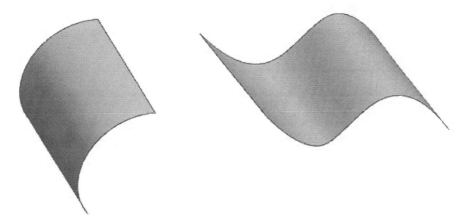

- Select Bridge from the Surface tab.

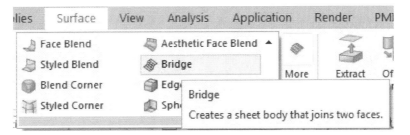

- Select the edge of the arc as Edge 1 and the Edge of the Studio Spline as Edge 2.

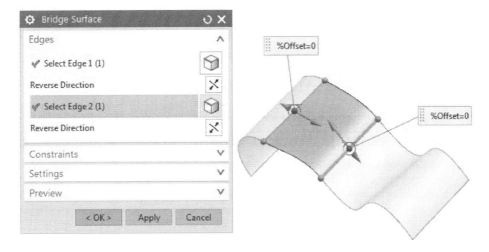

- Compare with the figure below.

- This operation creates a bridge surface, but if you want to make modifications, drag the Magnitude sliders.
- The Flow Direction can be changed to alter the course of the drag.

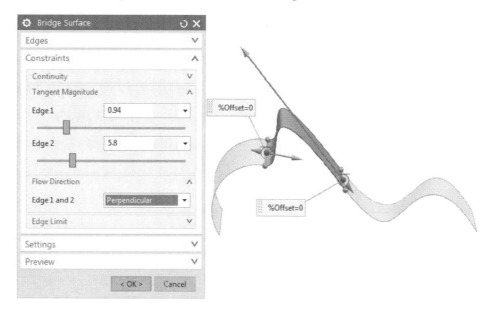

- Compare with the following figure.

8.6 Rib

NX makes it possible to easily create ribs, this new command can take a sketch and extrude, draft and thicken them all at once. This functionality is an amazing time saver for creating ribs or rib like features.

- Sketch a 100 mm x 65 mm rectangle in the X-Y plane, centered about the absolute origin of the part file, and Extrude it by 20 mm with a draft angle of 5 degrees.
- Use Edge Blend to apply 5 mm blends to all the corners shown in the following figure.

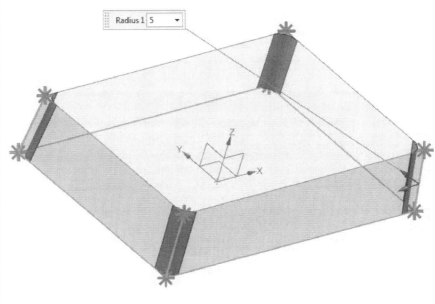

- Use Shell (see 10.2), select the top face and specify a thickness of 2mm.
- Your model should now look like the following figure.

- Click on Sketch and create a sketch on the top face of the part as shown in the following figure. Make sure the lines meet the inside edges of your shell. Notice the two applications of the of the Mirror Curve command in the sketcher.

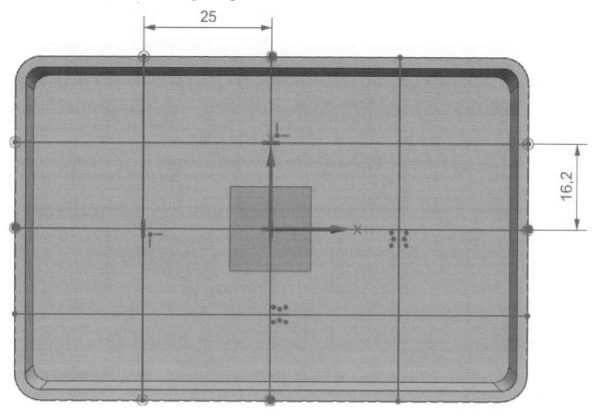

- Now click on the Rib command, and select all the intersecting curves that you created in your sketch. Enter the parameters shown in the Rib dialog box below. Enter a value of 2 degrees for your Draft, then click OK.

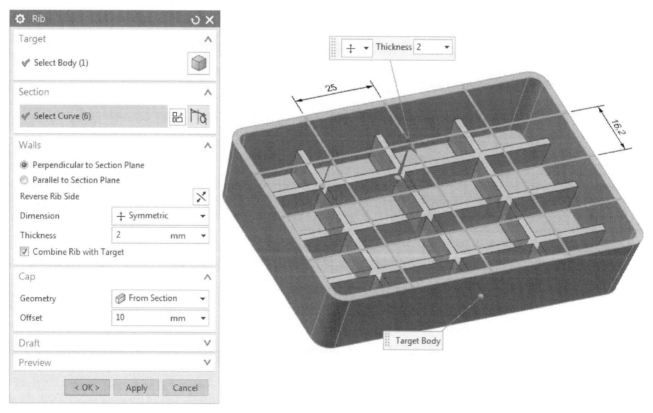

- Your model will now look like the following figure.

8.7   Project – The Pool Rack, Part II

Use the Hole, Pocket and Blend features to add detail to the pool rack model that you made in an earlier project. The finished pool rack is shown below.

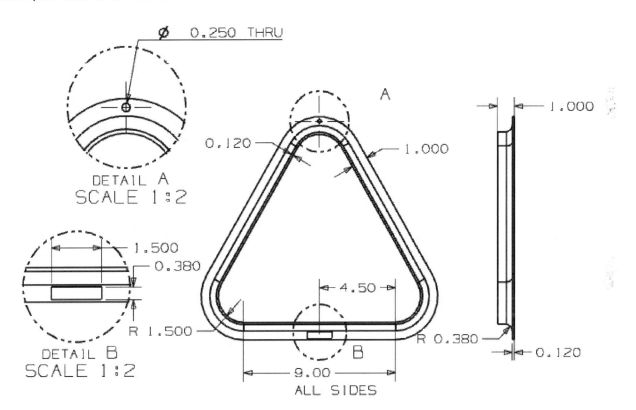

The new details in the pool rack are the 0.38" and 0.5" blends, a pocket in which to place the part number, and a hole for hanging the rack on the wall.

Note: The edges to be blended are a closed loop comprised of several individual edges. For each blend, all adjoining edges must be selected before selecting OK. To make selecting easier, use the Tangent Curves option in the Selection Intent menu. This option will chain all the tangent edges of any edge pick.

- The pocket has a horizontal positioning dimension of 4.5in. If you pick one of the rack's horizontal edges for a target dimension edge, picking near the right endpoint will place a dimension as shown in the figure above. You could also pick one of the rack's curved edges for a target edge. If that is the case, you will get a menu that allows you to dimension to the arc end point, tangent point, or center point.
- The hole is a simple through hole.

9 Datums

9.1 Introduction

Modeling challenging geometry parametrically often requires the use of *reference entities* (or *datums*) such as *datum planes*, *datum axes*, and *datum points*. These can be found in the Datum drop-down menu in the Feature group on the Home tab.

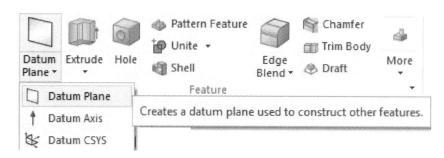

Reference entities are also useful for many other modeling operations such as mirroring, circular patterns, and positioning holes. Defining a reference entity often requires a combination of model geometry and other reference entities. For example, in the figure below, the plane is placed at an angle to the top face. Creating an angled datum plane requires a straight edge or datum axis to define the rotation axis. Since the model in the figure below has no straight edges, a datum axis was created to accomplish this.

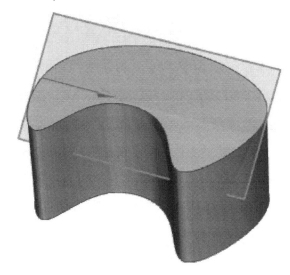

9.2 Datum Plane

Datum planes are very useful for creating sketches, constraining and positioning features, and defining cross-sections for solid models. You may use solid geometric entities (such as faces, vertices, and control points) or other reference entities when defining datum planes.

Thus far, when you have created for sketches, you have used the WCS to locate them. However, datum planes can also be defined using existing solid geometry.

9.2.1 At Distance

Datum planes can be offset from a planar solid face, or from another datum plane.

- Create the following sketch and Extrude by 3in.

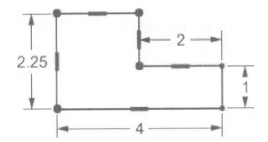

- Select the Datum Plane tool from the Feature group on the Home Tab.
- Set the Type to At Distance.
- Select the top face of the solid. The Datum Plane menu will have an Offset field in which to enter a Distance value and the number of planes to create.

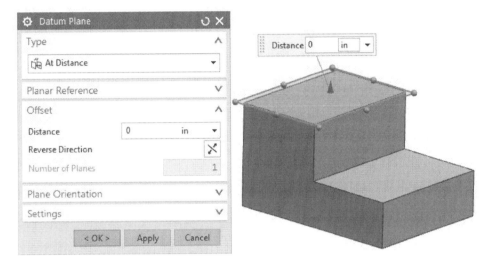

- A preview of the datum plane, along with an arrow appears in the Graphics Window, as shown in the following figure. The arrow indicates the positive offset direction.

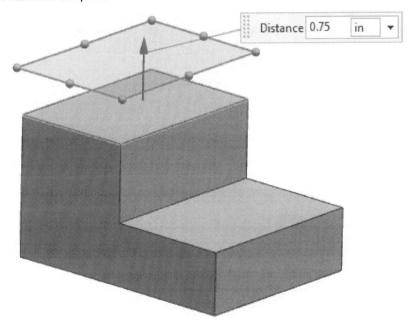

- Enter an Offset Distance of 0.75 in and set the Number of Planes field to 1.
- Repeat this process, but this time the datum plane that you just created as the Planar Reference.
- Type in an Offset Distance value of .38.

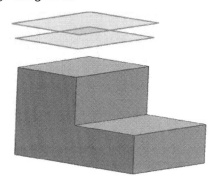

9.2.2 Bisector

The datum plane shown below is centered between the two side faces.

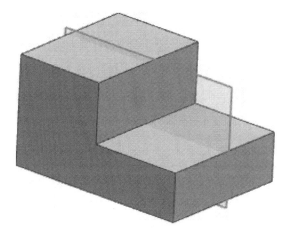

- Either Undo or Delete the datum planes you created in the previous project.
- Select the Datum Plane tool and set the Type to Bisector.
- Designate the left face (shown below) as the First Plane.

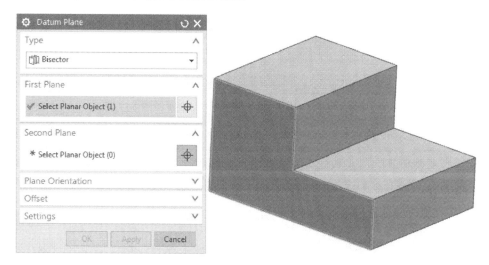

- Rotate the model and select face on the opposite side. *NX 10 automatically creates a center plane.*

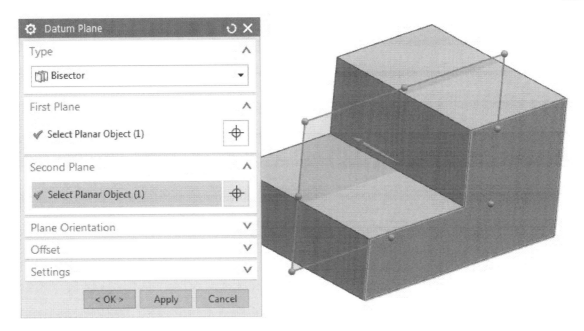

9.2.3 Through Edges

The datum plane in the figure below is placed though two edges. If you pre-select geometric entities prior to invoking the Datum Plane menu, NX 10 will use these entities to infer the datum plane's constraints.

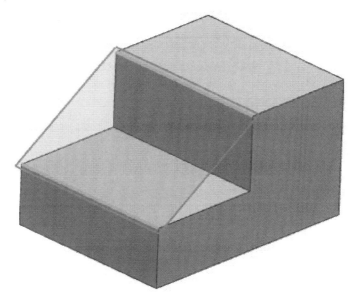

Note: In this project you learned that you can pre-select the objects to create a Datum Plane.

- Either Undo or Delete any datum planes that you created in the previous project.
- Select the Datum Plane tool and set the Type to Two Lines.
- Select the edges of the two steps. NX 10 will display a preview of the datum plane in the Graphics Window.

9.2.4 At Angle

Datum planes may be constrained at an angle to a planar face or a datum plane. In order to accomplish this, it must pass through a linear model edge or a datum axis. The figure below illustrates a typical example of an angled datum plane.

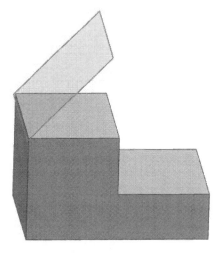

- Either Undo or Delete any datum planes that you created in the previous project.
- Select the Datum Plane tool and set the Type to At Angle.
- Select the planar face as shown in the figure above.
- Select the edge as shown in the figure above.
- In the Angle value field input ±45.

9.2.5 Through Three Points

A datum plane can be determined by three points, as shown in the figure below. To accomplish this, you may select either the vertices or the control points of solid edges. Note the three orange points selected to generate the datum plane shown.

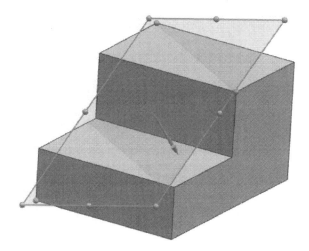

- Either Undo or Delete any datum planes that you created in the previous project.
- Select Datum Plane.
- Set the Type to Inferred.
- Ensure that the End Point icon is toggled on in the Snap Points section of the Selection group.

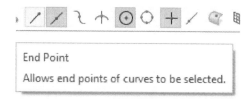

- Select each of the three corners shown above, and click OK!

9.2.6 Tangent

Datum planes can be constrained to be either tangent to cylindrical faces or through the center axis. To explore these options, construct the geometry shown below.

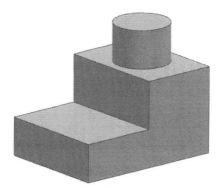

- Either Undo or Delete any datum planes that you created in the previous project.
- Add a boss, centered on the top face, with Diameter = 1.5 and Height = 1 as shown above.
- Select the Datum Plane tool and set the Type to Tangent.
- Select the cylindrical face of the boss. A datum plane preview will appear.

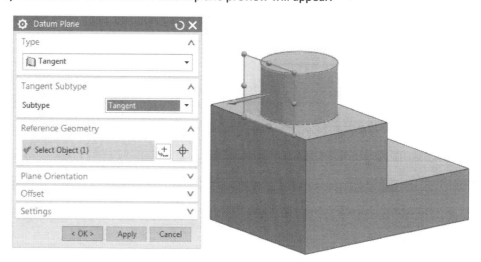

Note: For most types of Datum Planes the Inferred type will yield the correct results.

9.3 Datum Axis

Datum axes are useful for creating angled datum planes and circular patterns, as well as for bodies of revolution. They are defined by specifying constraints and solid geometric entities, just as for Datum Plane features.

Typical objects used to define datum axes include edges, two points on a solid body, the axis of a cylinder, or the intersection of two planes.

9.3.1 Intersection

You will create the two Datum Axis features shown below.

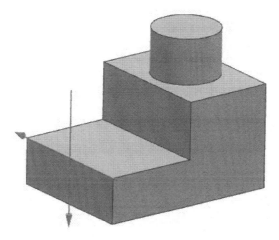

- Continue working on the same part you used in the previous project.
- Select Datum Axis in the Datum Plane drop down.
- Select the horizontal edge as shown above. You should see a preview of the Datum Axis appear.
- Create a Bisector Datum Plane.

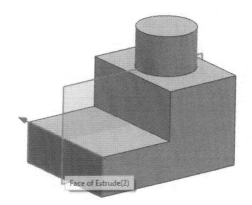

- Create a new Datum Axis.
- Select the Datum Plane as shown above.
- Select the front bottom face as shown. You should see a preview of the second Datum Axis appear.

9.4 Datum Point

The *Datum Point* feature creates a point entity that is fully associative and parametric, meaning that design features can be moved around according to the point to which they are set.

The following exercise shows how to create a point entity and demonstrates its parametric capability.

- Create a Block with dimensions 5 in x 3 in x 1 in.
- Select Datum Point under the Datum Plane dropdown menu.
- The following figure shows the Point dialogue window to control the placement of points. Points can either be placed by the cursor or by typing in the coordinates of exact locations.

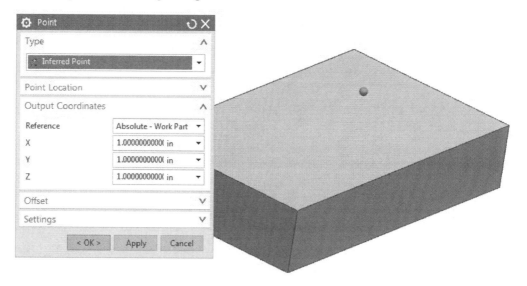

- Create a Point by inserting coordinates into the box shown above, making X, Y and Z all 1in. A point will be created as shown above.
- Create a Boss with a height of 1in and a diameter of 0.5in. Place the boss on the top surface and then use the Point onto Point positioning function to position the Boss onto the newly created Point entity.

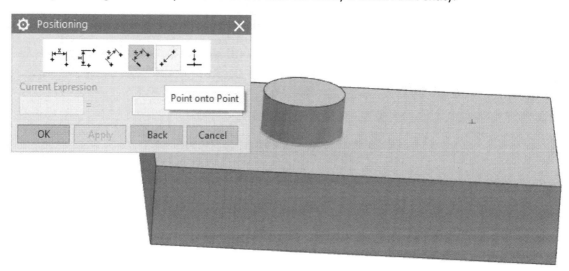

- Click the Datum Point.

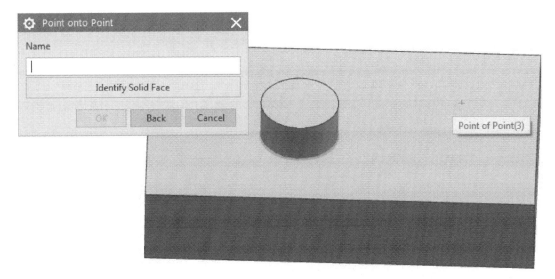

- The boss will move to the center of the point as shown in the following figure.

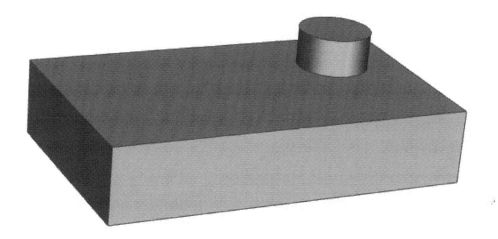

10 Trims, Offsets, and More

10.1 Introduction

NX 10 contains a swath of useful tools for sculpting a complex model out of a simpler shape, such as a block. Trims and offsets are fundamental operations in solid modeling, and we would be remiss not to share some of the most basic and effective of those tools with you. Many of the tools you will use in the exercises below are found in the Trim and Offset/Scale groups in the More gallery in the Feature group on the Home tab.

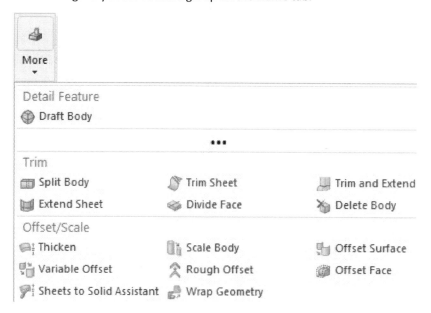

10.2 Shell

The Shell tool removes material from an existing solid body, resulting in a solid body of constant wall thickness. In defining a Shell feature, you specify faces that to be removed by the tool. The figure below shows two solids that are shelled with a 0.25 in wall thickness. The body on the left had the top face removed, while the body on the right had the top, left, and right faces removed.

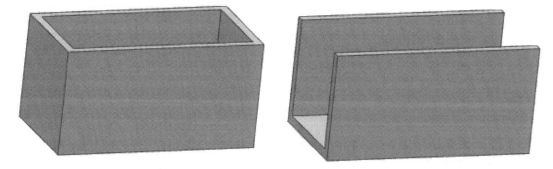

In this exercise, you will create the flanged bushing shown on the following page by shelling an extrusion. The Shell tool is found in the Feature group on the Home tab.

- Extrude a circle of diameter **3 inches** by **4 inches** in the +Z direction and create a secondary **Extrude** with a depth of **0.38** and an offset of **0.75in** outward to create an annular cylinder, as shown in the following figure.

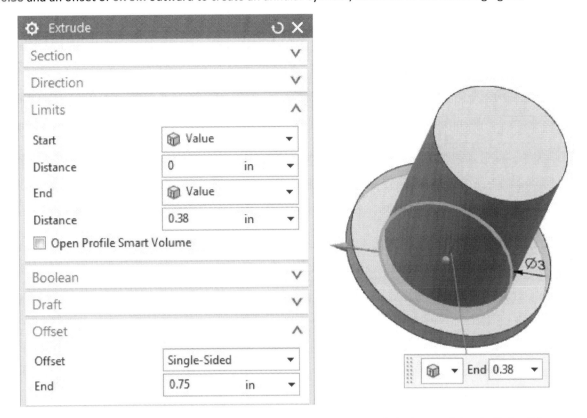

- Select the **Shell** tool, and input a **Thickness** of **0.38in**. This will be the wall thickness of the shelled solid.

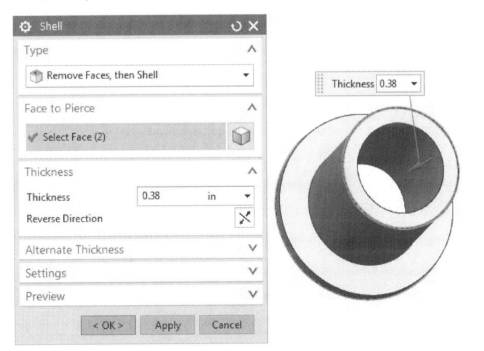

- Pick the top and bottom faces of the bushing as shown in the previous figure.
- Your model should look like the following figure.

- **Save** the model and rename it as *'bushing_<your initials>.prt'* .

Note: If you simply want to give an entire body a wall thickness, i.e. to hollow it, use the shell all faces option as shown in the left figure.

10.3 Delete Body

Delete Body is an extremely useful trim operation that we will use in the next few exercises (and throughout the remainder of the book). Quite simply, it deletes a sheet or solid body from your model. You might ask – why use Delete Body over Delete? The difference is that Delete Body is a parametric operation, and appears in the model history.

This means that Delete Body is suppressible, and can itself be deleted! This tool is fantastic for cleaning your model of construction geometry, but allows for modifications to that construction geometry, should the need for changes arise.

10.4 Trim Body

The Trim Body tool is used to remove part of a solid body using either a datum plane or a sheet body as a trimming tool. You can specify which part of the body you wish to remove by changing the direction of the red trimming arrows.

Note: Trim body features fail if the operation splits the body into multiple pieces.

10.4.1 Trimming with a Datum Plane

In these examples you will create a solid body and trim it using a datum plane and a face.

- Create a **4in x 4in x 8in** block, and place a Bisector datum plane at the midpoint of one of the **8 inch** edges.
- Select Trim Body from the Feature group of the Home tab, and select the block as the Target.

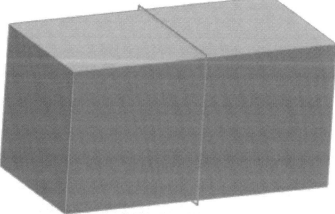

- Select the datum plane as the Tool.

- After selecting the block as the target and the datum plane as the tool, a direction arrow appears. You can choose to reverse the trimming direction using the Reverse Direction button.

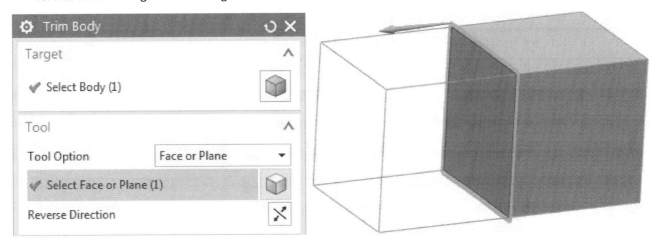

- Compare your results to the figure below.

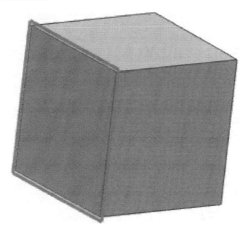

10.4.2 Trimming with a Sheet Body

- Undo the trim operation from the last project.
- Create a curve and Extrude it to create a sheet body, as shown in the following figure. Make sure that all edges of the sheet body extend beyond the block.

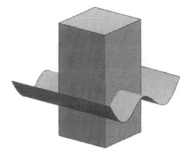

- Select Trim Body, and choose the block as the Target.
- Select the sheet body as the Tool.
- Use Delete Body on the extruded sheet.

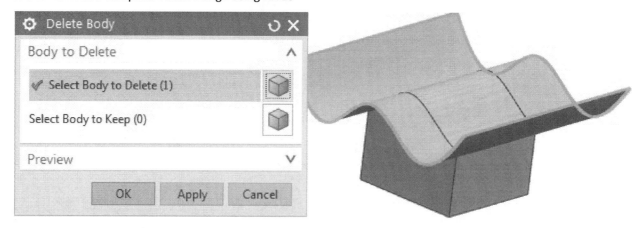

- Compare your results to the figure below.

10.5 **Split Body**

In this exercise, you will use the extruded sheet body to split the block, rather than to trim it.

- Undo the Trim and Delete Body operations from the previous project.
- Select Split Body, and select the block as the Target.
- Select the extruded sheet body as the Tool.

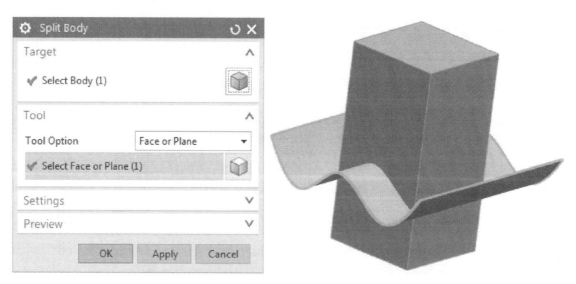

- Compare your results with the following figure. Don't be fooled by your cursor - the output of the operation is two separate solid bodies. The block will still highlight as a single entity when you put your cursor over either of the two bodies, but that is because of your Selection Filter settings. Change your Selection Filter to Solid Body and you will be able to select each of the bodies individually.

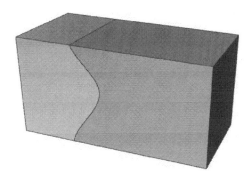

10.6 **Offset Face**

The Offset Face feature offsets one or more solids along their normal vector. The Offset Face feature is very useful when making small changes to existing models and can be applied to both parametric and non-parametric models.

In this exercise you will use the bushing from the previous section and offset the upper face of the flange such that it is only 0.18in thick.

- Open the part file *bushing_your_initials.prt*.
- Select Offset Face.

The flange is 0.38 in thick; the goal is to decrease the thickness to 0.18 in. Thus, this face must be offset by -0.2 in.

- Input an Offset Value of -0.2.
- Pick the face as shown in the following figure.

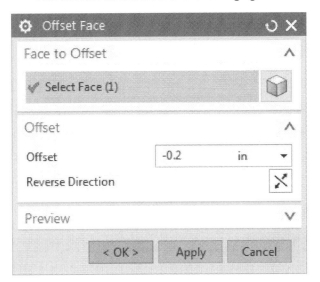
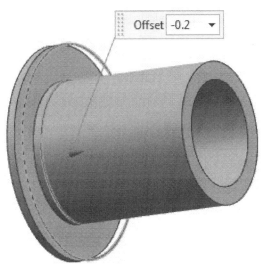

- After selecting OK you will see the thickness of the flange decrease, as shown below. Save when you are done!

10.7 **Thicken**

Thicken is a useful feature when importing surfaces from external software packages. The command allows you to create a solid body from a sheet (surface) body.

- Create a spline curve similar to the following figure and Extrude it into a sheet body.

- Select the Thicken tool. In the Thicken window, enter Offset 1 = 0.2 as shown in the following figure.

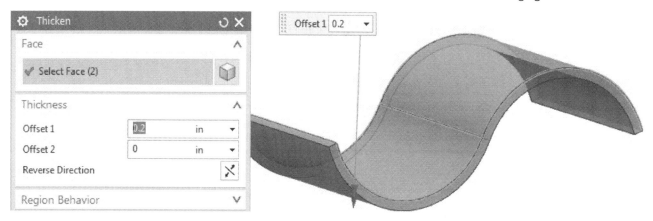

Note: the direction of the arrow. Input a negative value or click the Reverse Direction button if you would like to reverse the direction.

- Select the curve sheet as the Face to thicken.
- Compare your results to the figure below.

10.8 **Tube**

The Tube tool is a special case of the Sweep along Guide feature. It creates solid geometry by sweeping a circular section along an arbitrary guide curve.

The figure below shows a tube feature that has been created using a helical guide curve.

Note: This is a common way to create a spring. Use the Helix command from the Curve tab as your guide string.

Tube features can also be defined using solid edges as the guide curve. The following figure shows a cylinder with a tube cutout at the end – perhaps the shaft needs to mate against an o-ring.

- Create a 2in diameter Cylinder that is 3in long.
- Select Tube.
- Input an Outer Diameter of 0.5 and an Inner Diameter of 0 in the Tube menu (shown in the following figure). Non-zero values for the inner diameter result in a hollow tube.

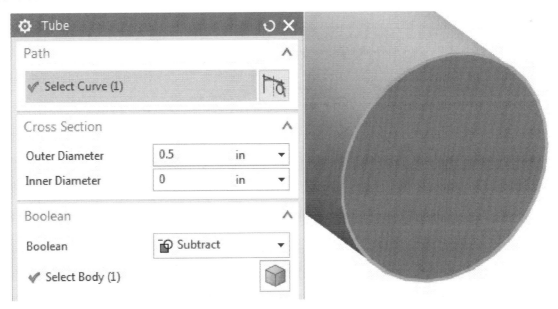

- Pick the top edge of the cylinder as shown in the previous figure.
- Select Subtract from the Boolean menu.
- Compare your results to the figure at the beginning of the project.

10.9 **Extract Geometry**

The Extract Geometry command allows you to make copies of existing geometry. The original geometry can then be hidden leaving you with only the face or region you desire. New geometry can then be created using your extracted feature, ensuring a perfect match.

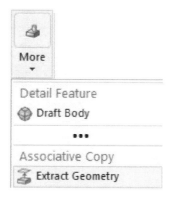

The following exercise is a very basic example of how this command is used.

- Create a model similar to the figure below.

- Select Extract Geometry, and set the Type to Face as shown in the following figure. Select the curved surface and the back vertical surface as your face to extract.

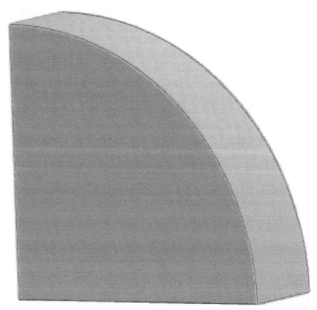

- Of the checkboxes at the bottom, the most important is the Associative checkbox. If you check this box, a link will be established between the original geometry, and the copy created. This means that as you modify the original, the copy will change as well.

Note: NX 10 has now created a curved surface identical to the one you selected. It is located in the same position as the original feature.

10.10 Emboss

The *Emboss* command is used to create geometry that might be punched into a thin sheet of metal or plastic. To use it, you start with a sheet solid and some contour curves such as a sketch or, in many cases, letters. Then the emboss command gives you the opportunity to use various options to create the geometry. You can apply draft angles and "end options" that allow you to control the way the top of the new surface will look.

Although the Emboss command allows only one closed profile at a time, it allows you to apply a draft to the geometry as well as a uniform offset from the surface you are embossing. This can be a bit confusing but we will walk you through it in the following example.

Open a new part file. Make sure you set the Units to Inches.

- Create a simple surface and a keyhole shaped sketch on an offset plane. Make the offset space about 2 inches away from the surface as shown below:

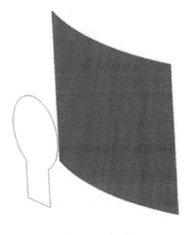
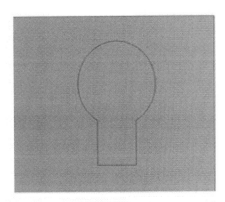

Isometric View   Head on view

- Select the Emboss tool from the More gallery in the Feature group on the Home tab.
- Select the Feature Curves from the selection intent pull-down menu.
- Select the sketch section curves and middle-click.
- Select the sheet body and middle-click.
- Set the End Cap in the following way.
  - Geometry = Selected Faces
  - Location = Translate
  - Distance = -0.2

- Set the Draft options to:
- o Draft = From End Cap
- o Angle 1 = 3°
- o Check Set All to Same Value.
- Set all other options as default.
- Select OK.

The result is shown below:

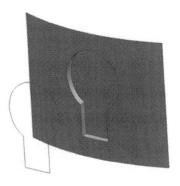

10.11 **Project – The Attachment Arm**

A simple approach to building an attachment arm for a robotic fixture, as shown below, involves a combination of the Shell, Offset Face, and Tube features.

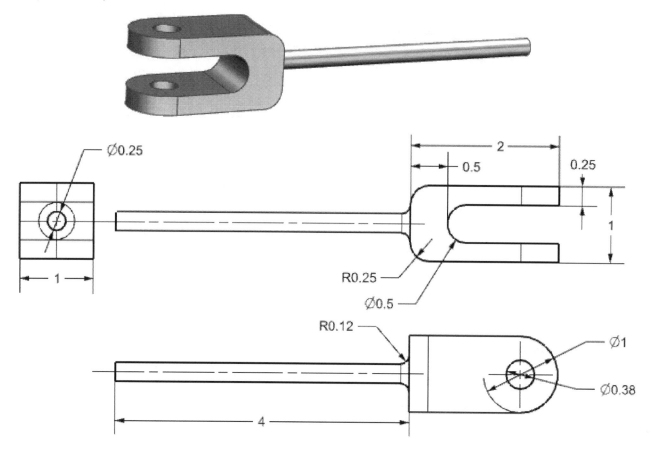

- Create the sketch as shown below. The shaft and the head will be created separately and then United.

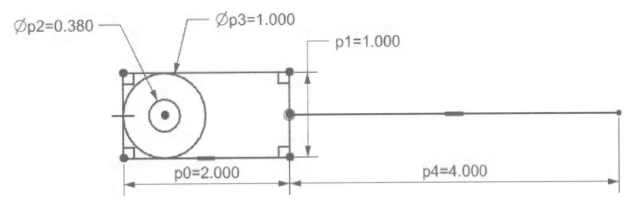

- Extrude the end profile by changing your Selection Intent to Connected Curves and Stop at Intersection.

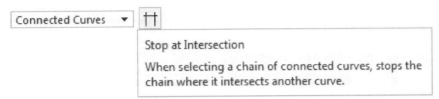

Stop at Intersection

When selecting a chain of connected curves, stops the chain where it intersects another curve.

- Use the option Symmetric Value and set the Distance to 0.5in.

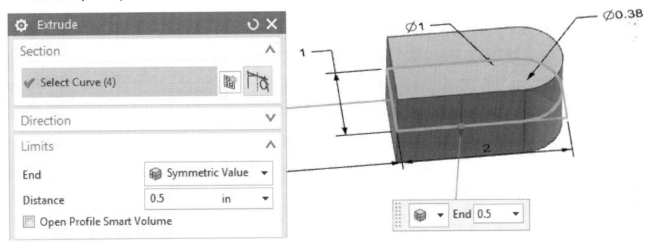

- Shell the end by piercing three faces with a 0.25in wall thickness. Compare to the figure below.

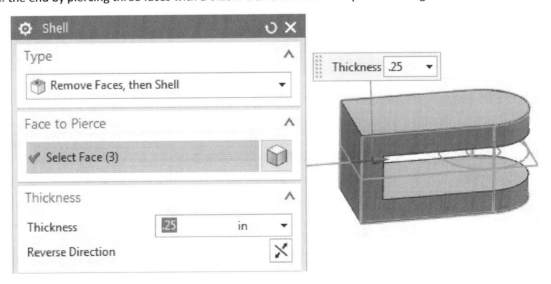

- Now, suppose a design evaluation has resulted in the necessity of making the base **0.5in** thick versus the current **0.25in** thickness.
- Use the **Offset Face** feature to achieve the correct thickness.

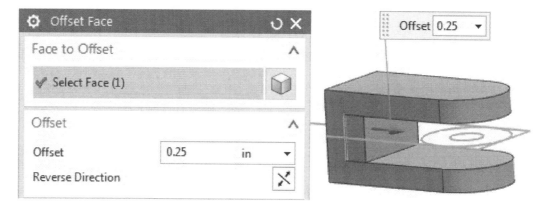

- **Extrude** the **0.38 in** circle to create a hole through both ends. Use **Through All** as the **Start** and **End Limits**.

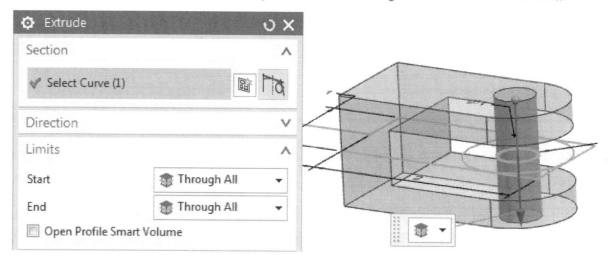

- Add the remaining **Blend** features to the end extrusion.

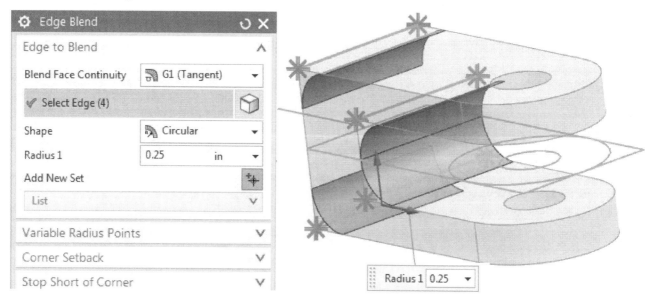

- Add a **Tube** feature to create the shaft.

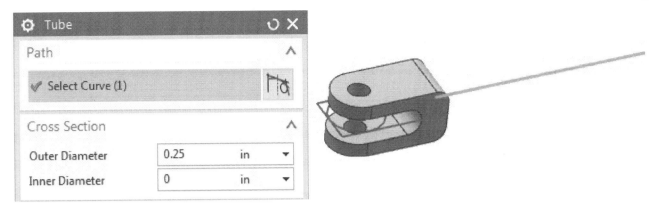

- Unite the shaft to the end extrusion and add the final 0.12in radius blend.

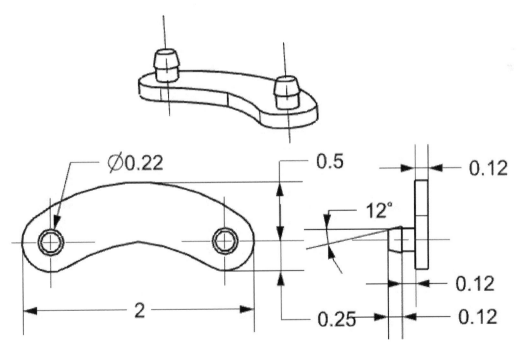

10.12 **Project – The Clip**

A good strategy to create the clip model shown below involves using the Mirror Geometry, Draft Faces, and the Boss features.

- Create the sketch shown in the following figure. The center of the side arc is point on curve to the bottom horizontal reference line. The center of the top and bottom arcs should be aligned to the vertical line. Make the top and bottom arcs concentric. (Be careful not to over-constrain the sketch – it's pretty easy to do.)

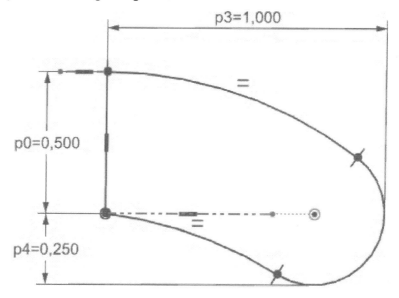

- **Extrude** the sketch **0.12 in** to build the base of the clip.

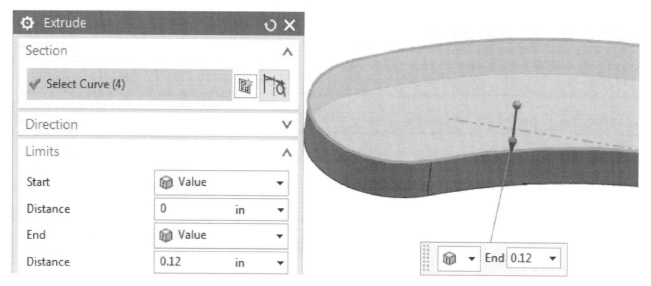

- Position a boss at the center of the outer arc.

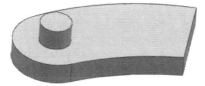

- Position a second boss centered on top of the first boss (*be sure to set the Draft angle in the Boss command*).

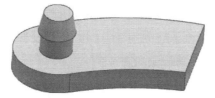

- Use **Mirror Geometry** and mirror across the planar face, then **Unite**.

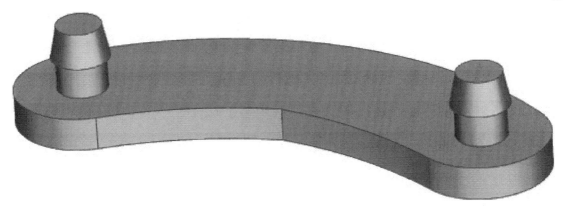

11 Three Dimensional Curves

11.1 Introduction

In NX 10, the definition of 'curve' includes lines, arcs, circles, ellipses, and splines, as well as other non-solid, non-sketch geometry (e.g. text can also be treated as a set of curves). Curves can either be parametric or 'dumb.' Parametric curves are defined in space by specific, numeric parameters. All parametric curves are listed in the Part Navigator. 'Dumb' curves are non-quantified entities which do not have parameters defining their position. A 'dumb' curve will not be listed in the Part Navigator.

The tools discussed in this chapter are all found on the Curve tab.

11.2 Basic Curves

The Basic Curves tool allows you to place lines, arcs, circles, and other simple curves from within one tool. The curves created in this way are non-parametric, so they will not be listed in the Part Navigator. The Basic Curves icon is found in the More gallery on the Curve tab.

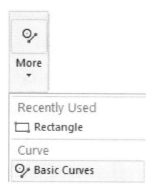

- Create a new file called *curve_<your initials>.prt*
- Open the Basic Curves tool.

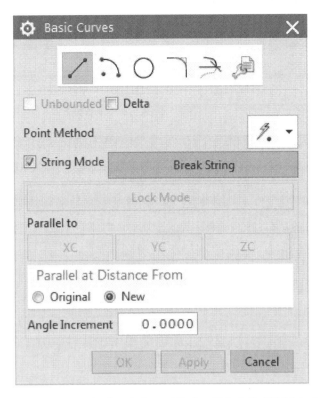

- Select the Line icon and set the point method to Inferred Point. This tells NX 10 to 'guess' how you want to create curves based upon where you pick in the Graphics Window – it does a pretty good job once you get used to it.
- Make sure that the String Mode box is checked. When this option is enabled, NX 10 automatically starts defining a new entity at the end point of the last entity that you created.

Note: In this detail, all screen picks are automatically placed in the XC-YC plane of the WCS. This is always the case for screen picks.

- Pick the screen locations 1, 2, and 3 in the Graphics Window to create the lines shown in the figure below. NX 10 will interpret the screen picks as the line endpoints. Remember to read the Cue; it will prompt you for a start and end point for each line.

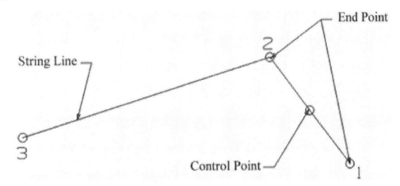

- Select Break String from the Basic Curves dialog box to begin a line with a new end point.

Note: Clicking the middle mouse button also interrupts String Mode.

- Uncheck the String Mode radio button.

Note: Although string mode can be very useful, it is often desirable to disable it temporarily.

- Create two or three more lines – *Have a ball!*
- Select the Circle icon.
- Click in the Graphics Window at the approximate location of the circle center as in the following figure.
- Click where you want the circumference of the circle to be. *Compare your results to the figure below.*

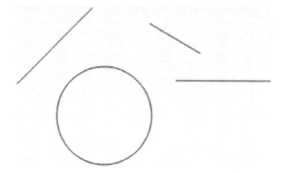

- Select the Arc icon .
- Select the Start, End, Point on Arc button.
- Pick the first endpoint of the arc.
- Pick the second endpoint of the arc.

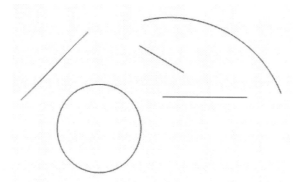

- Select a third point to define the arc itself. Compare your results to the figure shown above.

Note: The arc will drag more intuitively if the cursor is kept roughly equidistant from the endpoints.

11.3 Associative Lines and Arcs

The Line and Arc commands can be used to create associative lines and arcs with parametric values. Although these curves are planar, they are *not sketch curves* – they are defined by points in 3d space. Be careful not to confuse the parametric 3d curve tools with the sketch tools on the Curve tab – they are right next to each other and their icons are very similar!

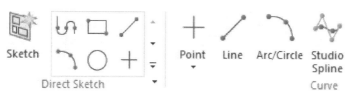

Project 3.6.1

- Create a new part.
- Select the Line tool from the Curve tab.

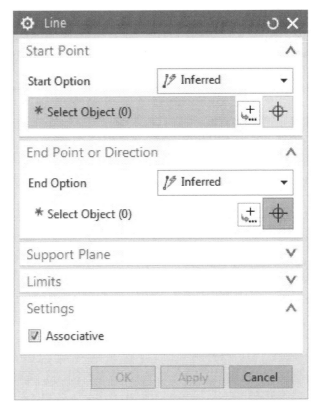

- Make sure that the Associative check box is checked as in the above figure. When this option is enabled, NX 10 *automatically creates parametric lines* with associations to other existing parametric curves.
- Click anywhere on the screen and create lines similar to those in the preceding geometry figure. Middle click after every line you create. Notice NX 10 has no default control points for Associative lines and arcs. Instead, Snap Points must be assigned to allow you to choose End Point, Mid Point, Point on Curve, etc. The figure below shows the Snap Point window.

> ***Note:*** *The Snap Point Toolbar is available in any command where it is required.*

- Select the Arc / Circle tool from the Curve Tab.

Arc/Circle

- Using the Line and Arc command with End Point and Mid Point Snap Points on, create lines and arcs similar to those in the previous geometry figure.
- Notice that by right-clicking on any of the lines or arcs and selecting Edit Parameters, an edit window appears as in the figure below. You can modify the parametric values associated with the curve – a feature not possible with Basic Curves.

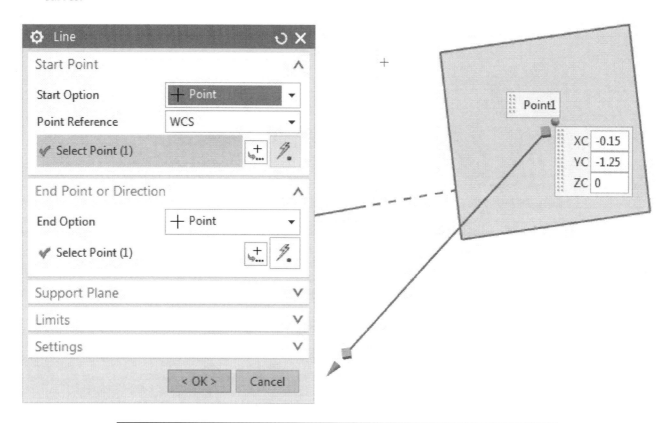

> **Note:** Click on the Part Navigator icon located on the left side of the screen. Notice how associative lines and arcs drawn are listed, whereas basic curves are not listed.

11.3.1 Tangent Lines

It is often necessary to create curves with certain relations to other curves, such as parallel, perpendicular, tangent, etc. The approach for creating such geometry is to pick an existing curve on which the new geometry will be based and then pick some second defining restraint. For this topic, make sure that the point method is set to 'Infer'.

To create tangent lines, simply pick a circle or an arc and choose an end point for the line. In the following project you will create a line tangent to a circle and to a point, as in the following figure.

- Create a new part file named *curve2_<your initials>.*
- Create a circle of any dimension.

- Select Home Tab / Datum Plane Drop Down / Datum Point.

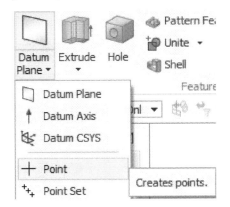

- Select the Associative Point icon from the dialog box as shown below.

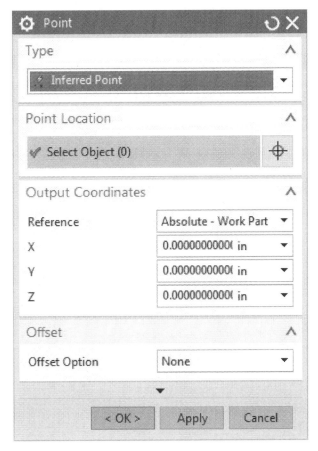

Note: The order of your picks is not significant here. For example, you could have picked the point first and the circle second and gotten the same resulting lines.

- Pick a point anywhere on the screen. Recall that this is done with the Quick View Pop-Up menu activated by the right mouse button.
- To create Line 1, select Curve Tab / Line.
- Pick the circle. Do not pick a control point. You will see a tangent line that can be dragged to an endpoint.
- Pick the point.
- Create Line 2 just as you did Line 1. If the tangent line comes from the wrong 'side' of the circle, simply pass the cursor through the inside of the circle and the tangency point will be corrected.

11.4 **Spline Curves**

The Studio Spline function allows you to create a closed/open loop, non-parametric General Spline curve. Spline curves are extremely useful when creating geometry that is of a free-flowing, organic, or smooth nature (e.g. prosthetic devices and highly designed consumer products).

11.4.1 **Spline**

The figure below is a Studio Spline curve made from 5 points.

- Select the Studio Spline tool from the Curve tab.

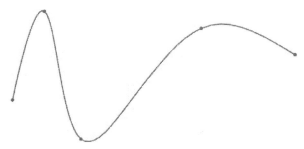

- The following dialog box is shown.

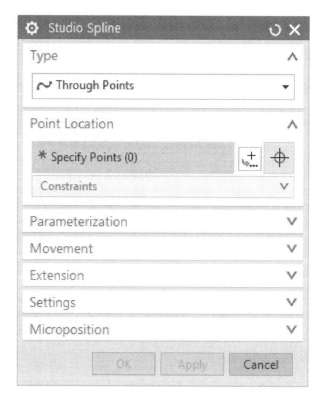

- Click Through Points for the spline Type.
- Type 2 in the Degree parameters dialog box as shown below.

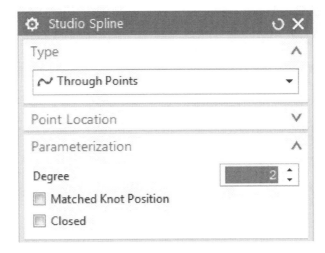

- Click in the viewport to create points for the Spline to travel across.
- Compare your results to the figure below

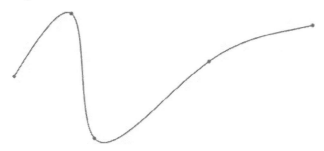

11.5 **Helix**

A helix can be created for use as a guide string. This is especially useful for designing springs like the one seen below.

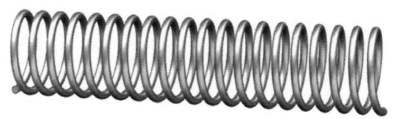

Parametric helices can be made quickly using the Helix command. The 'Use Law' switch allows you to vary the radius of the turns as you go. You will see a variety of choices, the most common of which is a linear law.

Project 3.7.1

- Select Curve Tab / Helix.
- Set the Length Method to Limits.
- Enter 20 in the End Limit dialog box under Length.
- Enter 2 in the Pitch dialog box
- Enter 2 in the Radius value dialog box, as shown in the following figure.

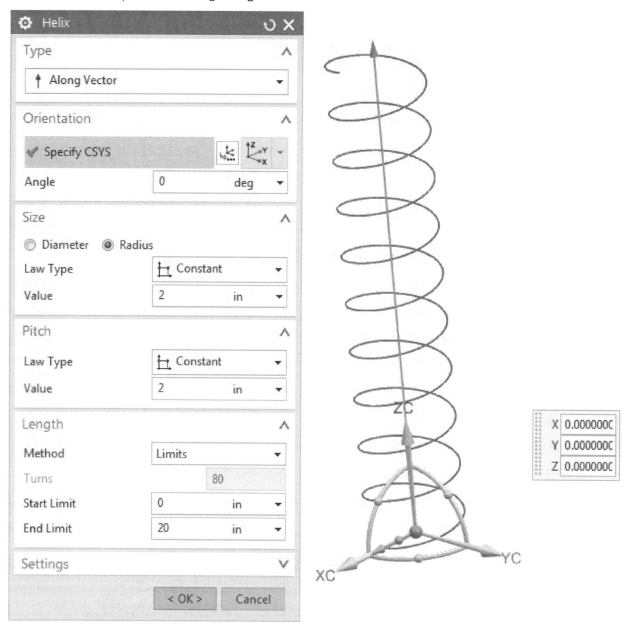

- Choose OK *or* middle-click. Compare your results with our previous geometry.

11.6 **Text Curves**

Text curves allow you to make solid models of actual text. For example, when creating a casting model with a brand name etched onto one side, text curves can be used to extrude letters of the brand name onto the part. But you need to know how to create text before you can extrude it.

11.6.1 **Text Curves**

Written text curves can be created quickly using the Text command.

- Select Curve Tab / Text.
- Select text Type to Planar.
- Enter any text with the font you want in the Text box shown below.

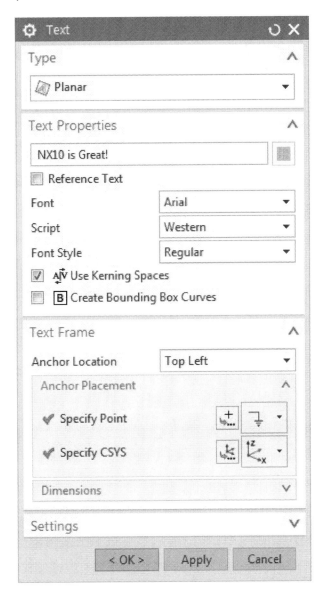

- Try to hold and drag the handles one at a time and see how you can stretch and rotate the text with the Dynamic Handles (see below). Have some fun stretching the text around.
- Left-click anywhere on the modeling screen to place the text and hit OK. Compare your results to the previous figure.

You can also choose to create the text with a bounding box by clicking the 'Create Bounding Box Curves' button shown above.

11.6.2 **Text on Curve**

Text curves can be created using a guide curve that determines the form of text.

- Create a Cylinder and draw an arc on one end of the cylinder.
- Select Curve Tab / Text.
- Select text type On Curve.
- Type the text using the Natural vertical direction as shown below.
- Select curve for text to follow.
- Adjust height and length using either the Dynamic or input boxes (*see below*).

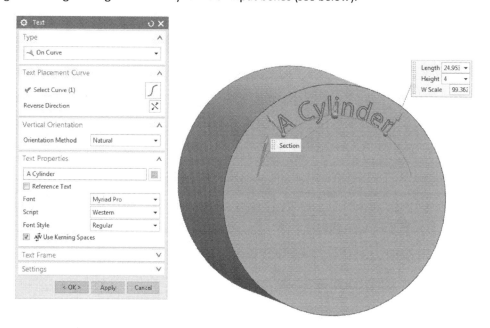

11.6.3 **Text on Face**

Text curves can also be created on a face using a guide curve.

- Create a Cylinder.
- Select Curve Tab / Text.
- Select text type On Face.
- Type the text as shown in the following figure.
- Read the Cue, select the cylindrical face to place the text.
- Select the edge curve as the location curve.
- Adjust the text using handles and input boxes as shown in the following figure.

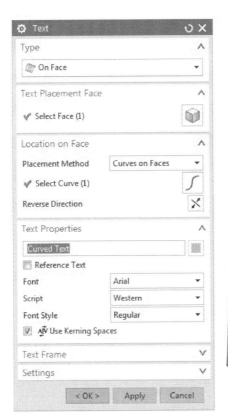

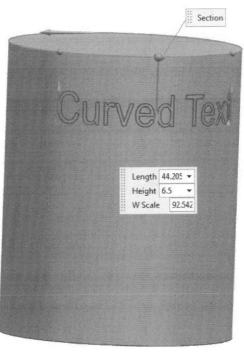

11.7 **Bridge Curves**

The Bridge Curve function allows you to select a pair of curves and connect them to provide one smooth curve. This function can create either non-parametric or parametric curves. The bridge curve is excellent for shapes that have to blend together smoothly, such as the geometry needed to transition from a rectangular opening to an oval shaped opening as shown in the following figure.

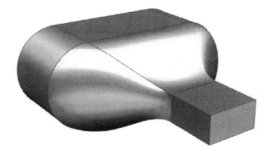

- Create the following sketch

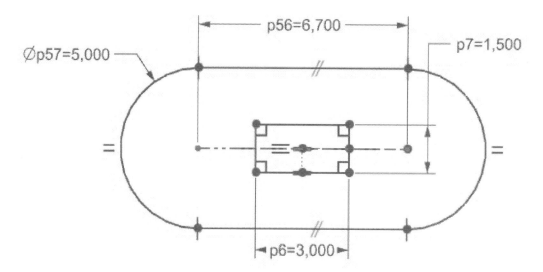

- **Extrude** the center rectangle with a Start Distance of -1in and an End Distance of -4in.

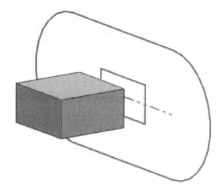

- **Extrude** the larger tangent section with a Start Distance of 4in and an End Distance of 8in.

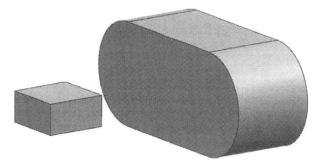

- Select **Bridge Curve** from the Curve Tab.

- Create a bridge curve between the top edge of the block and the tangent edge of the rounded body as shown in the following figure.

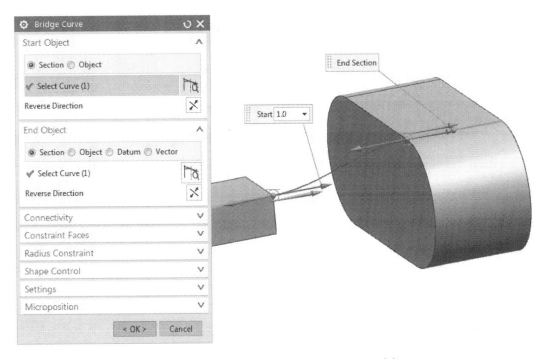

Notice how the Bridge Curve function automatically connects the two curves with a smooth line.

- Do the same for each side until you have 4 bridge curves, as shown in the following figure:

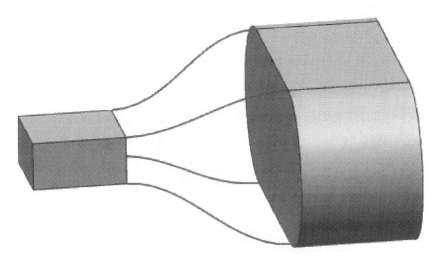

Note: Be careful when clicking on the curves to bridge. Clicking near the endpoint from which you intend to connect the curve will ensure the Bridge Curve command will operate smoothly. If you click on a curve nearer the other endpoint, the Bridge Curve command will attempt to create a smooth curve from that end instead.

- Next select Swept from the Surface group of the Home tab.

- Select the vertical edge connecting the two bridge curves as the first Section.

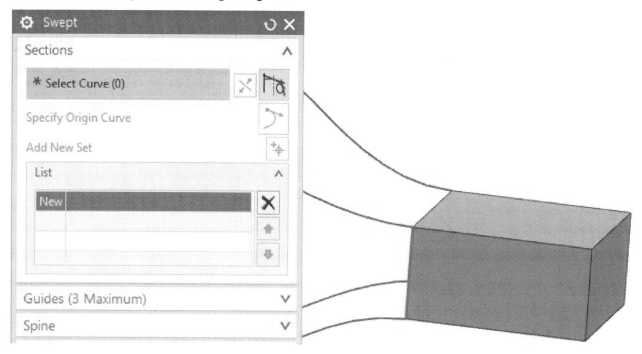

- Select **Add New Set**, Select the edge of the rounded side of the second body connecting the same bridge curves as the Second Section.

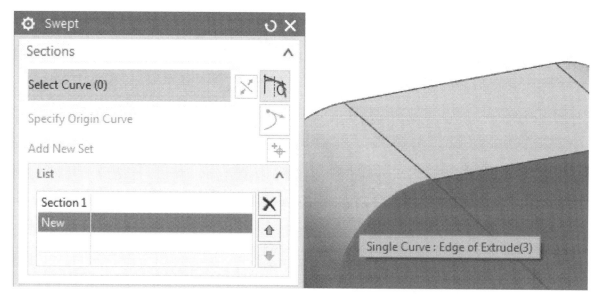

- Select one of the connected bridge curves as the first guide.

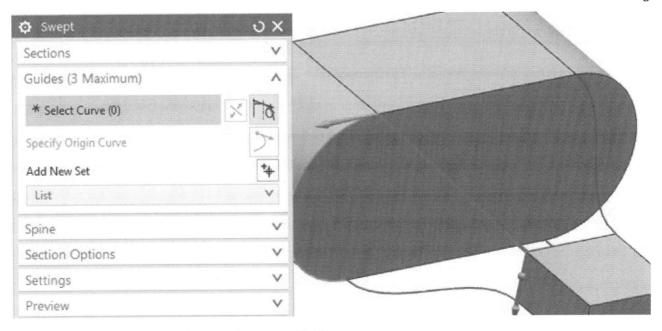

- Select **Add New Set**, Select the second connected bridge curve.

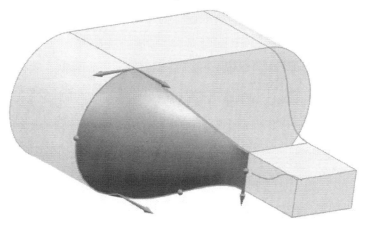

- A surface connecting the two shapes has been created. To the same for the other 3 open sections to complete the body.

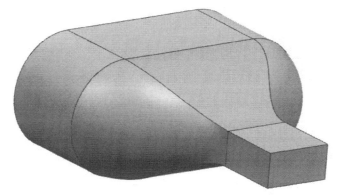

- Compare your results with the figure above.

11.8 **Join Curves**

The Join Curves command allows you to select distinct curves and connect them to provide one continuous curve. This function can create either non-parametric or parametric curves.

Below are shown three curves in 3D space. One curve was created on the XY plane and two curves (one line and one arc) were created in the YZ plane.

The following figures illustrate the difference between swept features created with and without the Join Curves command. Notice the line separating the swept feature in the first model illustrating two separate lines. The second feature does not have this line and thus illustrates how the Join command was used to connect the two lines shown in the previous figure.

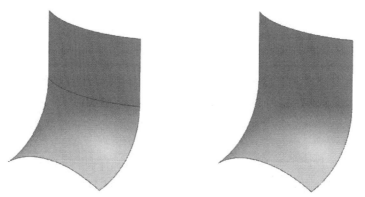

The following project will use the Join Curves command to create a smooth transition edge blend.

- Start by creating a 4in x 4in x 4in Block
- Create the following sketch on the side of the block.

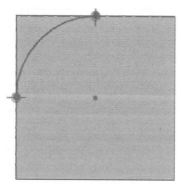

- Use Join Curves to create a tangent curve as shown in the following figure.

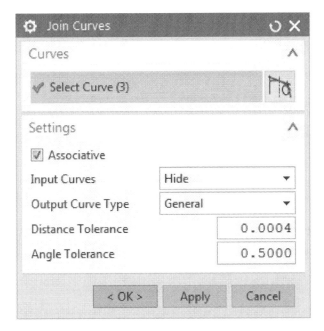

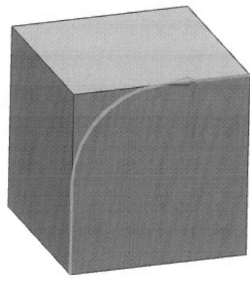

- Extrude the curve to create a cutting sheet.

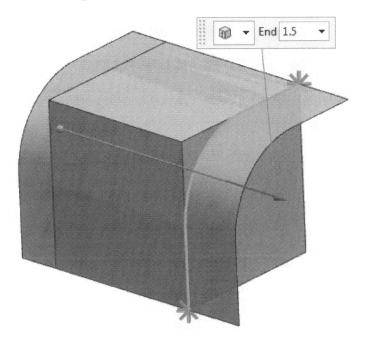

- Offset the front and top faces by 0.01 in.

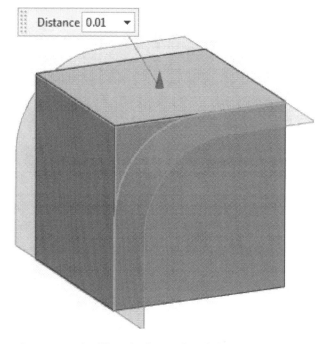

- Use the Trim Body command to create the filleted edge and and then use the Delete Body command to remove the unwanted sheet body.
- Compare your results to the following figure.

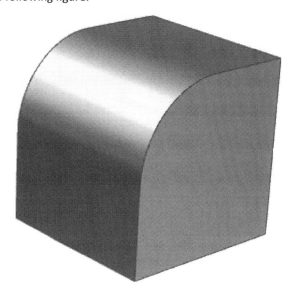

11.9 **Project Curves**

The Project Curve function allows you to select a curve and a specified plane and project the original curve onto a plane or face, as shown below. This function can create either non-parametric or parametric curves.

In this project, the focus will be on projecting curves onto a curved surface and using the Thicken command with region option. This will create a variable curved surface you might see on a high quality gaming mouse.

- Create the following sketch

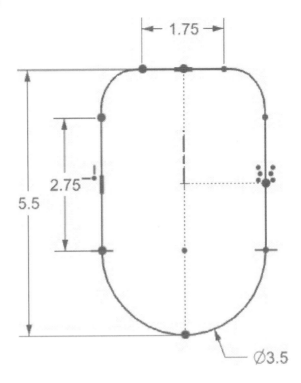

- Extrude the sketch by 2in.

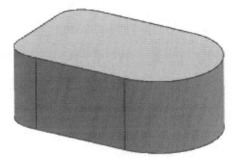

- Create the following sketch on the side face, this will be used as a cutting tool.
- Try creating the sketch using a Studio Spline.

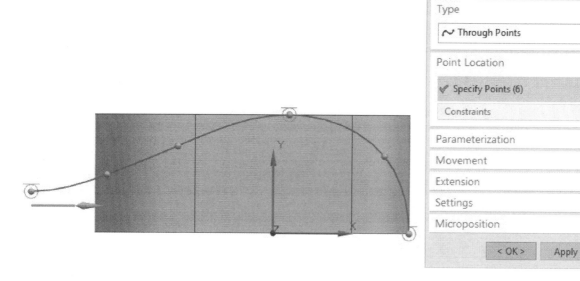

- **Extrude** the sketch so that the resulting sheet goes beyond the edges of the solid body as shown in the following figure.

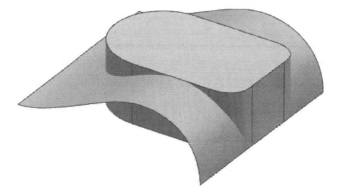

- **Trim** the top half of the solid body off using the newly created sheet. Use **Delete Body** to remove the sheet afterwards.

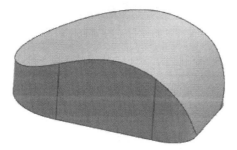

- Next **Extrude** a sheet body downward from the bottom edges and add a **40** degree **Draft**.

212

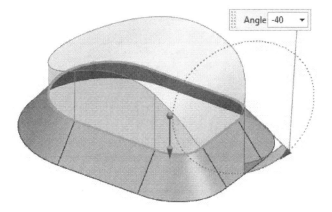

- Create an **N-Sided Surface** using the selected edges shown. Set the Type to **Trimmed**, Check the **Trimmed to Boundary** box.
- For the **Constraint Faces**, select the drafted bottom sheet body that was extruded.
- Compare to the following figure.

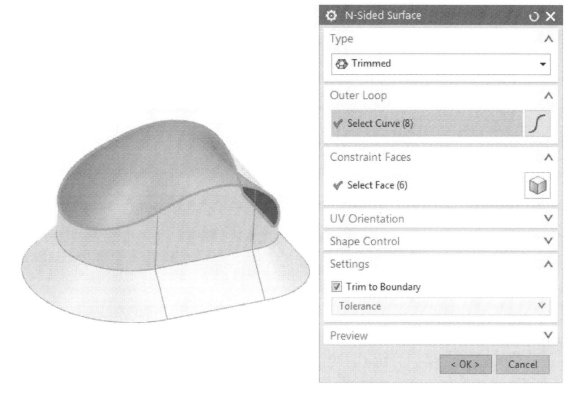

- Use **Replace Face** to switch the top face of the mouse body with the newly created **N-Sided Surface**.

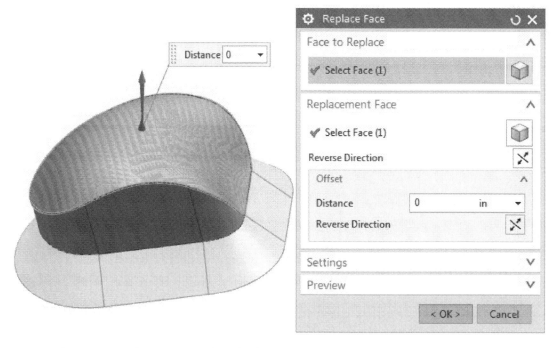

- Use Delete Body to remove the remaining sheet bodies and add a 0.5in Edge blend to the top edges as shown in the following figure.

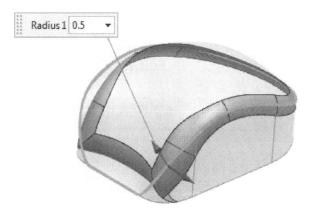

- Do the same for the bottom edges as shown.

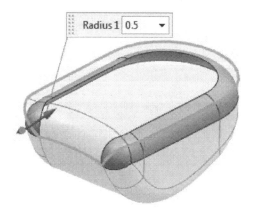

- The resulting geometry should look like the following.

- Create a Datum plane above the mouse body by offsetting the datum plane by 3in from the bottom face as shown.

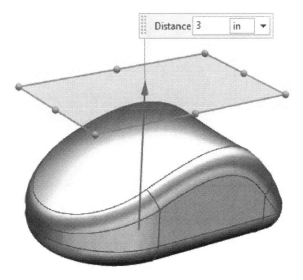

- Create the following sketch on the datum plane, use Pattern Curve.

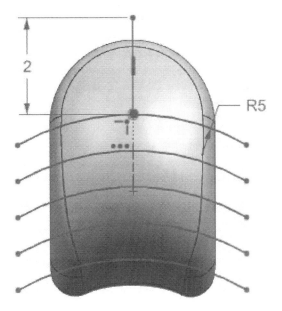

- Select Project Curve from the Curve tab

- **Project** the sketch downward onto the curved face of the mouse as shown in the following figure.
- Select the sketch as the **Curves to Project**.
- Select the top faces on the mouse as the **Objects to Project to**.
- Set the **Direction Vector** downward along the Z axis as shown.

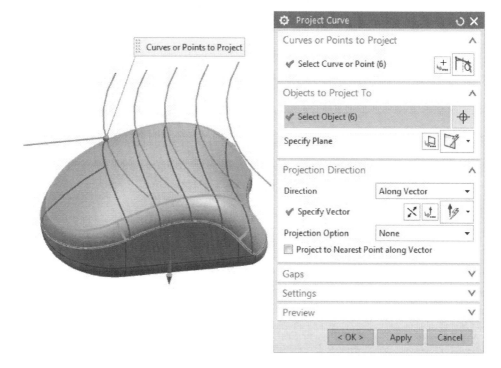

- Next select the **Thicken** command.
- Select the same top faces.
- Set the **Offsets** both to **0**, you will get a warning about a *zero-thickness body*.

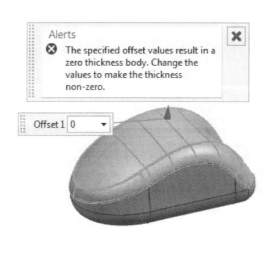

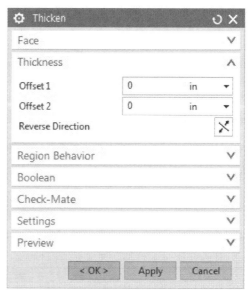

- Expand the Region Behavior section.
- Under the Region of Different Thickness, select the option for Boundary Curve, then select the region as shown.

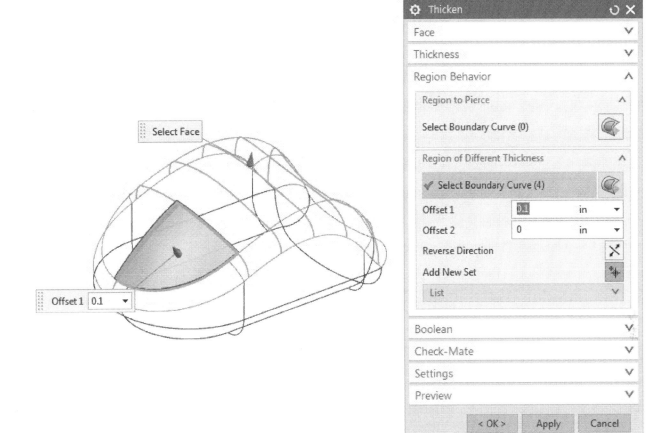

- To ensure that two separate mouse buttons are generated select the back regions as shown for the first set of thicken faces.

Due to the fact a zero offset was used in the original thicken parameters thicken will generate multiple bodies. Before in previous versions of NX a thicken command had to be used for each individual body that was created. Now in NX10 this is no longer the case.

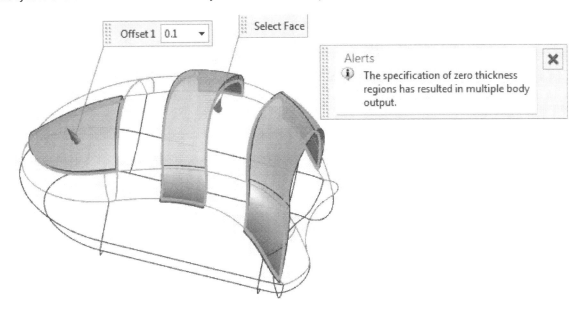

- Next select a new Thicken command and do the same for the remaining faces.

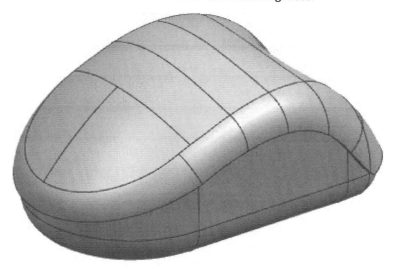

- Using Chamfer on the thicken edges will result in an interesting mouse design.

11.10 **Isoparametric Curves**

Isoparametric curves are incredibly useful. They've been available in NX for many years and are parametric entities that update. You can use them to distribute curves along a surface in a rectangularized pattern. Once you have the curves, you can use them as the underlying construction geometry for almost anything. In the example below a handle is created and 2 sets of isoparametric curves are distributed on it. The surface is sewn into a solid and the curves are used to create solid ribs.

You see, every surface has a U and a V direction. The isoparametirc curve creation tool just lets you access it and make curves on it.

- Create the following sketch.

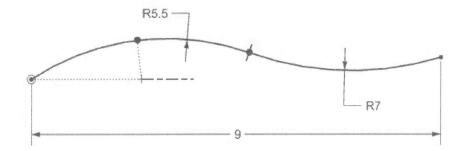

- Create a Datum Plane that is 6in away from the sketch as shown in the following figure.

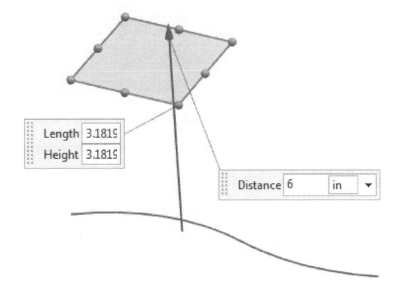

- Create the following sketch on the new Datum Plane.

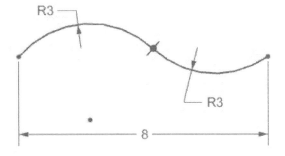

- Use the Through Curves command to create a sheet body between the two sketches as shown.

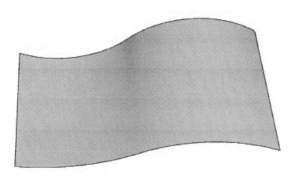

- Select the Isoparametric Curve command and create 10 U-curves.

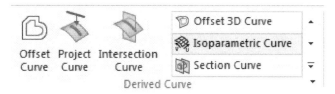

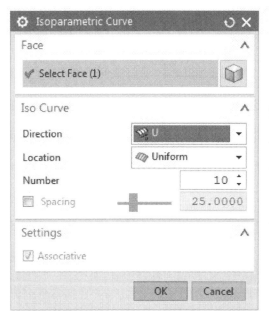

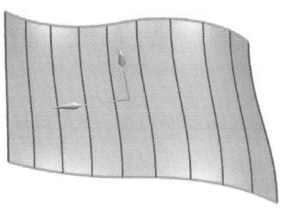

- Create the same number of V-curves.

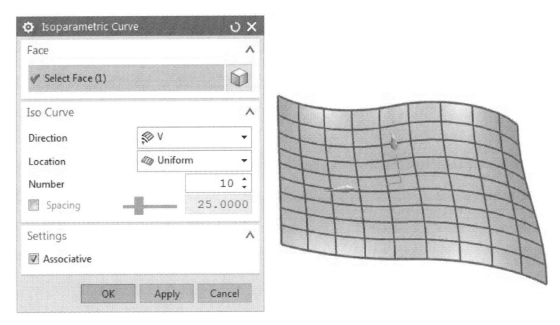

- Select **Point Set** from the **Datum Point** Dropdown.

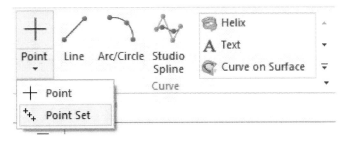

- Select **Intersection Points** as the **Type**.
- Change the *Selection Scope* to **Infer Curves** and select all of the U curves for the first Set.

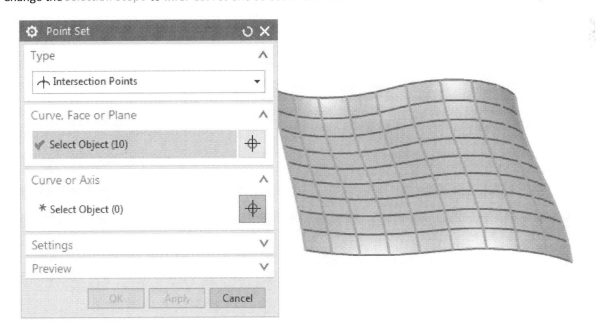

- Select all of the V curves for the second set.

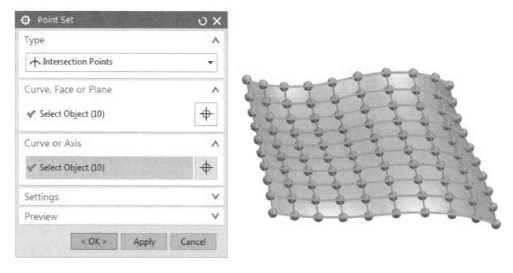

- Select the Hole command, choose all of the interior Datum Points.

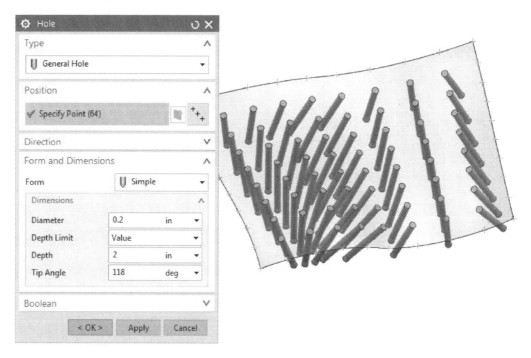

- Set the Diameter to 0.2in
- Using this technique a "linear" Hole pattern can be created on curved surfaces that would otherwise be a difficult challenge.

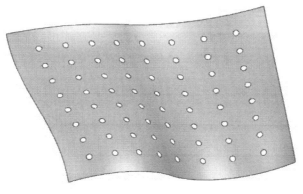

11.11 Trim Curve

There are many situations where existing curves must be extended to some boundary, or a perhaps curves may overlap and require trimming. In NX 10, this is accomplished using the Trim Curve operation.

11.11.1   Trimming a Curve

The figure below shows a horizontal line that must be 'cut' at the boundary of two other lines.

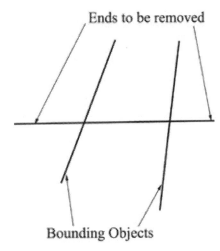

- Create the three lines approximately as shown above the Basic Curve function.
- Select Curve Tab / Trim Curve.

Note: *Feel free to experiment with the setting shown next. Notice that when the associative toggle is activated and the input curves are set to "keep" you will see evidence of your original curves after the trim operation.*

- Pick either end of the horizontal line that is to be removed.
- Choose the vertical lines as bounding objects.

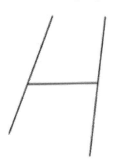

> **Note:** When trimming to shorten, always pick the portion of the curve to be removed

- Hit the middle mouse button for NX 10 to accept this step. Compare your result to the figure above.

11.11.2   Extending a Curve

The Trim Curve function may also be used to extend a curve, as shown below.

- Create the three curves approximately as shown in the left hand side of the figure above.
- Select Curve Tab / Trim Curve.
- Pick the horizontal line to be extended and middle click.
- Choose the two vertical lines as bounding objects.

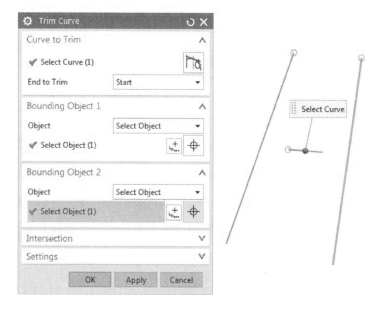

11.11.3   Trimming with Only One Bounding Object

Often there may be only one bounding object, as shown below. The Trim function can accomplish this by skipping selection of the 2nd bounding object.

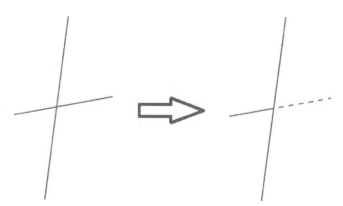

- Create the two lines as shown in the left hand side above.
- Select Curve Tab / Trim Curve.
- Pick the part of the horizontal line that is to be removed.
- Pick the vertical line as the first bounding object.

The cue is prompting you for a second bounding object, which is an 'Optional step'. Since there is none, middle-clicking tells NX to 'move on.'

- Middle click or press OK, compare your results to the figure above.

12 Patterns

The Pattern Feature tool is a powerful method of creating an array of identical features in an associative manner meaning the copies will all take after the original, like cool little children. When you make a parametric change to the mother, the children all do the same. The variety of entities that you can pattern is endless. Imagine a speaker gill, gear teeth, the knurl on a tool handle or any such repeated geometry and you should immediately think Pattern Feature. Due to the variety of ways you can pattern geometry the Pattern Feature command is extensive.

12.1 Linear Pattern

The Linear option of the Layout menu within the Pattern Feature command allows you to pattern features in a rectangular fashion, such as shown below.

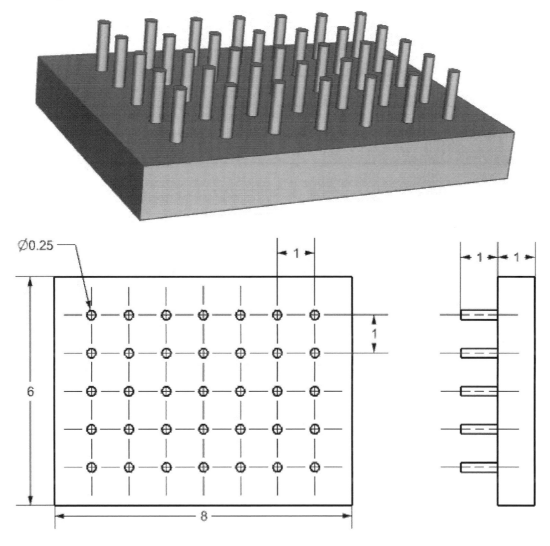

- Create an 8in x 6in x 1in block using any method that you wish. (Orient the 8in dimension along the XC axis and 6in along YC.)
- Create the initial Boss in the bottom left corner using the dimensions shown above.
- Select Pattern Feature in the Feature group of the Home tab.
- Select the Boss and a small yellow cube will appear. This is the feature reference point. It helps you understand what the pattern will look like before you actually have the system calculate the entire array.
- Select Linear from the Layout choice within the Pattern Definition menu.

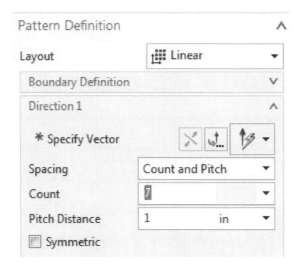

- For this project make sure the Spacing method is Count and Pitch. Input a Count of 7 and a Pitch Distance of 1. To specify the vector you may select one of the blue vector arrows that appear.

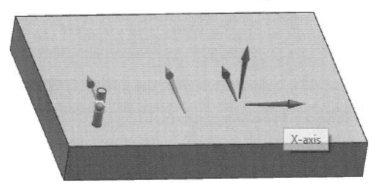

- Next you must click the checkbox labeled Use Direction 2.
- A similar portion of the dialog box will appear where you can input a Count of 5 and a Pitch Distance of 1.

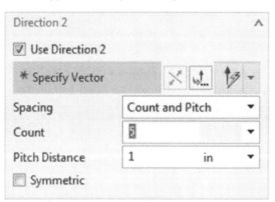

- Select the Y Axis for the Direction.

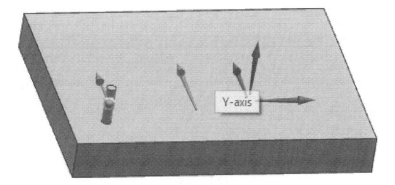

- You will get a preview of the positions of the bosses before you OK it.

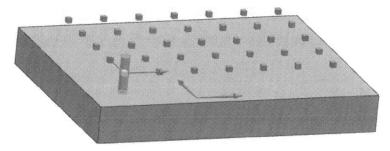

- The finished product should appear as below.

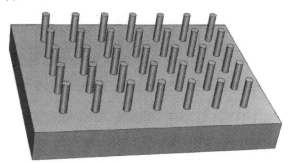

12.2 **Circular Pattern**

You can also use the Pattern Feature command in a Circular, Polygon or Spiral mode. The most common is Circular.

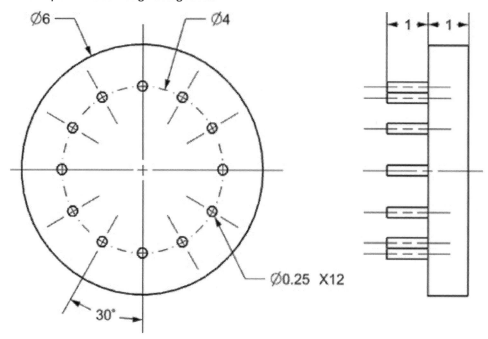

In addition to learning how to create a circular array, this project requires a new technique for positioning the boss – by dimensioning to datum planes.

- Create Datum CSYS at the WCS origin if you don't have one by default in a new part file.
- Sketch a 6in diameter circle.
- Position its center at the center of the datum plane, as shown in the following figure.
- Extrude the circle 1in.
- Create the initial boss and position it relative to the datum planes as shown in the following figure.
- Use the Point onto Line command within the positioning window to center the boss onto the Z axis.
- Use the Perpendicular command to create the 2 inch dimension away from the X Axis.
- Enter in 2in for the distance away from the X Axis.
- The boss should now be aligned to the center of the Z Axis and 2in away from the X Axis as shown.

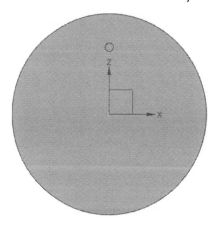

- Select Pattern Feature.
- Set the Pattern Definition / Layout to Circular and select the boss feature.
- Set the Spacing to Count and Pitch and select the datum axis that is aligned with the Y Axis.
- Enter the values shown below: Count = 12 and Pitch Angle = 360/12. These values determine the number of members in the pattern and the angular spacing between each instance. Notice that you can let NX evaluate mathematical expressions. Here we have specified a full 360-degree set of pattern instances.

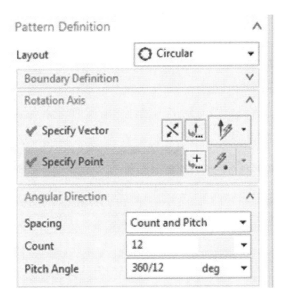

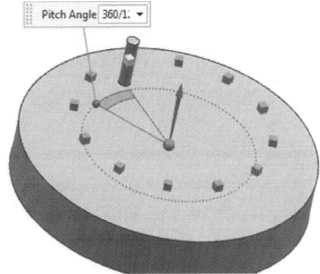

Note: when you select the vector, as long as the Specify Vector option is set to Inferred, you will not need to Specify Point.

Compare your results to the following figure.

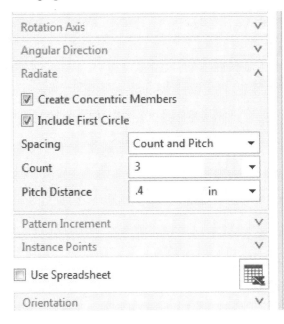

- Next come to understand the Radiate command. Just edit the pattern feature that you just created and open the Radiate Sub-Menu.
- Click Create Concentric Members. Once checked several options become available, enter the values as shown in the following figure.

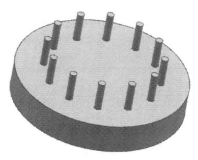

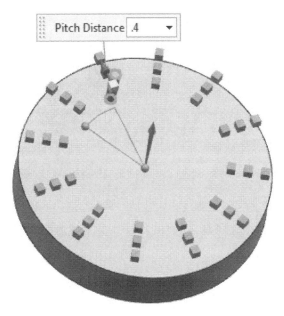

- Next come to understand the meaning of Stagger within the Pattern Settings dialog. Set the Stagger choice to Angle.

- The result is shown in the following figure:

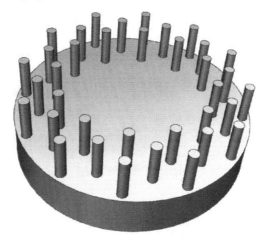

12.2.1 **Follow Face**

In the old days, when you wanted to repeat a feature on some pattern and you wanted that feature to remain normal to a surface, it was difficult and tedious. The technique is useful when you want to model anything that looks like a hair brush, a heat exchanger, or the texture on anything that is cloth or rubber.

In NX 10 there is powerful functionality in the Pattern Feature command. It's awesome. In one step you are now able to create a pattern that Radiates according to a Count and a Pitch Angle, and will also Follow Face if you want. This means each associative copy of the original feature will maintain the same relationship relative to a normal vector and selected surface as the original. The next figure shows how a pattern of spines are distributed along a face.

In the following figure the initial feature is located on the face near the center of the revolved surface.

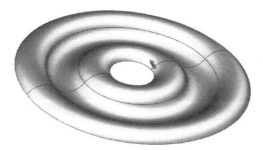

Using a Circular Pattern in conjunction with Follow Face, Stagger, and Delete Body. The resulting pattern can be accomplished.

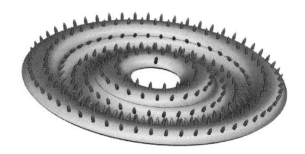

12.3 **Along Pattern with Pattern Increment**

In addition to the Stagger and Follow Face options, there is another truly amazing ability in the Pattern Feature. It's called Pattern Increment. It gives you the ability to add an incremental amount onto one or more of the defining parameters of the feature you are patterning. For example, if you have a series of bosses on a solid block and you want them to get taller and taller as they progress as a pattern, you can use the Increment option and add a value to the expression that controls its height.

This project will teach you how to use the Pattern Increment option in the Pattern Feature command. You will also learn about the Along command.

- Create a Cylinder that is 1 inch in diameter by 6 inches high.

- Next Offset the top and bottom by .25 inches. This way the shape will be a little bit lower than the WCS and a little bit higher. Build a Helix with a Radius of .5 a Pitch = 1 and number of Turns equal to 6.

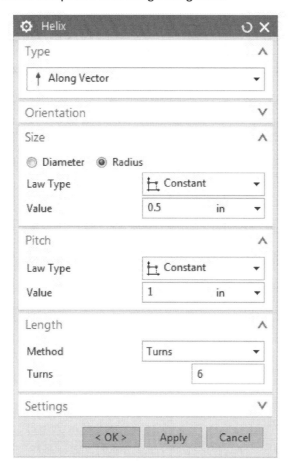

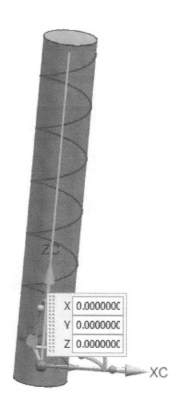

- Using the Sphere command, place a .1 diameter sphere right at the beginning of the helix and unit it on as shown below:

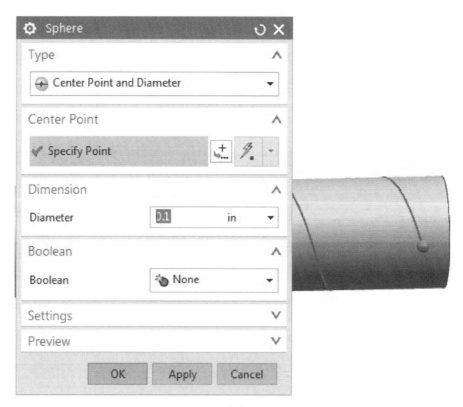

- Next use the **Pattern Feature** command with **Pattern Definition** set to **Layout = Along** and all other parameters as shown below. You will select the sphere as the feature to be patterned and select the helix as the curve to follow along.

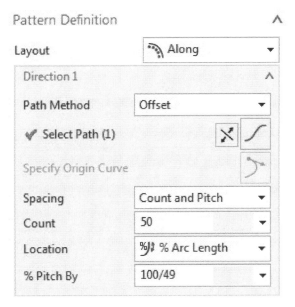

- Also set the **Pattern Increment** to .01 on the sphere diameter. This means for every new member of the array, there will be a sphere that is .01 larger than the last one.

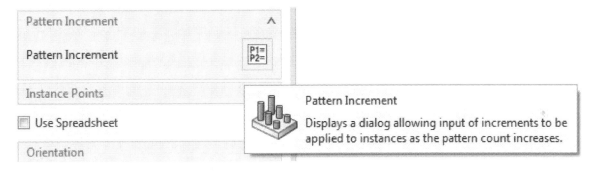

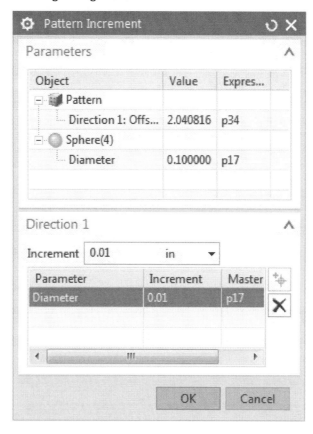

- The result will be a shape that resembles a cudgel as shown below.

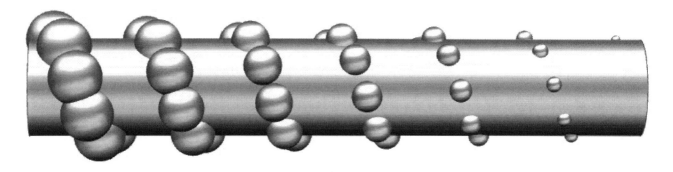

12.4 Pattern Boundary Definition

The Boundary Definition option in the Pattern Feature command allows you some additional control over where the pattern instances can and cannot go.

For this project a boundary will be created so that instances of the pattern will not be added. For example, say there is a grate cover that has holes in it however the holes should not go over the space with the logo nor should it go over the handle section to lift it. Before in NX, you would have to manually delete the instances in order to remove them. This can be a lengthy process of search and destroy through the part navigator to find the correct instance.

Now in NX10 this process is very simple.

- First create a Block that is 10in in length, 6in in width and 0.25in in depth.
- Next create the following sketch on the top face of the block.

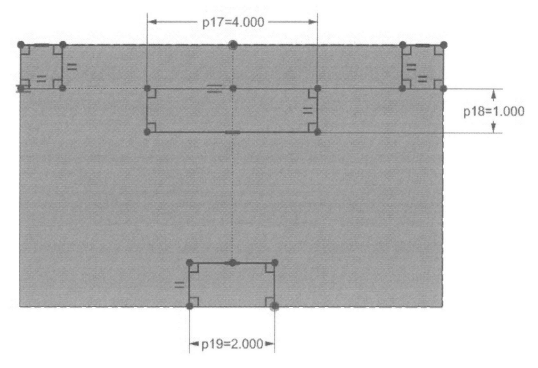

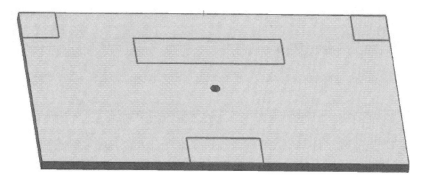

- Next create a 0.25in diameter Hole in the center of the block as shown.

- Select Pattern Feature.
- Select Linear as the Pattern Type.
- Select the Hole as the Feature to Pattern.
- Select the X-Axis.
- Set Spacing as Count and Pitch.
- Set Count = 10.
- Set Pitch Distance = 0.5in
- Check the Symmetric checkbox so that the pattern goes both directions on the X-Axis.

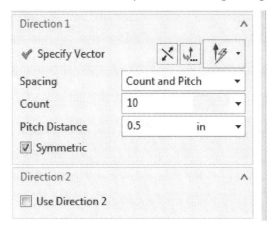

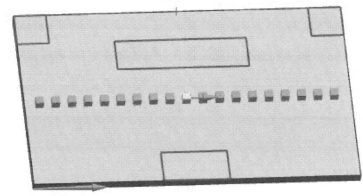

- Next check Use Direction 2
- Select the Y-Axis and check Symmetric
- Set the Count = 6.
- Set Pitch Distance = 0.5in.
- The Pattern Preview should look like the following figure.

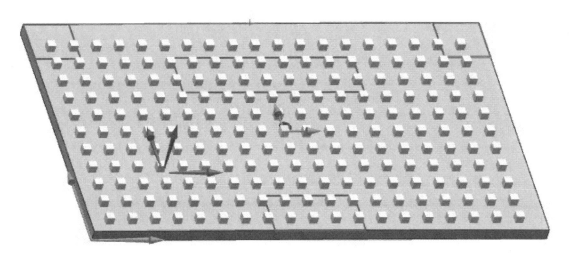

- Change the Boundary Definition to Exclude.
- Select the Sketch on the top face as shown in the following figure.

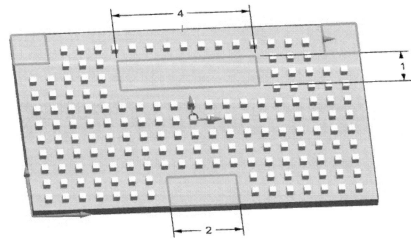

- Notice the instances do not enter the sketched areas.
- If more space is needed from the sketch lines the Margin Distance can be used to put an offset barrier around the sketch lines that the pattern instances cannot pass.
- Compare your pattern to the following figure.

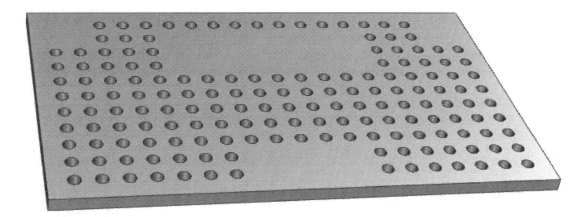

12.4.1 **Simplified Boundary Fill**

Using the same model from the last project undo or delete the Pattern Feature used.

- Create a new Pattern Feature.
- Select the hole again as the Feature to Pattern.
- Select Boundary type Face.
- Select the top face as the Boundary Face.
- Check the Simplified Boundary Fill checkbox.

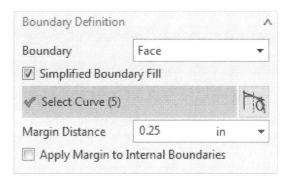

Notice NX fills the area within the face and margin specified with instances.

- A new rollout menu called Simplified Layout will appear.
- Several layout options are available, Square, Triangle & Diamond.

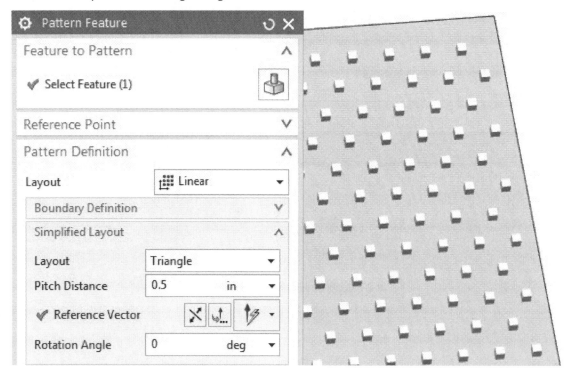

- This allows a quick way to create staggered patterns easily and quickly onto faces without the need to specify Axis or Symmetry.
- A rotation angle is provided which can be dragged dynamically or a value can be entered.

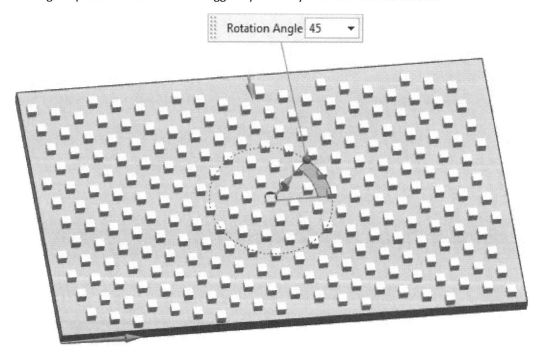

- **Simplified Boundary Fill** is a new easy way to create amazing patterns quickly.

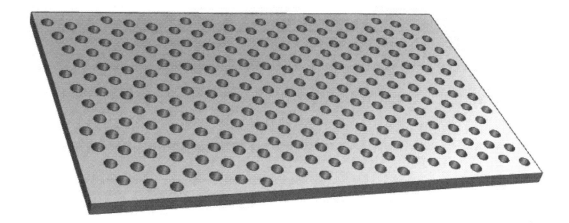

12.5 **Mirror Feature and Mirror Geometry**

The Mirror Geometry tool mirrors an entire solid body about a datum plane. It is useful for simplifying the construction of symmetric models. It can be found under the More gallery in the Feature group of the Home tab.

Mirror Feature is similar but mirrors individual geometric features that have been united to a base piece of geometry. When using Mirror Feature, it is important to make sure that the resulting mirrored geometry remains on its original base geometry.

There are many ways to create the geometry shown below. One alternative is to build half of the entire solid and then use the Mirror Geometry tool. Another alternative would be to create the entire solid geometry with only one of the Hole features and then use the Mirror Feature tool. In any case, the use of Mirror Geometry or Mirror Feature can save you time. In this exercise, you will create the body shown below.

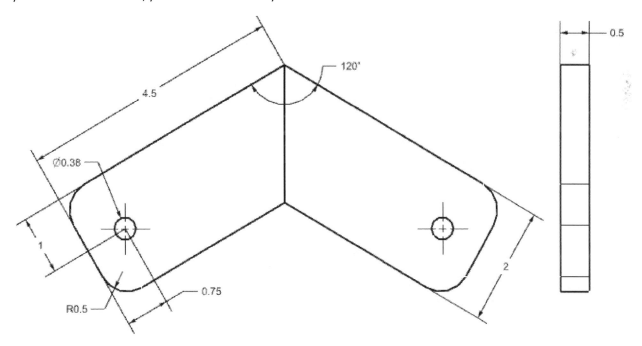

- Sketch the geometry shown below and position it using vertical Reference Line.

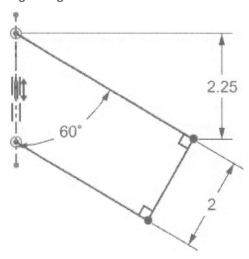

- Extrude the sketch 0.5 in.
- Create the 0.38 in diameter hole and the two 0.5in blends.

You should now have the model shown below.

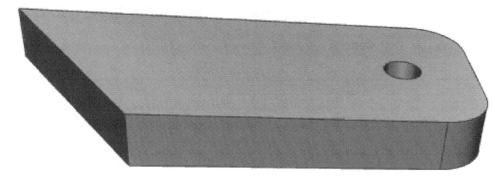

- Select Mirror Geometry. Pick the solid body. Pick the left most face as the mirror plane.

You should now have two solid bodies, as shown below.

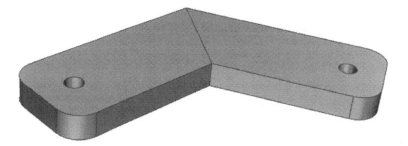

Note: Using Mirror Feature to copy a threaded hole will reverse the thread direction! Use with caution!

12.6 Pattern Geometry along a Path

The Pattern Geometry command adds even more power to the idea of reusing already existing geometry in an associative manner. With Pattern Geometry you can create associative patterns

In addition to allowing more types of geometry, Pattern Geometry also provides the ability to accomplish more complex patterns than just Mirror, Rectangular, or Circular. The geometry below shows a product that would be easier to design if there were some way to pattern geometry along a randomly shaped path.

The good news is, the Pattern Geometry command provides a function for this exact purpose. Appropriately named Along, this function is one of the patterns that can be very useful.

- Create a sketch to represent the top shape of the part.

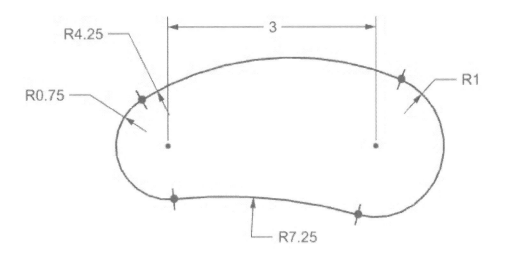

- Extrude by 1.5in.
- Create a sketch on the appropriate orthogonal plane that will be used to modify the bottom of our extruded shape.

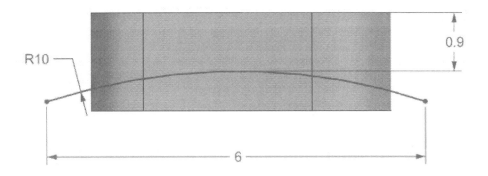

- Add a 10 degree Draft to the extruded body.

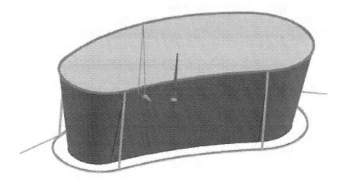

- **Extrude** the cutting sketch, Make sure it's long enough to cut through the entire model as shown in the following figure.

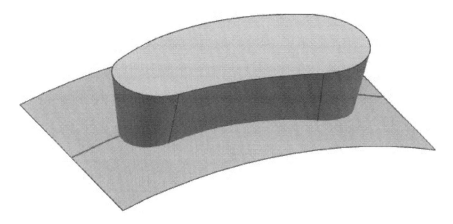

- Trim the body using **Trim Body**.

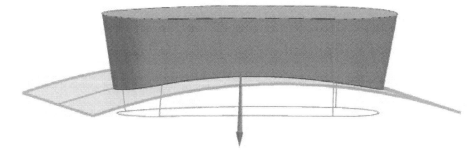

- Clean up your display by hiding the sketches and the sheet: Use **CTRL+W** as the keyboard shortcut, or use **Delete body** to remove the sheet.
- Add a **0.35 in Edge Blend** to the bottom of the part.

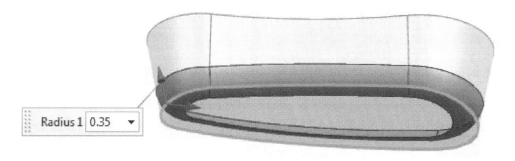

- Shell the part to a wall Thickness of 0.1in.

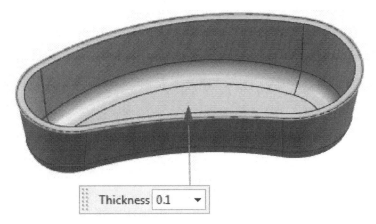

Thickness 0.1 ▼

Now, begin the creation of the first triangular feature. There are many easy strategies available. One is to create a sketch with two offset curves and one line connecting the two offsets. The two offset lines act to provide the position for the feature and is constrained to the inner and outer wall edge curves. The shorter line acts as the guide during a subsequent use of the Sweep along Guide feature. This is one of many easy strategies to create a feature that has uniform spacing from the outer and inner edges.

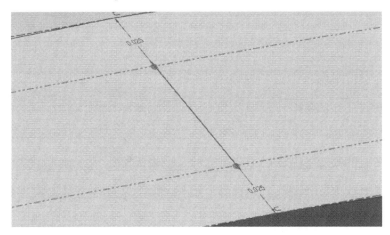

- Create this sketch on the top face at any one of the intersections of radii.
- Use Offset Curve to offset the outer edge and inner edge by 0.025 in as a reference line as shown in the previous figure.
- Draw a line connecting the outer offset with the inner offset.
- Take advantage of the sketch type called On Path. Create a sketch as shown at either 0% or 100% of the short line from the previous sketch.

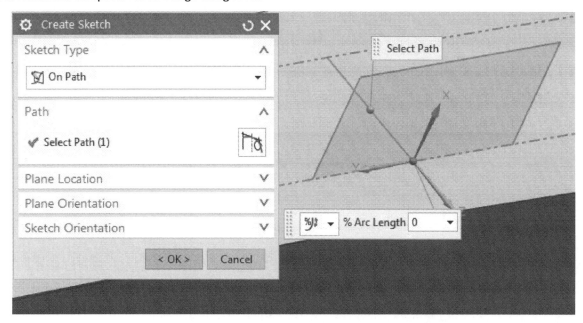

- Use the Polygon tool to create a triangle on the sketch as shown in the following figure.

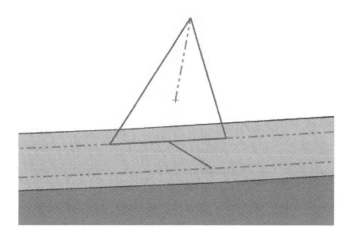

- Create the triangular prism using the Sweep along Guide tool.

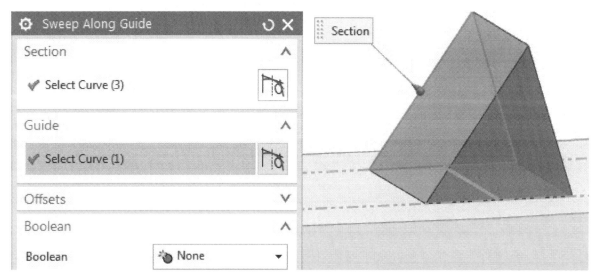

Note: This step is very similar to that used for creating a Tube. The difference here is that instead of the default circular cross-section utilized in the Tube option, you will use the triangular sketch as your swept cross-section and the shorter line as the guide. This tool is covered in more detail in a later chapter.

- The goal is to have 100 triangular features distributed evenly around the perimeter of this product. Unlike the previously discussed patterning tools, Pattern Geometry Along Path does not ask you for the total desired number; instead, it asks you for the number of copies. In this case we want 99. Begin creating your associative pattern by accessing the Pattern Geometry command and setting the layout type to Along.
- Select the tooth as the Geometry to Pattern, then select the path (either the inside or outside edge of the product is suitable for the path).

- All of the individual pieces of geometry can be united using the standard Unite command.
- Identify the shelled large piece of geometry as the target and drag a selection rectangle around all of the little pieces of geometry to identify them as the tools. Combining bodies is covered in more detail in a later chapter.
- The finished piece of geometry is fully associative; making this is an extremely powerful design feature.

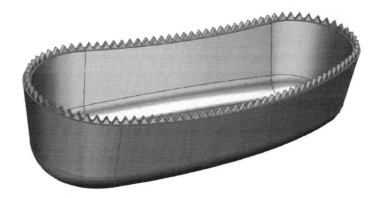

13 Expressions

13.1 **Introduction**

In NX 10, an *expression* is a parameter that determines the output of an operation. Each parametric feature created in NX 10 has a set of expressions that define its geometry. An expression can be written as a single numeric value (p24=4.125), a mathematical operation (p17=sin(30)), or a combination of other parameters (p49=p22+3*p7). The Expressions editor is found on the Tools tab, in the Utilities group.

The feature expressions created by NX 10 are designated sequentially beginning with p0; the second is p1, then p2, etc. It also automatically creates units based on how the expressions are used. You can create new, or edit existing expressions using the Expressions ([Ctrl] + [E]) dialog box, shown in the following figure.

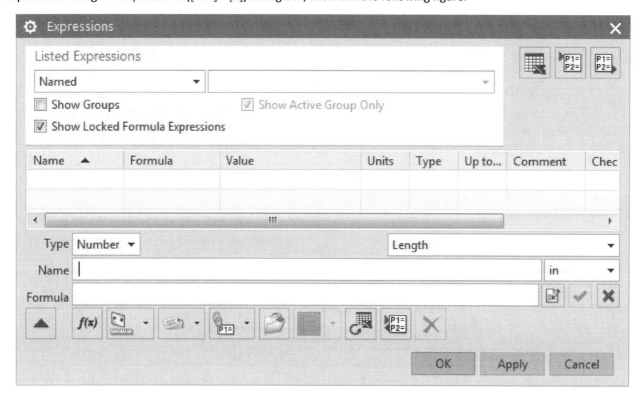

Note: NX 10 provides you with several filters in the Listed Expressions drop-down menu. Choose All when unsure what method to use.

Clicking the Spreadsheet Edit icon allows you to export the expressions into an Excel format file to edit. If several expressions need to be modified or viewed rapidly, use Listed Expressions.

13.2 **Pre-Determined Expressions**

A model that has meaningful parameter names is easier to edit. For example, the parameter that controls the extrusion distance of a feature could be renamed *"extrude_dist"* instead of the standard *"pXX"* name, enabling immediate recognition of the feature to be edited.

Perhaps the simplest way to create meaningful parameter names is by entering equations into the Expressions menu prior to constructing a model. The parameter names can then be used during the definition of the solid feature geometry.

13.2.1 Basic Expressions

The following figure illustrates a model constructed with a simple extrusion and a boss feature. All dimensions of the model are to be controlled by the equations that are listed. In this project, these expressions will be defined prior to creating the solid model.

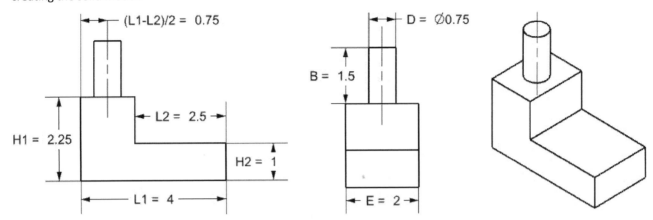

- Select Expressions from the Tools tab. NX 10 will display the Expressions window.

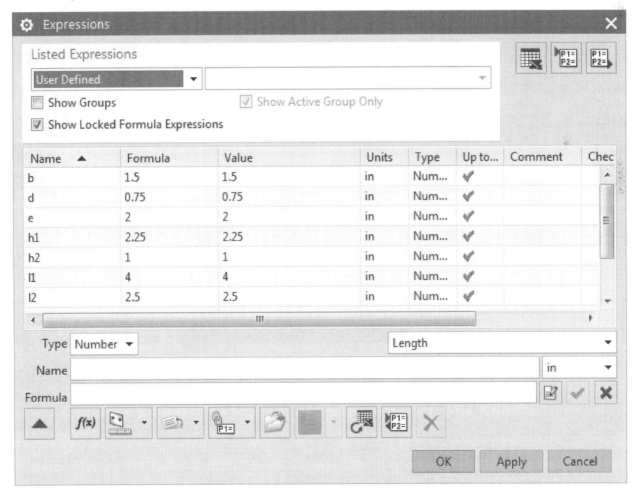

- Type *"b=1.50"* in the Name input box. The *"="* will automatically tab the cursor down into the Formula box.

- Hit [Enter]. Your equation will be added to the list of expressions, and the cursor will return to the Name input box.
- Type in the other six expressions listed in the figure above. Hit Enter after typing each expression. You are finished when seven expressions are listed. Choose OK to exit the Expressions editor.
- Create the sketch and apply dimensions and constraints according to the figure, but don't bother to adjust the dimension values yet.
- Modify the sketch dimensions, and enter the expressions shown below.

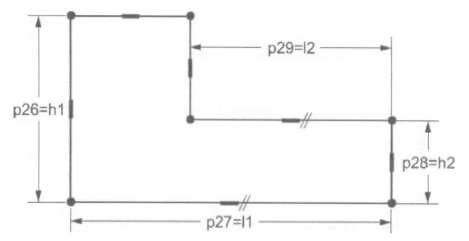

Note: Variable names are case sensitive.

- Extrude the sketch, entering Start Distance = 0 and End Distance = e.
- Create the boss, entering Diameter = d and Height = b (see below).

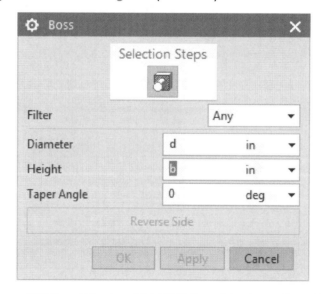

- Position the boss a distance of E/2 from Edge 1 and (L1-L2)/2 from Edge 2 (see figure below).

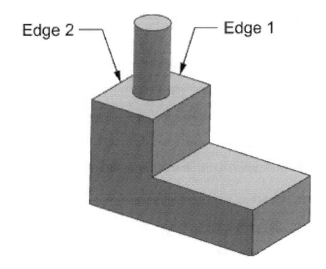

Edge 2 — | — Edge 1

- Save the file and rename it as *'expression1_<your initials>.prt'* .

13.2.2 **Changing Expressions**

The following figure shows a variation of the model that you created in the last detail section. To create it, simply change the variable values using the Expressions editor.

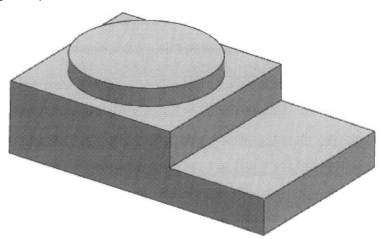

- Ensure that you are working in the file *'expression1_<your initials>.prt'* .
- Open the Expressions editor ([Ctrl] + [E]).
- Highlight the expression *"b"* in the Expressions editor. *The expression will appear in the input box.*
- Click in the input box and change it to: *"b=.25"* and hit [Enter].
- Edit the remaining expressions until they all match those listed in the figure below. Choose OK. *The model configuration will change to that as shown above.*

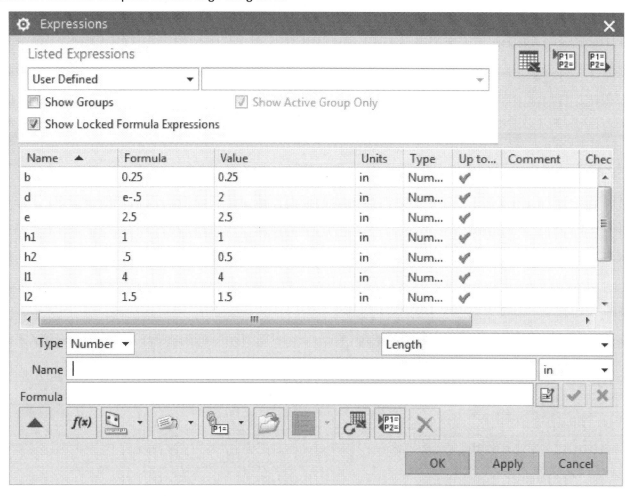

Note: The equation "d=e-0.50" defines the expression d in terms of e. Expressions can be used to set variables equal to a function of other variables and to use mathematical operators such as sin, cos, tan, etc.

13.3 Creating Expressions during Modeling

You have seen that expressions can be directly input during feature definition. Most of the time, you may not know all the required variables at the beginning of the design process. In this case, you can create variables on the fly as features are defined.

13.3.1 Creating Expressions on the Fly

You will create the model shown below using named variables. This time you will define the parameters as they are needed during the design process.

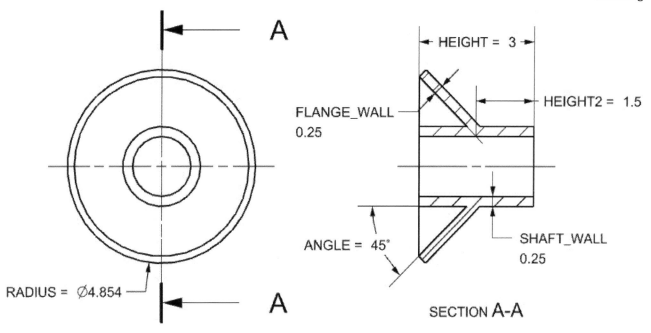

SECTION A-A

- Create the sketch shown in the next figure. Constrain the reference line with an Equal Length constraint.

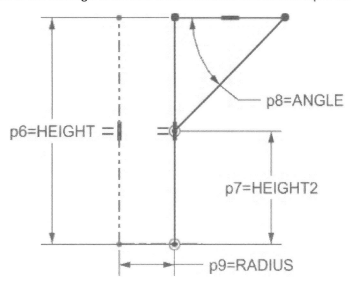

- Type *"HEIGHT"* in the dynamic input box (See following figure) and hit Enter. *Note that HEIGHT will replace the 'pXX' variable name in the sketch.*

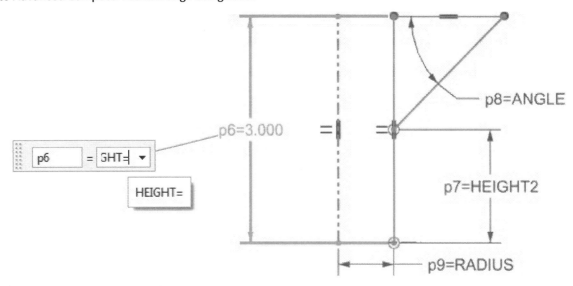

- Change the value of *HEIGHT* to **3** and hit **[Enter]**.
- Continue dimensioning the sketch and renaming the dimension variables as shown in the following figure.

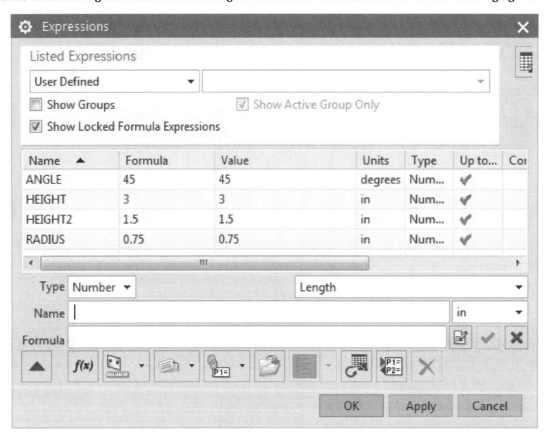

- Use constraints to position the sketch with respect to the origin as seen below and exit the sketch command.
- Select **Revolve**.
- Use the **Single Curve** filter and pick the **3 in** vertical sketched line (not the reference line).
- Select the vertical reference line to define the object to infer a vector (axis of rotation).
- In the **Revolve** dialog box (shown in the following figure), enter **Start Angle** = 0; **End Angle** = 360; and **Start Offset** = 0; **End Offset** = *"SHAFT_WALL = 0.25"*.

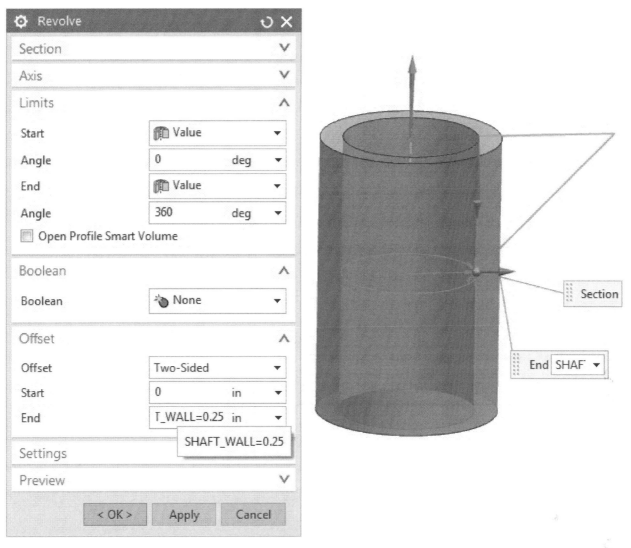

Note: *that you entered an expression rather than a value. This can be done anytime NX 10 requires you to enter feature parameters. You may need to enter* "SHAFT_WALL = +0.25", *depending upon which direction the rotation axis arrow is pointing.*

- Repeat the same Revolve operation for the angled sketch line with Start Offset = 0
- End Offset = "FLANGE_WALL= .25".
- Unite the two bodies.

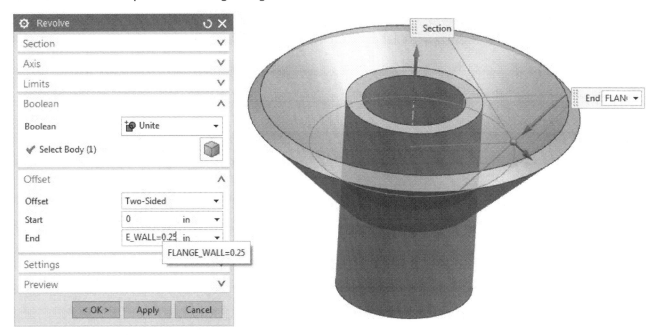

- To check your work, select Expressions (Ctrl + E). The Expressions list should contain all the variables that you created, such as *HEIGHT*, *ANGLE*, and *SHAFT_WALL*.

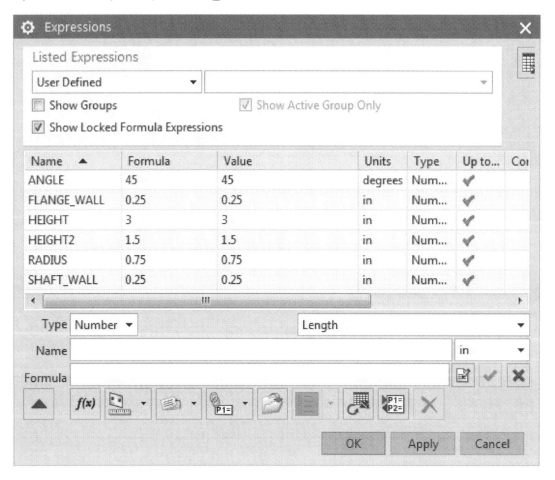

Save this model and rename it as *expression2_<your initials>.prt*

Note: Entering variables on the fly is a great way to document important model parameters. As a practical example, consider the design of a machine element which contains a shaft. Quite often, the length of the shaft may change during the design process, so if you define a shaft length variable, modifications to this value are easy to make.

13.4 **Renaming Existing Variables**

After building a model, you may find that renaming a few variables would help to document it. Renaming variables is easily accomplished with the Expressions editor.

13.4.1 **Renaming Existing Variables**

Using the part you built in the previous project, you will rename two variables that control the rotation angles of the sketch lines to *'THETA1'* and *'THETA2'*. You will then change both of their values to 180 degrees.

- Open the file called *'expression2_<your initials>.prt'*.
- From the Expressions editor, find the two angular parameters that control the span of each Revolve operation. Select each one, and then change the strings in the Name input box to THETA1 and THETA2, respectively.

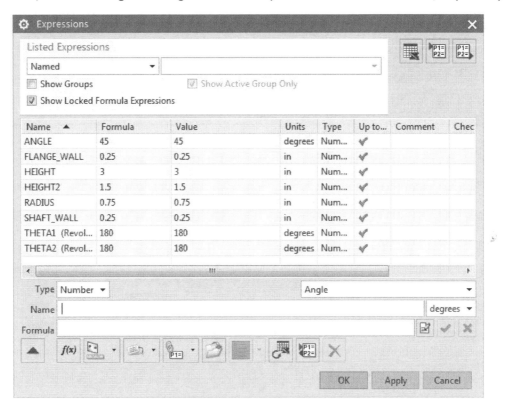

- Change the values of *THETA1* and *THETA2* to equal 180 degrees. *(Use the method that you learned earlier in this chapter.)*
- Compare your results to the following figure.

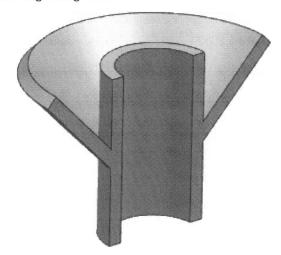

Suppose that you wanted *THETA1* and *THETA2* to be equivalent. You can use the Expressions editor to accomplish this by changing the expression *THETA2=180* to *THETA2=THETA1*.

Note: You do not need to change the variable names to edit their values. You can just as easily change parameters that retain their default 'pXX' name.

13.4.2 Adding Comments to Variables

NX 10 allows you to place comments next to the value of the variables. Comments should be placed in the Formula entry box after two forward slashes *"//"* (without the quotation). These comments are for the user's reference only as NX 10 does not recognize any text placed after the slashes.

- Select Expressions.
- Select the *HEIGHT1* variable.
- In the formula line after the number 3, enter *"// This is the overall height."*
- Select Apply. Notice NX 10 adds your comment to the Comment column.
- Continue to add comments to other variables as shown next.

Name ▲	Formula	Value	Units	Type	Up to...	Comment
ANGLE	45	45	degrees	Num...	✔	
FLANGE_WALL	0.25	0.25	in	Num...	✔	
HEIGHT	3	3	in	Num...	✔	This is the overall HEIGHT
HEIGHT2	1.5	1.5	in	Num...	✔	
RADIUS	0.75	0.75	in	Num...	✔	How big is it

Note: Comments can also be added by right-clicking over the name of the expression or double-clicking in the comment field of the column. Select Edit Comment and type in your comment in the provided text block and choose OK. The text is automatically converted to comment format with the necessary "//".

13.5 **Project: The Door Latch**

The door latch model shown in the following figure is controlled by a single variable, E, that was defined prior to modeling. Expression values are entered as a function of E to control the thickness and other dimensions of the part.

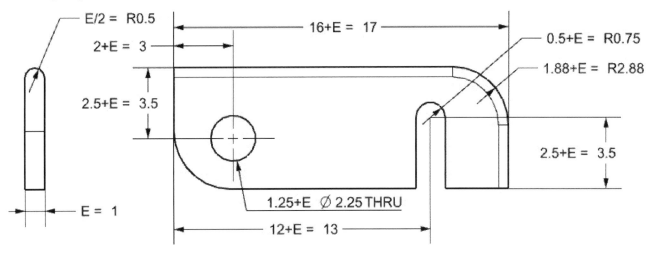

13.5.1 **Practice Outline**

- Using **Expression**, create the expression *E=1*.
- Create a sketch similar to the figure below. Note that variable names, such as *LENGTH* and *HEIGHT*, use the Dimensions menu of the sketcher.

E	1
HEIGHT	5+E
LATCH_DEPTH	2.5+E
LATCH_DISTANCE	12+E
LENGTH	16+E
RADIUSI	.5+E

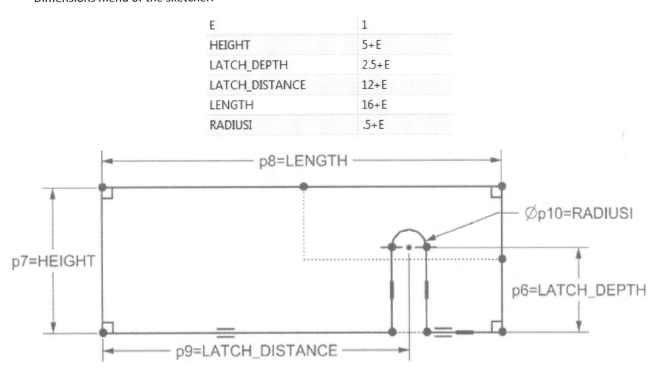

- **Extrude** and add features until you have the model shown in the following figure. Enter feature parameters as a function of *E*. e.g. **Edge Blend Radius** = *"0.5+E"*
- Test your completed model by changing the value of *E* to **1.75**. Your model should change size.

14 Synchronous Modeling

14.1 Introduction: A Double-Edged Sword

If there is one good argument against parametric modeling in general, it is that when used, models get too complicated. It becomes difficult to make edits because one must understand everything that was done before in that model.

NX has a fantastic suite of tools suitable for modifying both parametric and non-parametric models that do not require the designer to understand the complete model history – these tools are found in the Synchronous Modeling group on the Home tab.

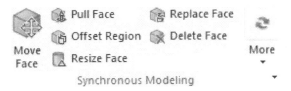

The danger in using Synchronous Modeling is that all design rules that are captured in a parametric model get overridden and the model no longer works in the way that was originally intended to.

14.2 Move Face

The Move Face command is in some sense the fundamental Synchronous Modeling operation. You select a face or chain of faces and specify a transformation. Adjacent edges/faces will adapt to accommodate the change. A good grasp of this tool will equip you with the insight to predict the behavior of other Synchronous Modeling tools.

- Create a Block with dimensions 200 mm x 100 mm x 50 mm. Use the Hole tool to place a simple thru hole of diameter 30 mm on the top face of the block, centered and at a distance of 75 mm from one of the 100 mm edges.

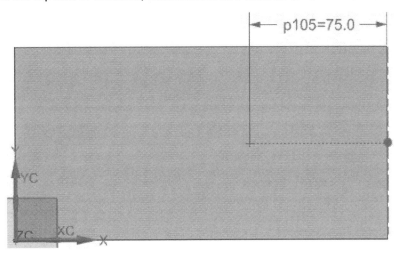

- Apply an Edge Blend of radius 5 mm to the four vertical edges and the top edge of the hole, as shown below.

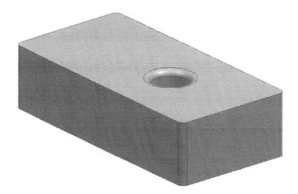

- Select the Move Face tool from the Synchronous Modeling group on the Home tab.
- Notice all the options in Move Face. You can set the motion to Distance, Angle, Distance between Points, Radial Distance, etc. For this exercise, set the Motion to Distance. Select the face shown below. You can specify the distance by either dragging the blue arrow, or entering a numerical value. Set the Distance to 50 mm and click OK.

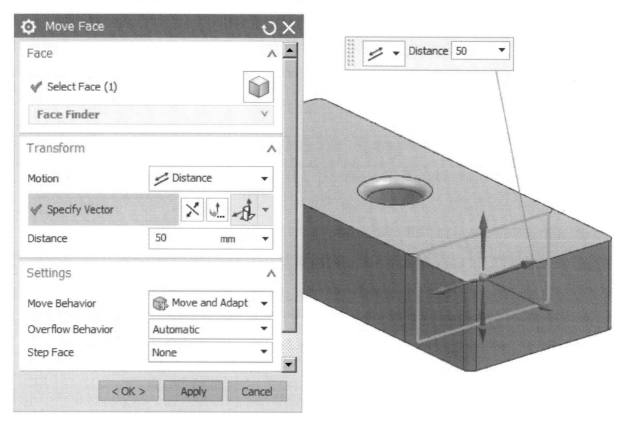

IMPORTANT: The hole was placed by specifying a dimension of 75 mm from the edge of the block, but after applying Move Face, that dimension does not update based on the change to the face of the block! The hole remains positioned 75 mm from the original position of the edge of the block.

- If you wish for the hole to move along with the face, you can select it too. Double-click on *Move Face* in the Part Navigator and select the interior face of the hole, as shown below. Click OK.

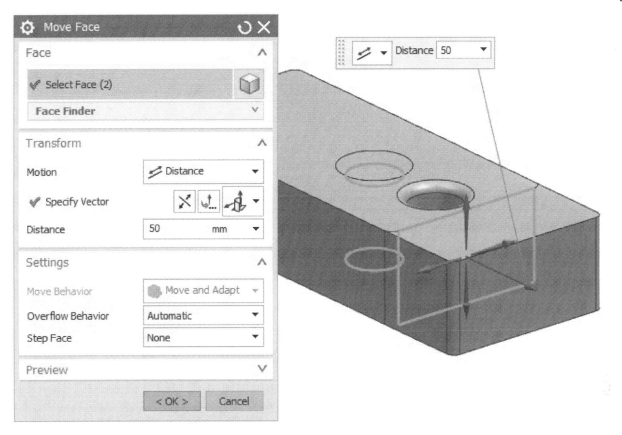

- You will see you have two options: the distance you want to move the face and the angle. You can either type them into the Move Face window or move the arrow and the ball around in the graphical display.

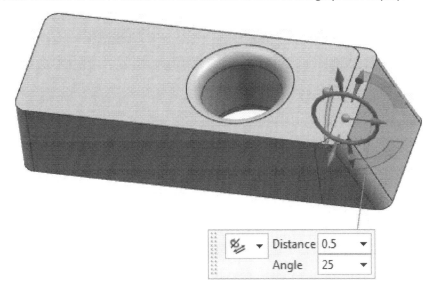

- You can change the direction of rotation by changing the distance vector as shown in the following figure.

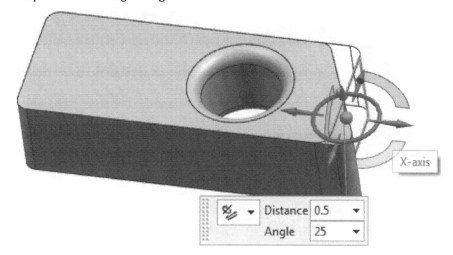

- Making **Z** the distance vector, change the angle and see what magically happens.

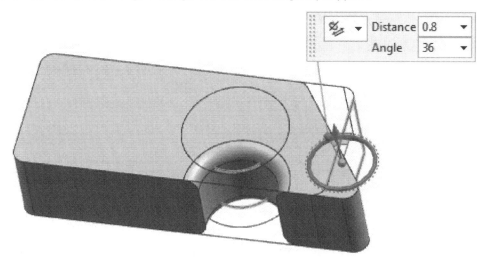

- Even the hole changed angle! That's the best thing since sliced bread!!! (It's hard to tell we're really excited about this.)
- As with all synchronous modeling tools, it's best to experiment and see how endless the possibilities are.

14.2.1 Face Finder

There is a Face Finder function in the Move Face command which allows you to move additional faces to the one you selected. For example, you can select a face and then say that you want all tangent faces to move with it. The move face window is shown in the following figure with the face finder expanded. Just tick off what additional faces you want to move from the Results tab.

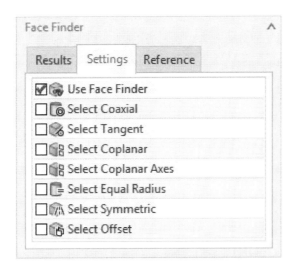

14.3 **Resize Face**

The Resize Face command is used to change the diameter of cylindrical, conical, or spherical faces. The position of the faces remains unaffected when the Resize Face feature is created.

- Continue working with the model from the last exercise. Open the Resize Face tool and select the interior of the hole.

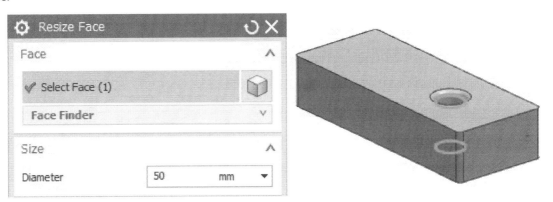

- Enter a Diameter of 50 mm and click OK. The result is below!

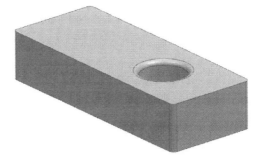

14.4 **Pattern Face**

Pattern Face is both a Synchronous Modeling operation and an Associative Copy operation, with its inputs restricted to *faces only*. This means that it is capable of creating linked copies of a set of faces (much like Pattern Feature) on a non-parametric model. You will see in the exercise below that Pattern Feature will not produce the same results when used on non-parametric bodies.

Thus far, you have applied Synchronous Modeling operations to an already-parametric model and seen how the new parameters interact with the old. For the present exercise, you will begin by removing the parameters from your model.

- Continue working with the model from the last exercise, and select Menu / Edit / Feature / Remove Parameters. You will be shown the following prompt.

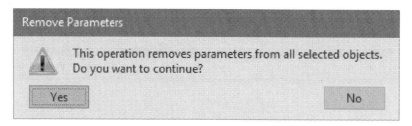

- Select Yes. Note that the Model History in the Part Navigator is now reduced to *Body*.

- Open the Pattern Face tool and select the interior face of the hole. Enter the values shown in the dialog box below.

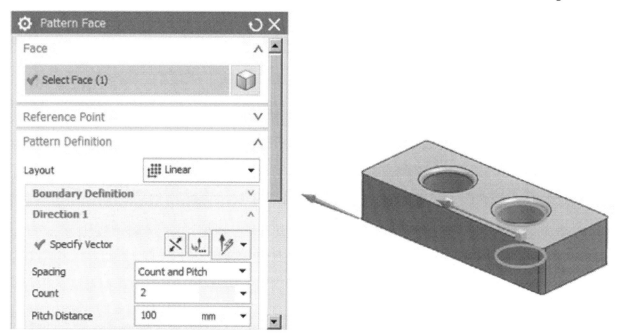

- The effect achieved is seemingly identical to that of Pattern Feature - but, if you try to select the interior face of the hole with Pattern Feature, you will find that your only option is to select the entire body, as shown below.

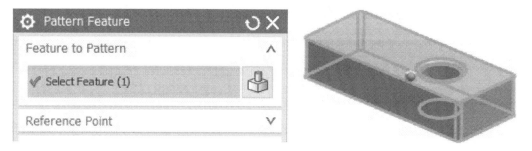

14.5 **Delete Face**

The Delete Face command deletes a face or set of faces on a body and extends or contracts the neighboring faces to adapt to the change. Not all faces can be deleted with Delete Face - if the adjacent faces cannot close the void left by the face you intend to delete, you will be faced with an error message. This limitation can be circumvented by changing the Cap Face settings.

- Continue with the geometry from the last exercise, and select the Delete Face tool. Select the face shown below and note the error message that arises.

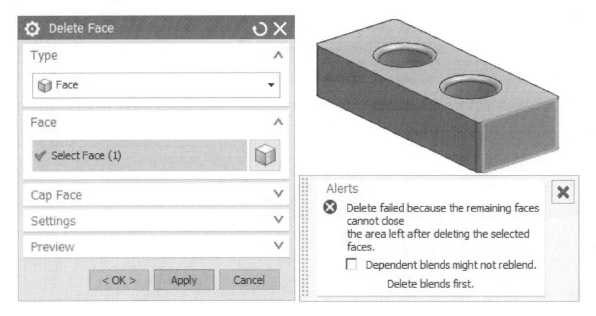

- Instead, select the edge blend on the hole created using Pattern Face in the last exercise.

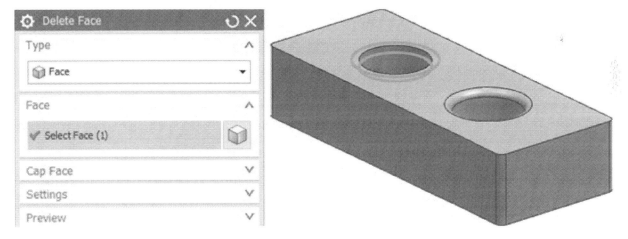

- Note that you can also delete the hole which Pattern Face references in the last exercise. This illustrates that you can use Synchronous tools to modify the original feature upon which a pattern is based without interfering with that pattern.

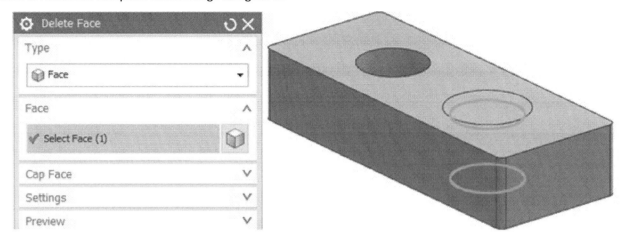

14.6 Replace Face

The Replace Face tool requires two inputs. The face to replace should be attached to a solid body, while the replacement face need not be part of a solid. The tool will extend or contract the body as necessary to accommodate the replacement face.

- Continue with the geometry from the previous exercise, and sketch an arc on the top face of the block centered at the center of the remaining hole, spanning the 180 degrees between the two longer edges of the block.
- Open the Replace Face tool and select the face shown below as the Face to Replace. Note that you do not need to select the faces of the blended edges for the tool to work!

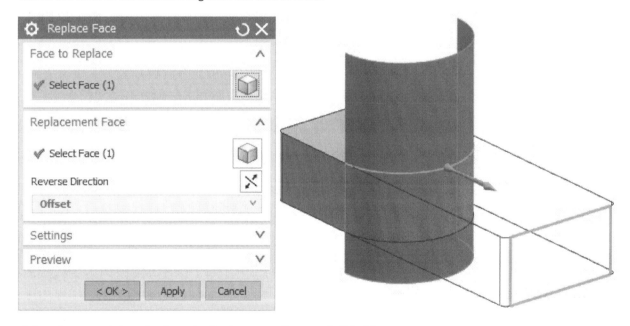

- Select the curved sheet body as the Replacement Face, and click OK.
- Use the Delete Body command (found in the Trim group of the More gallery in the Feature group on the Home tab) to delete the curved sheet body.

14.7 Offset region

The Offset Face command, as the name suggests, offsets a face or set of faces and - as you might expect by now - extends or contracts neighboring faces to accommodate the change to the selected face(s).

- Select the Offset Region tool and choose the face shown below. Notice that the tangent faces are also automatically offset.

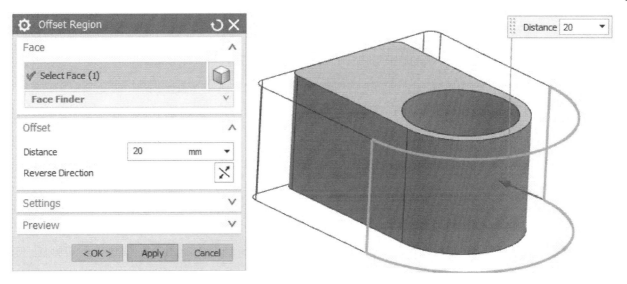

- After applying the Offset Region tool, open the Resize Face tool studied earlier. Change the Diameter to 80 mm. Note that the tangent faces do *not* automatically reposition when Resize Face is used.

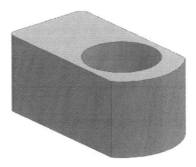

14.8 **Move Edge**

The Move Edge command acts in much the same way that Move Face does, except that it applies to edges rather than faces. The same transformations are available for both Move Face and Move Edge, but the effects of those transformations are quite different.

- If your model does not already contain a Datum CSYS, place one at the origin. On the X-Y plane, place a sketch of a hexagon with an Inscribed Radius of 100 mm and Extrude it 300 mm in the +Z direction to create a hexagonal solid.
- Select the Move Edge tool and select the top six edges of the hexagonal body, as shown below. Set the Motion to Angle.

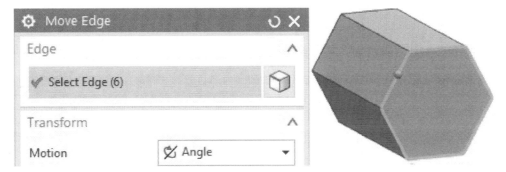

- Select the Z axis of the datum CSYS as the axis of rotation, as shown below.

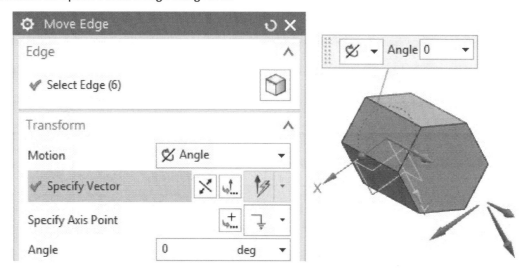

- At this point, you can either drag the blue sphere to dynamically control the motion, or enter a value for Angle to specify the transformation numerically. Either way, set the Angle to 60 deg.

14.9 Pull Face

The Pull Face command is similar to the Move Face command, but rather than adapting neighboring edges, it creates new ones. It's very easy to use!

- Continue working with the part file from the last exercise, and select the Pull Face tool. Select the face shown below and enter a value of 100 mm.

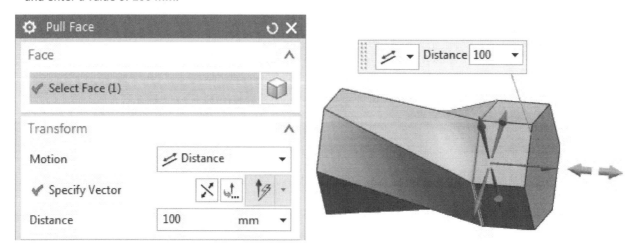

- Note that the selected face retains its shape, as do the neighbors. In order to accommodate the change, new faces are introduced adjacent to the transformed face.
- For comparison, select Move Face and apply it to the opposite end of the body. The result of this operation entails that the face grows and the neighboring faces extend.

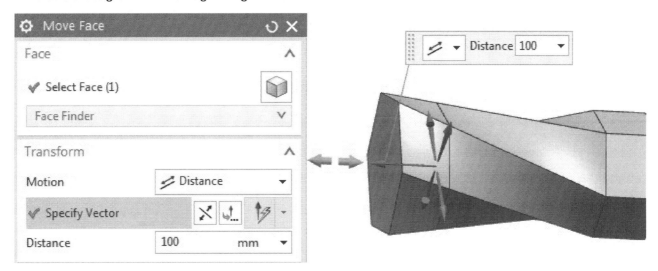

- Move Face and Pull Face are both incredibly useful – it is important to know the difference so that you can decide which is best for your model!

14.10 Synchronous Dimension Tools

The Synchronous Modeling group contains a suite of dimension tools that can be used to apply dimensions to non-parametric bodies, where there are none. They can also be used on parametric models to override existing dimensions, if the design intent is buried in a complicated model history.

14.10.1   Linear Dimension

The Linear Dimension tool allows you to change a dimension that you have placed between a point/edge/face and the face you wish to move. This function is not dependent on the history of your model and overrides the original placement of that face.

- Create the part shown in the figure below.

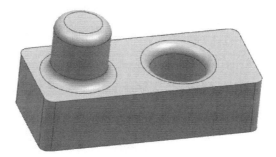

- Select Linear Dimension.
- This will bring up the window shown in the following figure.
- It first asks you to select the Origin Object of your dimension – this is where you're going to measure from.
- Select the edge as shown in the following figure.

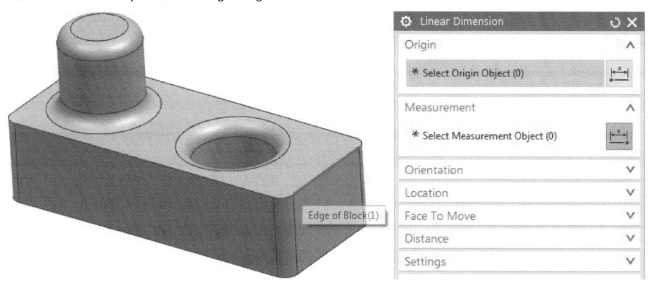

- Next, select the measurement object. This is what you're going to move.

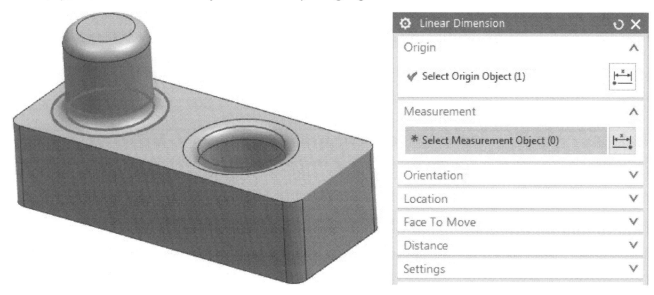

- As soon as you click on the circular edge you will see a dimension appear, as shown in the following figure. Select a place for that dimension by clicking on the screen.

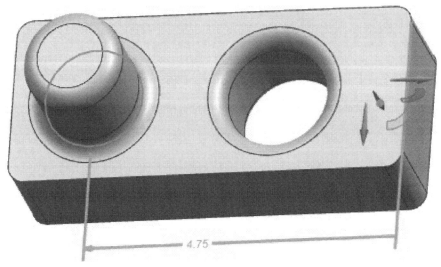

- Now you can change that dimension. The following figure was moved from 4.75in to 4in from the edge.
- Alternatively, you can just drag the blue arrow shown on the dimension. The automatic preview allows you to see what the changes are instantly.
- Your model should now look something like the following figure.

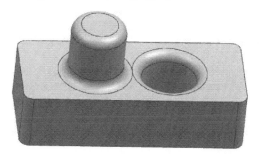

14.10.2   Angular Dimension

The Angular Dimension tool changes the angle between two faces. You start by selecting the reference face, then selecting the face you want to move, and finally by defining the angle. Let's try it together!

- Undo (or delete) the linear dimension you created in the last project.
- Select Angular Dimension, and specify the Origin face. This is the face you want to reference from, i.e. it will not move. This is shown in the following figure.

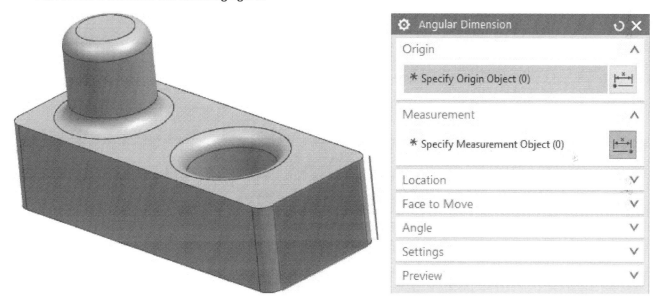

- The next step is to choose the Measurement object (the face that will change angle).
- Select the face shown in the following figure.

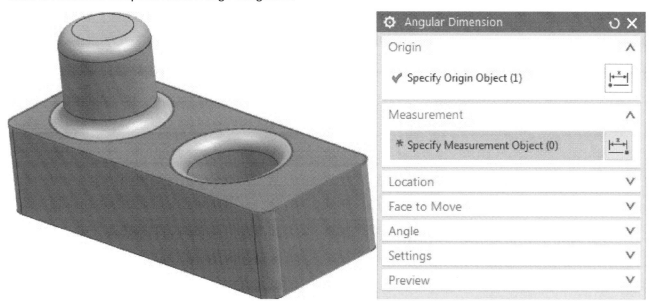

- Click on the screen somewhere to place the dimension you created (just like the last exercise).
- Then proceed to either specify the angle you wish or drag around the sphere that is circled below.

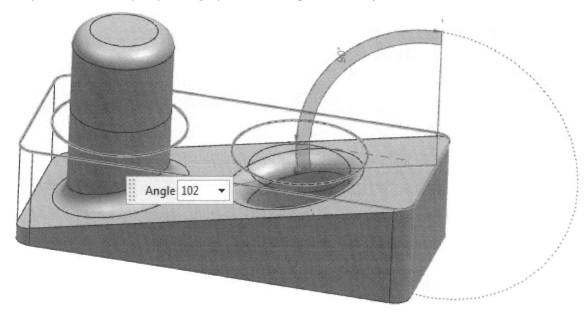

- Your model should now look something like the following figure.

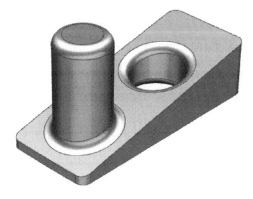

14.10.3   Radial Dimension

The Radial Dimension tool allows you to change the size of cylindrical components and similar geometry.

- Undo (or delete) the angular dimension that you created in the last project.
- Select Radial Dimension, and select the face you want to change the size of, as shown in the following figure.

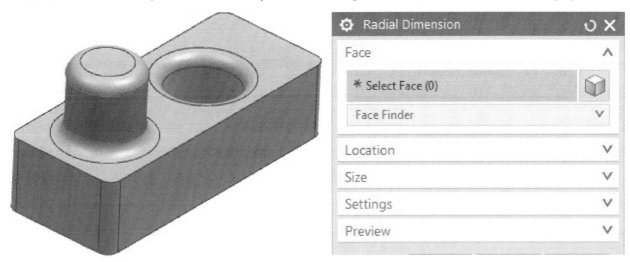

- Then simply change the size by either dragging the arrow or editing the value of the radius. Your model will now change, like the following figure.

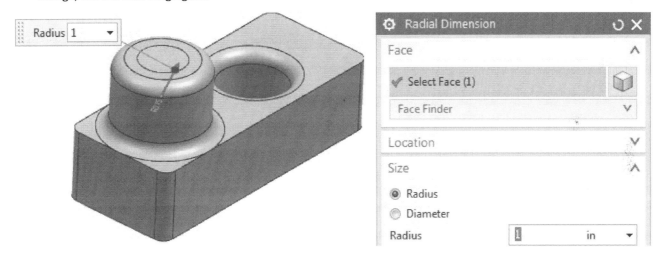

14.11 Synchronous Constraints

The constraint tools in Synchronous Modeling are very useful when making quick changes to your model. There is a plethora of easy to use tools under this command, from making faces parallel to making cylindrical faces coaxial. In this section, we are going to go through each of these tools. Because these tools are under the Synchronous Modeling menu, it means that it over-rides the parametric history of your model, allowing you to make changes easily.

14.11.1   Make Coaxial

This project is very simple. There are only two steps. First you select the face you want to move. Then you select the stationary face. This is like most of the constraint tools in synchronous modeling.

- Create the part shown in the figure below. Select Make Coaxial. Select the Motion Face you want to move as shown in the following figure.

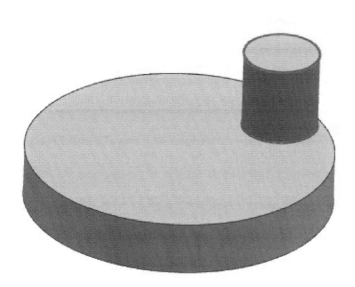

- Next, select the **Stationary Face**, the one you want to stay still, as shown in the following figure.

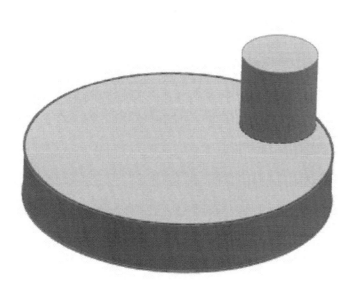

- As soon as you do so, the body will move to show a preview of what you are doing. Click **OK** to accept the operation.

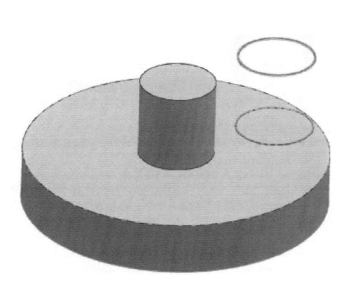

14.11.2   **Make Tangent**

A similar constraint tool in synchronous modeling is Make Tangent. This does exactly as you would expect – it makes two cylindrical faces tangent.

- Select Make Tangent.
- First select the Motion Face you want to move, as shown in the following figure.

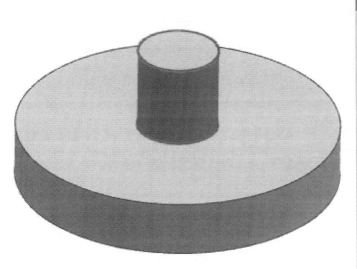

- Then select the Stationary Face you want it to be tangent to, as shown in the following figure.

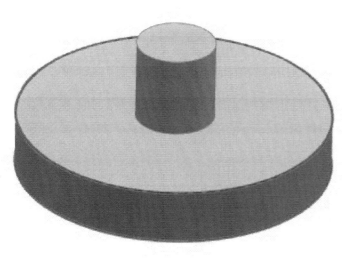

- Select the Through Point as a point on the edge of the larger cylinder as shown.

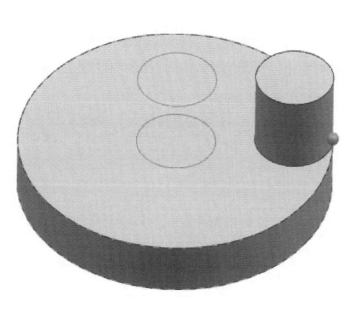

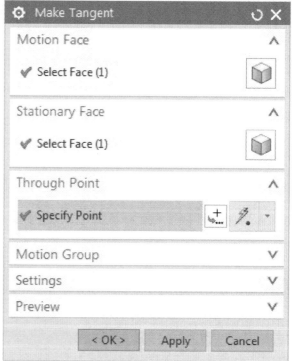

Note: There are several more constraint functions within synchronous modeling. They are as simple as the co-axial and the tangent constraints so go ahead and try them all!

14.11.3   Make Offset

The Make Offset command is another fantastic synchronous modeling tool. One of the best things about the synchronous suite is that some of the tools are quite similar so that if one of the tools doesn't work, another one will. In this example we are going to use Make Offset in a case where Replace Face would not achieve the same effect. This type of tool is also excellent for working with solid exports from other CAD software or for manipulating industrial design surfaces.

- Create a sketch that looks something like the following figure. Feel free to be creative! This one includes three lines and a studio spline.

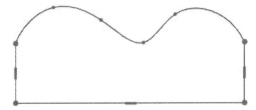

- Extrude the sketch so your model looks something like the figure below.

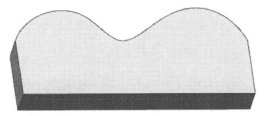

- Select Make Offset, and choose the planar face as the Motion Face as shown in the following figure.

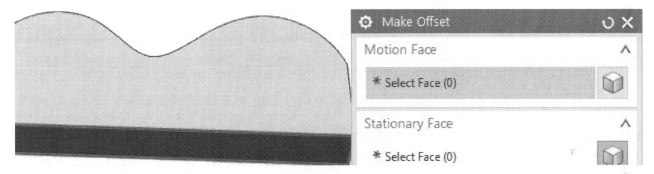

- For the next step select the curved face as the Stationary Face. You will be given the current distance between the faces. Change the value to roughly 1/3 of that value. If the change fails, try making your curved face simpler.
- Your model will look like the following figure.

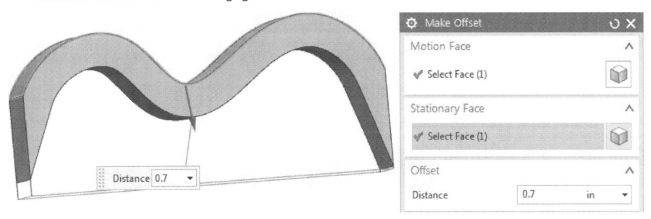

- Try and repeat this process using Replace Face and see if you get the same results.

14.12 **Resize & Label Chamfer**

The Resize Chamfer tool allows the user to change the parameters of any angled face. If you make any other changes, such as moving a face that is adjacent to a chamfer, the Label Chamfer tool will make the whole chamfer move instead of elongating the chamfer.

- Create the sketch shown below.

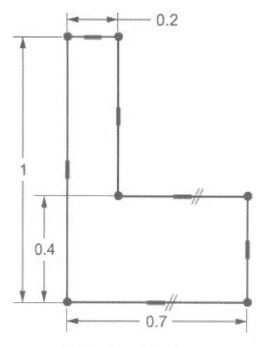

- Revolve the sketch 360 degrees to create the following solid body.

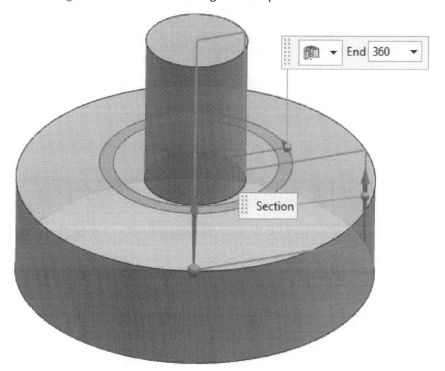

- Create the following sketch of a single line on the XY plane.

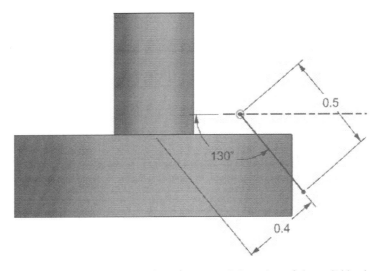

- Select Sweep along Guide. Select the sketch as the section and the edge of the solid body as your guide. Make sure you change Settings / Body Type to Sheet.

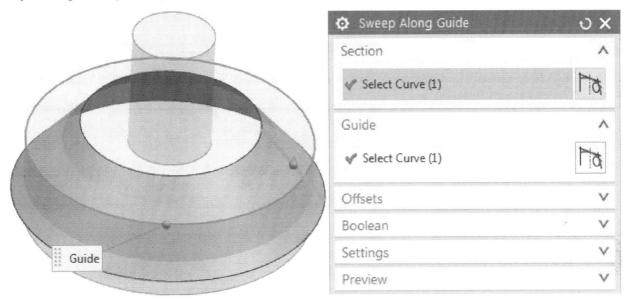

Note: You could also use the Revolve tool to create this sheet body.

- Select Trim Body. Choose the solid body as the Target and the sweep as the Tool. Make sure you are choosing the right side to trim. Hide the sweep, and your result should look like the following figure.

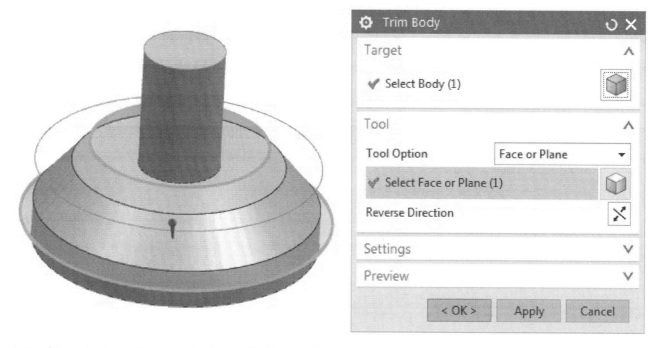

Note: *if the body trims in the wrong direction use the* *Reverse Direction* *button.*

- Now go to Label Chamfer. You accomplish this by selecting the angled face that you want NX to recognize as a chamfer. Most times that is all you will have to do, as NX is smart enough to infer the construction faces. If that is not the case, just select the two faces that the desired chamfer is adjacent too. The selection is shown in the following figure.

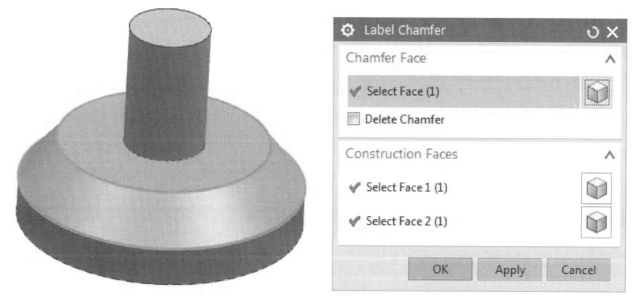

- Click Move Face. Select the face shown in the following figure and drag the arrow in the Z direction. Because we have labeled the chamfer, NX maintains the chamfer's parameters (*2nd figure*).
- The figure shown below (*1st figure*) illustrates the changes made when the chamfer has NOT been labeled as a chamfer.

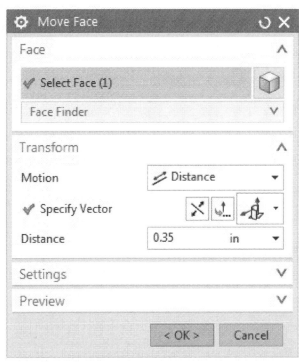

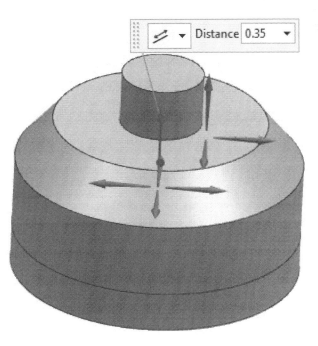

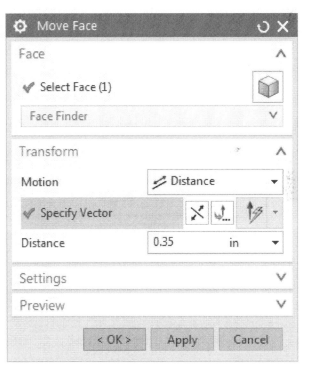

- Finally select **Resize Chamfer**. Click on the face of the **Chamfer**, choose the cross section as **Asymmetric Offset** and fill out the following parameters.

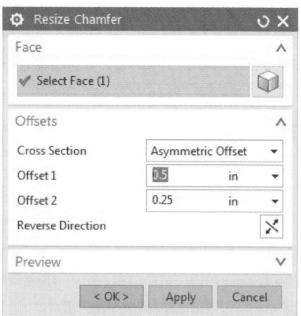

15 Surfaces

15.1 **Introduction**

The Surface tab contains a variety of powerful tools that are used to construct organically sculpted geometry. The surfacing tools available in NX 10 encompass many types of geometry, including zero thickness, infinitely thin sheets (surfaces), closed profiles swept along a drive curve, certain kinds of blends, and offset faces.

The figure below illustrates two typical examples of surfaces – the left is an example of a *mesh surface*, and the right is an example of a *swept surface*.

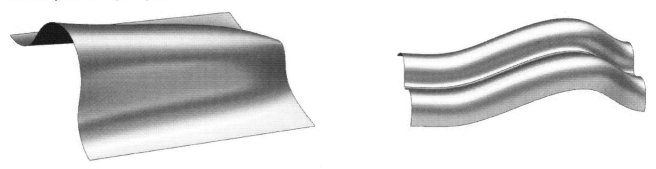

By their nature, surfaces are highly dependent upon other geometry. In the most rigorous situations, surfaces are created using fully parametric sketch curves, offset curves, or projected curves. By using these intelligent entities you can create the most difficult of geometries.

Surfaces are also known as sheet bodies in NX 10. Many other tool options that you have used so far to create solid bodies, such as extrude and revolve, can also be used to create simple surfaces or sheet bodies. In addition to the Surface tab, a limited set of surfacing tools can be found in the Surface group, on the Home tab.

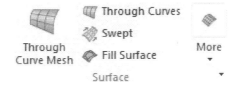

15.2 **Bounded Plane**

The *Bounded Plane* option enables you to build a sheet surface contained within a chain of connected curves. These section strings must be coplanar, closed and connected to form the sheet boundaries.

In this exercise, we will use the Bounded Plane command to create a glass block inside an existing solid as shown below.

- Create a Block with dimensions of 6in x 4in x 1in.

- Create a sketch on the top face and apply the Offset Curve tool to the top edges of the Block with an Offset Distance of 1in inwards.
- Extrude the curves through the model to subtract.
- Add 0.5in Edge Blends on the inside edges of the slot created in the last step, as shown below.

- Select Extract Geometry.
- Select the Face option from the Type drop-down menu and select the blended faces of the slot.
- Hide the original solid.
- The surfaces should look like the following figure.

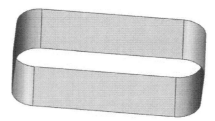

- Select the Bounded Plane tool.

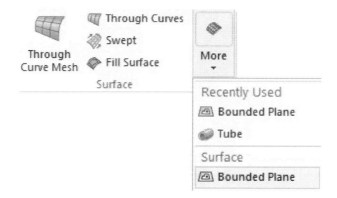

- Select all eight (top) edges of the curved surface.
- Repeat the same to create a lower end cap.

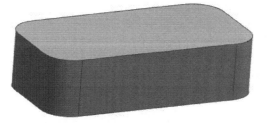

- Select Sew and sew all the sheets together to create the solid.
- Change the Object Display to better illustrate the translucent property of glass.
- Change the Selection Focus to Solid Body.

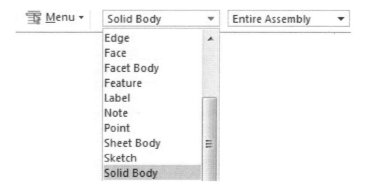

- Select the body you just created.

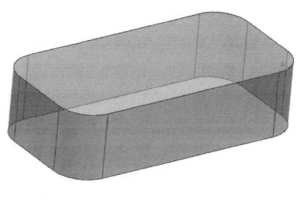

- Choose Edit Display.
- Set the Translucency to 50 as shown on the following figure.

- Make the original solid visible.

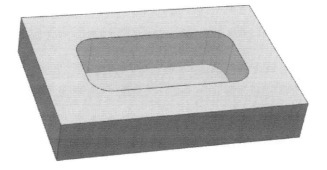

15.3 **Through Curves**

The *Through Curves* option enables you to build a surface that is *draped* over two or more rows of defining curves. Each row of curves must be continuous and are referred to as a Section String. It is important to pay close attention to the feedback that NX 10 gives you during the process of creating a Through Curve Surface feature, because it is rather complex. In other words, *read the cue!*

To avoid defining a *twisted* surface, each Section String must be spaced progressively farther from the initial row. The direction of section must also be defined in a consistent manner.

To obtain a fully parametric surface, each section should also be parametric. For example, each may be a sketch that is placed onto a parametrically-defined datum plane. When either the curves or the position of the datum planes is changed, the resultant freeform surface will update accordingly.

In this exercise, you will define the necessary construction geometry and create a surface using the Through Curves tool.

- Create a new file. Save it and rename it as *TC_<your initials>.prt*.
- Create at least four parallel datum planes, each spaced two inches apart.

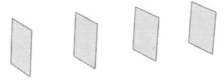

- Create at least four sketches on the datum planes, as shown next. You may use spline geometry or lines and arcs; however, be certain that each sketch has contiguous strings (no gaps allowed).

- Select Through Curves. (Read the Cue Display – the system is prompting you to select a Section Curve.)

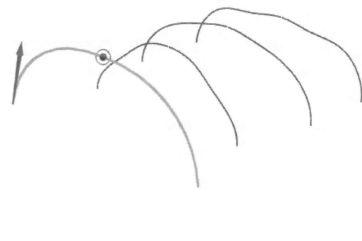

286

- Select the geometry at the left-hand side of the first sketch, as shown above. *(Read the cue again – the system is giving you two options.)*
- Add New Set to complete the selection of Section Curve 1. (The system should display a direction vector at the end of the sketch you selected and you will see Section 1 displayed in the Through Curves menu.)
- Select at the left-hand side of the second sketch.
- Choose Add New Set to complete the selection of Section String 2.
- Select at the corresponding location on the third sketch, and choose Add New Set. (Check the direction vector – if it is ever incorrect, you should expand the List highlight the previous and re-select the incorrect section string.)
- Select at the corresponding location on the fourth sketch, and choose OK.

Note: The subsequent dialog boxes contain several options that are not within the scope of this exercise.

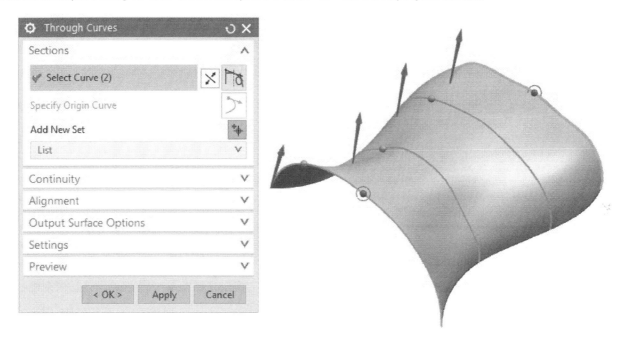

- Compare your results to the following figure.

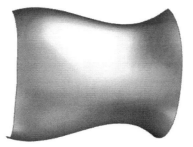

15.4 **Sweep Along Guide**

Sweep Along Guide can be used for creating any geometry that needs a uniform section to follow a curvilinear path. To use the Sweep Along Guide feature, you need two separate sketches in two different planes. One sketch will be the section string, which is the *"C"* shaped curve, and the second sketch will be the guide curve, which is the *"S"* shaped curve, shown below.

- Using the sketcher, create the Guide String on the default (X-Y) plane as shown below.

- **Finish** the guide string sketch.
- Create another sketch, this time with the **Sketch Type** set to **On Path**.

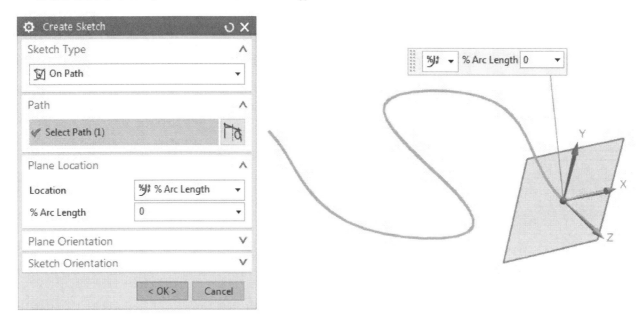

- Sketch a "C" shape, and make sure that the endpoint is coincident with the start point of the "S" shaped guide curve.

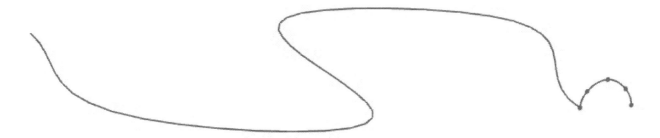

- Select **Sweep Along Guide**.
- Select the "C" shaped curve as section string.
- Select the "S" shaped curve as guide.
- Ensure that both offsets are zero. If you enter an offset value you can create a solid body instead of a surface.

You should now have the following model.

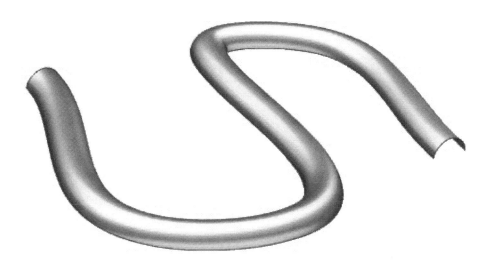

Note: *Sweep Along Guide features require that the start point of the guide string must intersect the section string plane. This is often overlooked by novice users. Another common mistake is defining the radius on the guide string so that, when combined with the section string, it results in self-intersecting geometry.*

15.5 Swept

The Swept tool allows you to specify not only multiple Section String curves, but also multiple Guide String curves to control the shape in between them. The number of guides is limited to three, but you can provide as many sections as you want.

It is worth mentioning a few points regarding the definition of Guide and Section Strings when defining Surface features:

- The orientation of each section must be consistent; otherwise the resultant surface feature will be twisted.
- Sections may be composed of one or many curve segments.
- Sections are not required to have a corresponding number of curve segments, but if so, the resultant surface shape will often be smoother.
- Sections do not have to be planar – but if they are, the resultant surface shape will often be smoother.
- If you use sketches to define the guides and sections, the surface will be fully parametric.

These comments are applicable to most surfaces created in NX 10. If the sections are closed loops, the resultant geometry will be a solid feature. If the sections are open loops, the resultant geometry will be a sheet body feature.

In this project, you will first build the construction geometry, which consists of the three default datum planes (CSYS) and one datum plane offset by **12** inches. Next, a square sketch is placed at each end with their centers aligned to the central datum planes. The final step is to create a sketch on the central datum plane that has a *"hump"* in the middle. Its endpoints must be aligned to the centroid of each end sketch.

- Create a new file. Save it and rename it as *swept_<your initials>.prt*.
- Create the Datum CSYS and the **12in** offset Datum Plane.

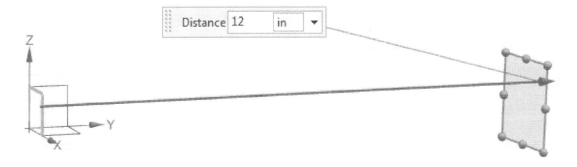

- Create the two section sketches as shown in the following figures. Be certain that the center of the rectangle is located at the center of the out-of-plane datum planes.

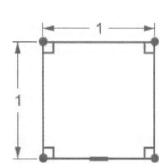
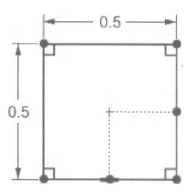

- Sketch the guide string, as shown below. Be certain that the ends of the sketch are aligned to the center of each section string.

- Select Swept.
- Select the left side of the first section (pay attention to which entity and end you select – you must select the other Section String in a consistent manner).
- Click Add New Set.
- Select the same side of the second section string (select this section string in the same way you selected the left side Section String e.g. both top box edges).
- Click on the Select Guide section of the menu, and choose the guide curve you sketched.
- Choose OK to accept other default options and the Swept solid will appear!

Compare your results to the figure above.

Note: *The Swept geometry defined by the sketches in this example resulted in the creation of a solid feature. If any of the Section Strings were not planar or closed, a sheet body would have been produced. Another important point is that if you do not <u>select corresponding locations on each Section String</u>, the Swept geometry will be twisted.*

15.6 **Through Curve Mesh**

The Through Curve Mesh option enables you to create a solid or sheet body from existing strings running in two different directions. You can create complex surfaces and surface patches using this method. As per the usual, using closed section string entities allows you to create a solid body; using open section strings will result in a surface body.

The main difference between Through Curves and Through Curve Mesh is that Through Curves only requires section curves, and Through Curve Mesh requires both section curves and guide curves.

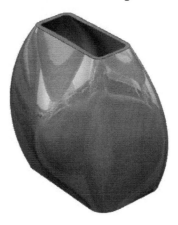

15.6.1 **Solid**

- Create a Datum CSYS if one doesn't already exist.
- Create a new datum plane offset by 3 inches in the +Y direction.
- Sketch a circle of Diameter = 1in on the offset datum. Center it in the sketch plane.

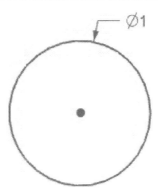

- On the original datum plane, parallel to the offset plane, sketch a rectangle with dimensions 3in x 2in with 0.5in fillets on all four corners as shown next. Center it in the sketch plane as well.

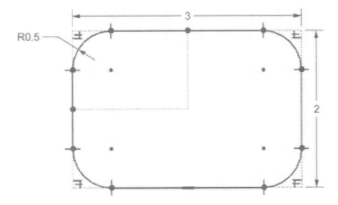

- Select Point from the Curve tab place four datum points on the circle.

Note: *Use Intersection between the CSYS planes and the curve.*

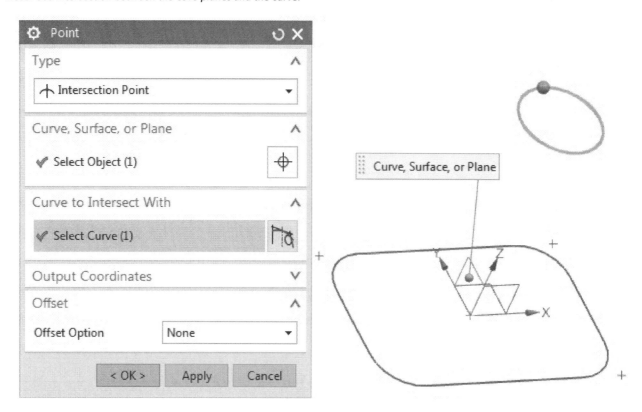

- Next, place four datum points on the rectangle. Use the intersection of the Datum CSYS and the curves

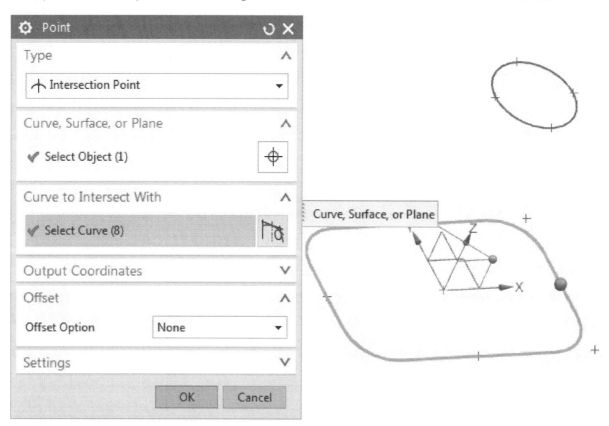

- Sketch two curves in the Y-Z datum plane to connect the datum points of the circle and rectangle as shown below.

292

Hint: You can mirror your sketch.

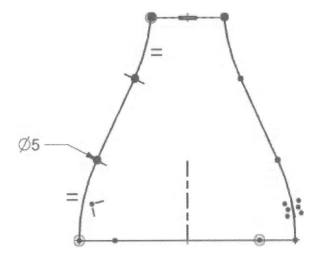

- Sketch two curves in the X-Y datum plane to connect the datum points of the circle and rectangle shown below.

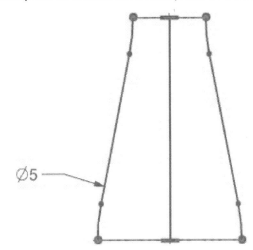

- Select Through Curve Mesh. NX 10 is prompting you to select Primary Curve 1. Make sure the option in the selection intent menu is set to connected curves.
- Select the circle as Primary Curve 1 and choose Add New Set. Select the rectangle as Primary Curve 2 and choose Add New Set.

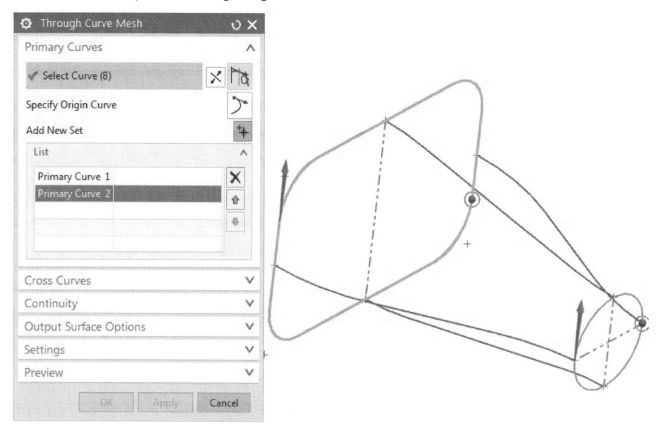

Note: *Be sure the arrows associated with both strings are pointing in the same direction. If they are not, NX 10 will probably freak out. If they do not match, select Back and be careful to select in a similar location on both primary strings.*

NX 10 is prompting you to select the first cross string.

- Select any of the cross curves as the first and hit **Add New Set**.
- Continue to select the remaining three cross curves in the same manner.
- When prompted for **Cross curve 5**, re-select your starting curve to let NX 10 know where to close the loop.

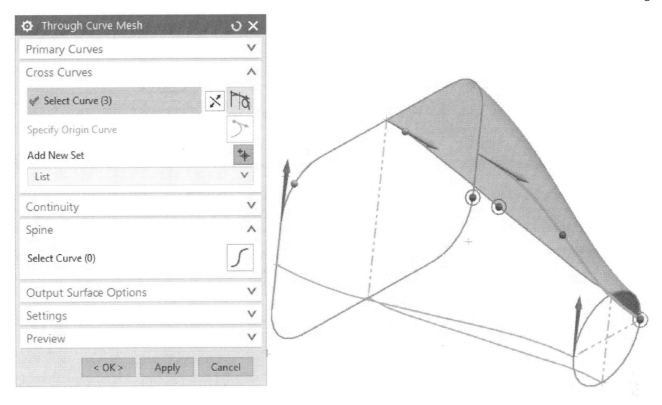

Note: *Be sure to go clockwise or counterclockwise, according to the direction in which the primary strings are directed, when selecting the strings to ensure a smooth, continuous loop.*

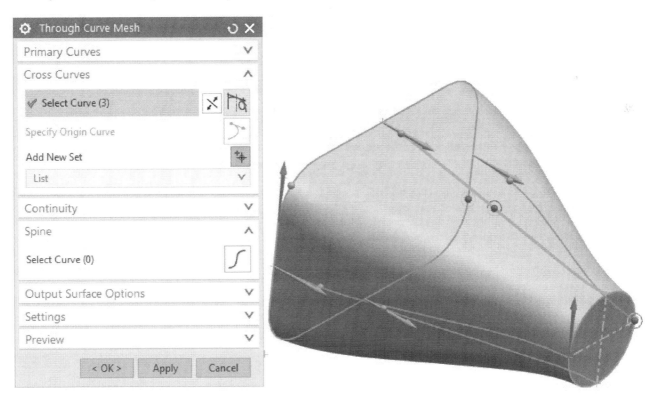

- Accept all the defaults in the Through Curve Mesh window.
- Select Shell.
- Select the two planar faces as the faces to pierce.

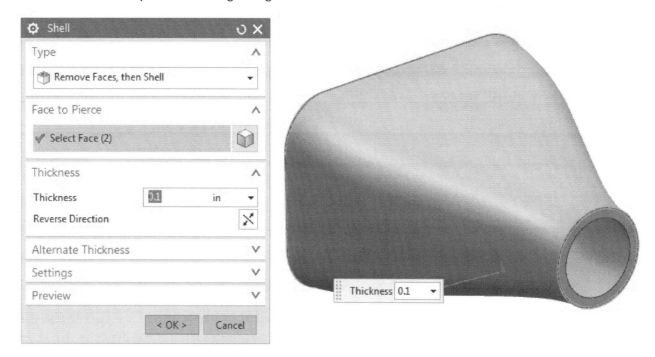

- Compare your results to the following figure.

15.6.2 Sheet

- Create the sketch shown in the following figure.

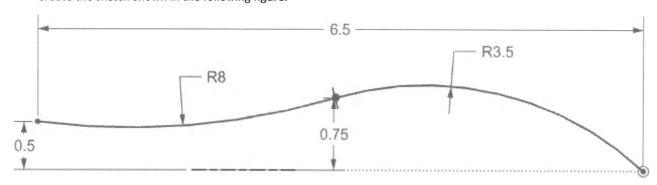

- Create another sketch on a datum plane perpendicular to the first one as shown below.

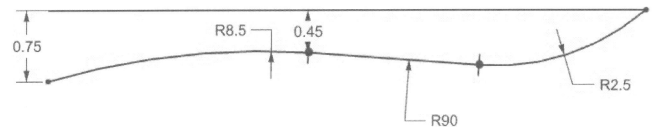

- Create the bridge curve to join the first two sketches.

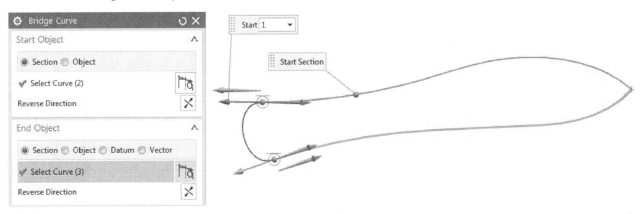

- Select **Through Curve Mesh**.
- Select the bridge curve and the datum point as the **Primary Curves** (you can specify a point as a curve!). Make sure that your arrows are pointing in the same direction.

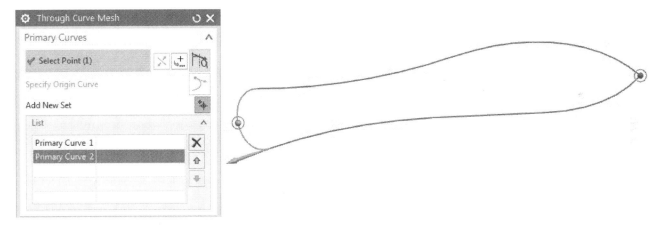

- Select the two **Cross Curves**.

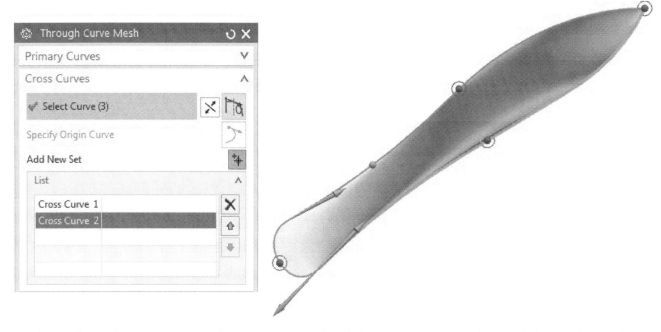

- Leave the options shown above. Notice the options for First & Last, Primary, and Cross Strings in the Continuity section of the menu.

- When you create surface patches adjoining another surface, you can constrain the resultant surface to the adjacent faces with varying degrees of geometric continuity – G0, G1, or G2.

15.7 **N-Sided Surface**

The N-Sided Surface tool produces a surface bounded by a specified chain of connected curves – much like the Bounded Plane tool studied earlier. Unlike Bounded Plane, the input curves for N-Sided Surface need not be coplanar. You can impose shape and continuity constraints to the surface along those boundary curves to produce beautiful and complex surfaces.

- Begin by creating the following sketch.

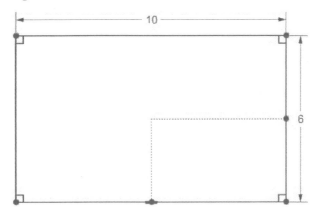

- Extrude the sketch by 0.5in.
- Create a G2 Edge blend on each corner.

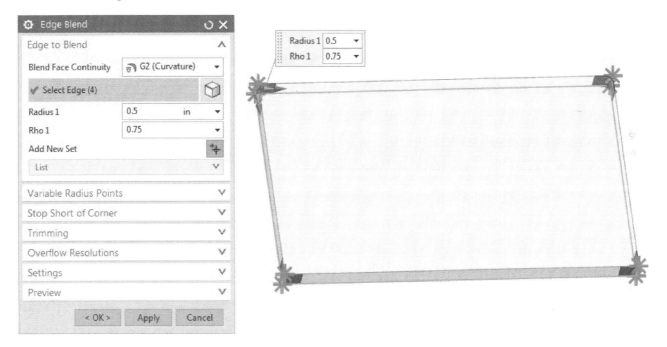

We want to end up with a domed surface that covers this profile. To help us control the shape of the dome, we are going to use an Extrude with a draft – where the draft angle will control the dome (N-sided Surface).

- **Extrude** the profile **0.25in**, include an **80 degree** draft, and choose **Sheet** as the body type, as shown in the following figure. This will create a sheet body instead of a solid.

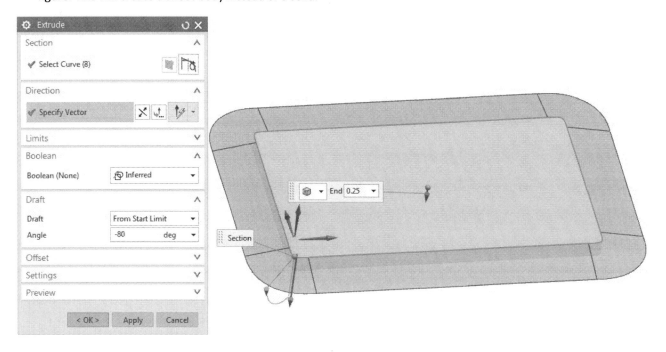

- Now select **N-sided Surface** from the **Surface** tab.
- Select the edge of the solid body as the **Outer Loop** and the select the sheet body as the **Constraint Face**, and finally check **Trim to Boundary** under settings, as shown below.

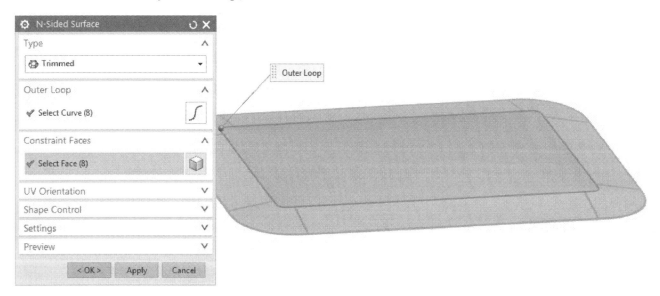

- Use **Delete Body** on the extruded sheet, you will have a domed surface – fit for any great consumer product.

- Use the Patch command to join the surface to the solid. Patch is similar to Sew (in that it produces a solid body) but requires a solid body and a sheet body as input, rather than only sheet bodies.
- Add a small chamfer around the edge as shown in the following figure.

15.8 **Advanced Surfacing Tools**

It's amazing how good surfacing, coloring and texture can affect the look of a thing. As many industrial designers know, a product's form can attract and delight the end user. The form can capture the eye of a prospective customer, beacon them over to the shelf, or click on the link and input their credit card info then proceed to checkout. Product form can give a product owner a sense of pride as they are seen using the product by friends, family members or even total strangers.

Form gives the user something that somehow appeals to an underlying sense of beauty and value. Although the function of a product is arguably more important than the form, and the function is somewhat inseparable from the form, it is instructive to consider the form as its own separate entity.

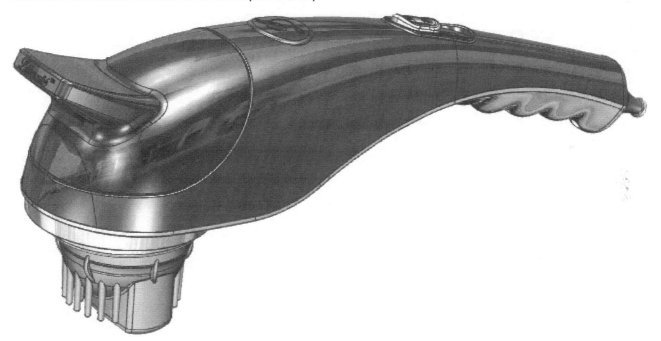

Massager unit designed by Design Visionaries

Great industrial design and the use of surfaces to achieve it is beauty and art. Unfortunately for the industrial designer trying to give a product a form that will help to sell it, art and beauty vary greatly from culture to culture, from age to age and from male to female. When defining a product that is supposed to sell worldwide, it is difficult to know what will be appealing to such a varied user community. That said, industrial designers who are trying to suit the tastes of a huge and varied audience benefit by considering what is universal. In NX 10, there are many more surfacing tools and many more options in tools than what we have covered. There are more than can be covered reasonably by this one book. However, here are a few more.

15.8.1 **Studio Surface**

The Studio Surface is an extremely powerful tool. You create section curves and guide curves, assign continuity, adjust the output surface options and the settings and you will create a great surface. You get a preview as you select the various options which enable you to work very efficiently. It is the humble yet strong opinion of the author that regardless of the surface type employed, the design will only ever be as good as the imagination and skill of the creator. The imagination must come first. The CAD system can be a hindrance if the vision of what you are creating isn't clear before you start "cading". To that end it can be very useful to begin with a series of hand sketches. You can solve many problems with hand sketches way faster than with a CAD system.

In the example below, a device is required to extract thermometers out of acid bottles. The thermometers are longer than the diameter of the opening of the acid bottles. The thermometer has a bulb on it that is about .28 inches in diameter. The user must use the tool to grasp the bulb loosely but securely. As the thermometer is lifted it rotates in such a way that it will align with the tool and come out of the 2 inch hole. The tool has a button on top which allows the user to tighten and loosen the grip on the bulb. We can begin this task with a hand sketch.

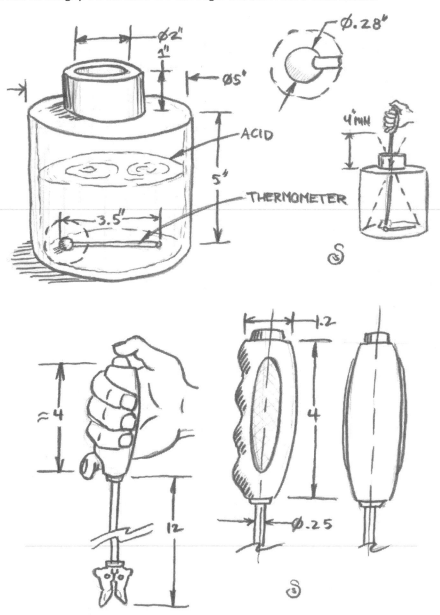

Once you've created the hand sketch, you can bring it into NX 10 using the Raster Image command. In this case and for this product a handle is needed. The shape of handles is extremely important because they provide both look and feel of a product. They are the most important interface that the user has with the product.

To begin this exercise, create a hand sketch and scan it. You may use the scanned image in the example pack. It's called *"hand sketches.JPG"*.

- Choose Raster Image under the Datum drop-down.

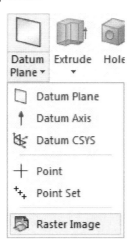

- Browse for the picture. It can be a *JPEG*, *PNG* or a *TIFF*. A preview will appear.
- Select the plane.
- Set the origin to Middle Center.
- You will have to play around with the Scale and the Aspect Ratio slider.

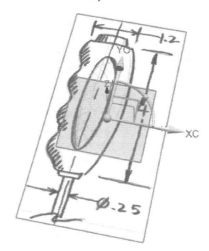

- Once you have placed the decal on the plane and scaled it using the scale button and the aspect ratio. You can start sketching over the image.

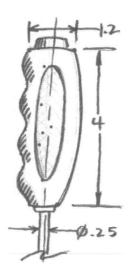

- Use the side view image of the handle and create a perpendicular raster image as shown.

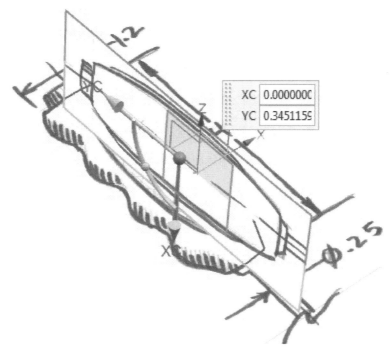

- Create a new sketch on the perpendicular plane to create the side profile.

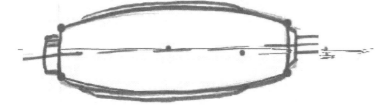

- Use a closed loop Studio Spline to connect the perpendicular sketches on each end.
- Select Studio Surface from the Surface Tab.
- Begin by selecting the two ends as the Primary Curves.

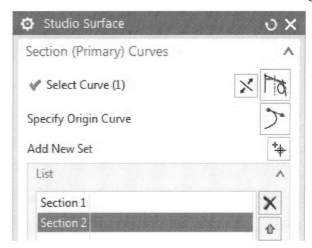

- Start selecting each side of the sketch as the Cross Curves.

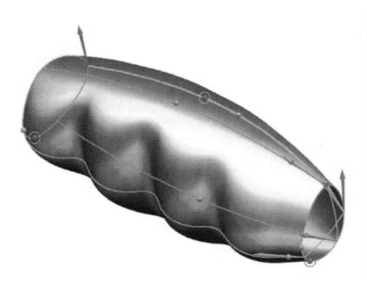

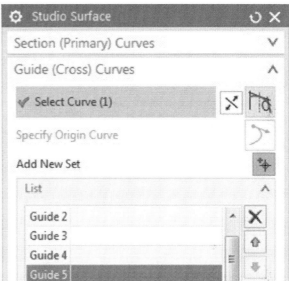

- Next create an offset curve of the top view sketch and project the curves onto the side of the handle as shown.

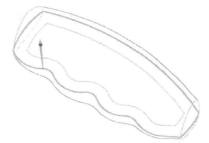

- Project the offset curves onto the side of the handle as shown below.

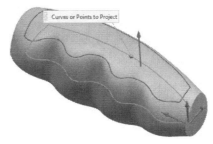

- Select Pull Face and move the Face inside the projected curve upward to thicken.

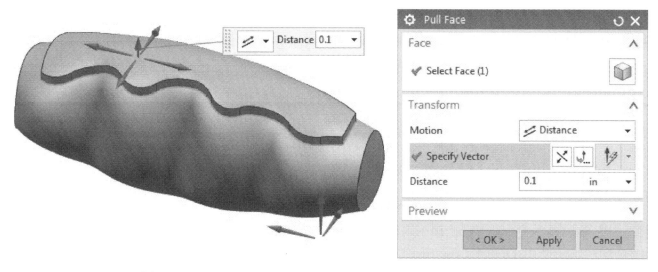

- Assemble the rest of the pieces, get a prototype, impress the customer and collect your check.

15.8.2 Realize Shape

Realize Shape is a new powerful new surfacing tool in NX 10 that allows free-forming of a body. It is similar to creating a clay sculpture which results in some very organic looking shapes.

- To use realize shape go to the Surface tab / Realize Shape.

Realize shape is like working with a clay model, to begin you have to start with a primitive shape. A few choices are available e.g. Block, Cylinder, Sphere.

- For this example select the Sphere.

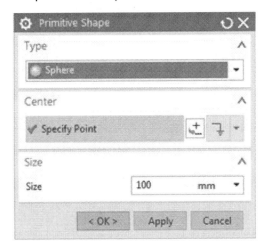 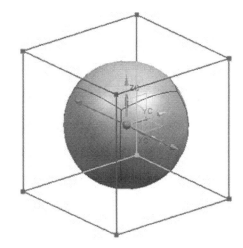

All shapes in Realize Shape are controlled within a cage, the cage is the control point to which the model can be deformed. By increasing the amount of cage bars the shape can be deformed in more precise ways, the cage can also be extruded, merged, projected etc. etc. to add more control over the shape.

- For this exercise a car-like model will be molded.
- The first step is to extrude this sphere to increase its length, to extrude you choose Extrude Cage then pick the wall of the change that needs to be extruded.

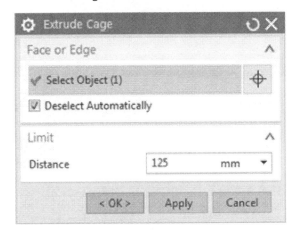 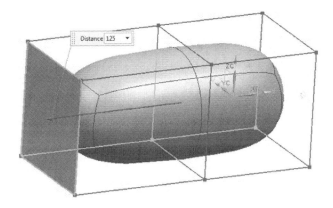

- A value can be typed or the blue axis can be pulled to increase the extrusion. Next the body should be flattened a bit, this can be done by choosing Transform Cage and then selecting the top cage faces and then pushing the orientation tool downward.

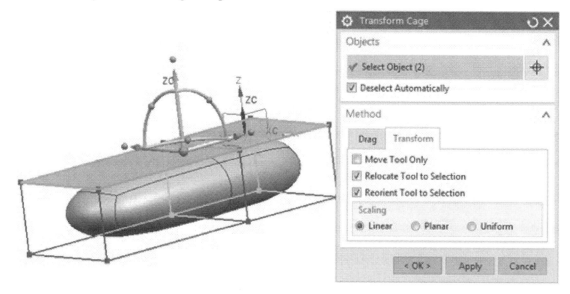

- The front of this shape which would be the front of the car needs to be less rounded, more weight can be given to the front face that will force the shape to conform to the cage more. Click Set Weight function and then increase the weight value for the front face.

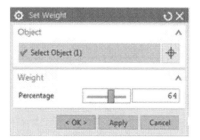

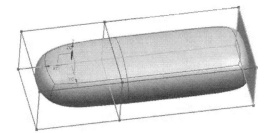

- Do the same with the back face of the cage. In the photo of the car above the front of the car has a draft angle on it, this can be done by transforming only the bottom edge of the cage and pull it outward or by rotating the cage face itself.

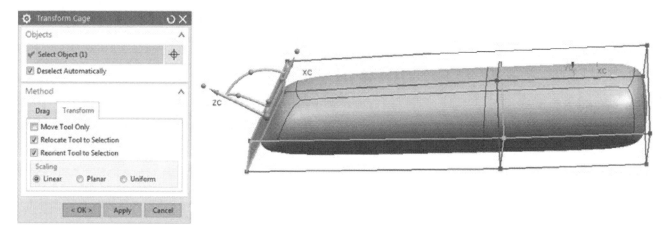

- Considering the car on the outside of the body is the same on both sides, symmetric modeling should be used to do any detailed deforming. To enable symmetric modeling choose the Start Symmetric Modeling button and then choose the plane that will cut this model in half and mirror all deformations to.

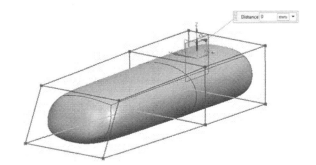

The model is now cut in half and all changes henceforth you make on one side of the model are mirrored to the other side.

- Next the top of the car should be Extruded, but if the top face is extruded it will pull what should be the hood and trunk along with it. To extrude a specific region of the cage, the cage has to be split. Click the Split Face tool.
- Split Face gives you a couple of options on how it will split. The split can be created in uniform which creates the split automatically based on the edge and count, or along polyline can be used. Along polyline is very useful and gives you a lot of control over how the cage is split. It allows you to draw split lines by clicking points on the cage edges shown in dark maize.

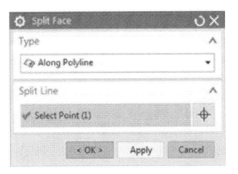

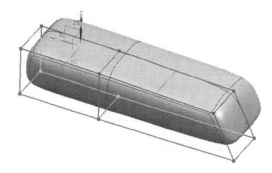

- Two splits are needed in order to extrude the cabin roof upward.

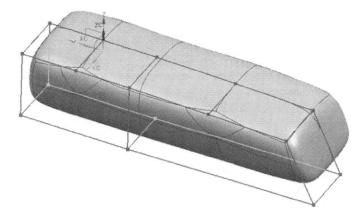

- Then Extrude.

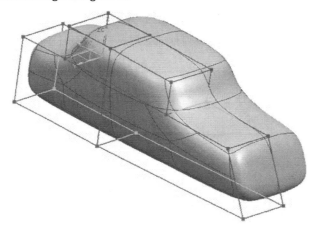

- Almost looks like a child's toy car at the present moment.
- More face splits and transforms can be used to give more detail to the model.

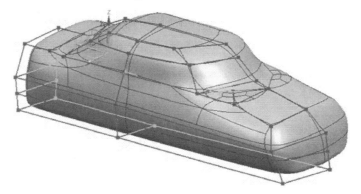

- The more you use split and transform, the more and more the body will take shape.

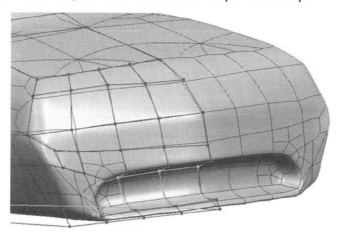

- Once finished with realize shape NX will return to the normal modeling environment where all other design features can be applied to the model.

16 Assemblies

16.1 Introduction

In NX 10, an assembly is a .prt file that contains other part files as components. An assembly contains not only the geometry within its component part files, but records the structure – the relations between those components.

There are two major ways to approach creating an assembly: by combining existing parts together (*bottom-up design*) or by creating new parts on-the-fly in an assembly file (*top-down design*).

In NX 10 there is no distinction between part files and assembly files. This can be a source of a confusion for new users familiar with other CAD tools. Note that it is also possible to produce geometry in the top-level assembly file – which is for most purposes a bad practice!

In order to create and manage assemblies in NX 10, you must enable the Assemblies application. To do so, click on the Assemblies icon in the Design group on the Application tab. Please do so at this time.

Once the Assemblies application is enabled, the Assemblies tab will appear on the ribbon.

16.2 Project – The Hinge, Part III

To illustrate the basic concepts in the Assemblies application, we will make use of the parts *hinge1* (created in Chapter 5.9) and *hinge2* (created throughout Chapter 6, but especially in Chapter 6.6). If you skipped those chapters or lost the files, please review those chapters and create the required part files. You'll need them to complete the next few exercises!

- Create a new file. Instead of choosing the *Modeling* template, as you have done up until this point, select the *Assembly* template, as shown below. Name your assembly *hinge assembly.prt*.
- There are two main differences between the *Assembly* template and the *Modeling* template:
    - If you create a new .prt file from the *Assembly* template, and the Assemblies application is not enabled, creation of the file will automatically turn on the Assemblies application.
    - When a new file is created from the *Assembly* template, the Add Component dialog box will appear automatically.
- Besides those two points, the *Assembly* template and *Modeling* template are effectively identical.

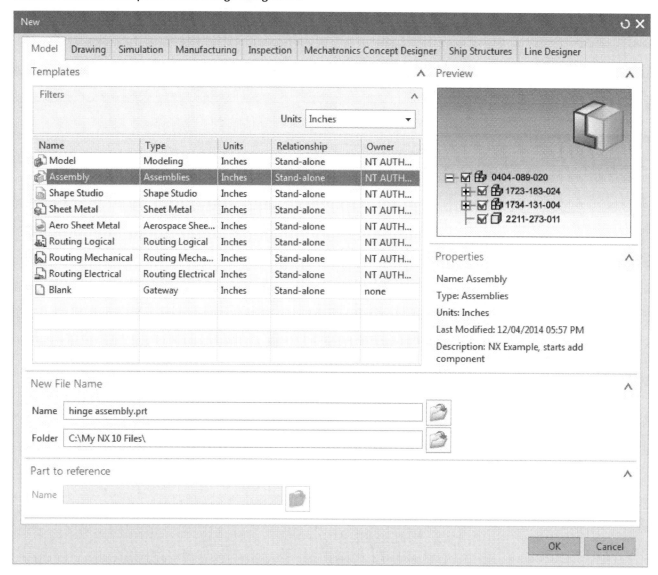

16.3 **Add Component**

The **Add Component** tool is the cornerstone of bottom-up assembly design. Quite simply, it adds a component into an assembly according to the positioning rules that you prescribe for it.

- Upon creating *hinge assembly*, you should see the **Add Component** dialog box immediately. You might see *hinge1* and *hinge2* in the **Recent Parts** section of the menu, but if not, click the **Open** icon, as shown below, to search for them.
- Select *hinge1.prt*.
- Fill out the rest of the **Add Component** dialog box as shown below. You will see a preview of *hinge1* as shown to the right.

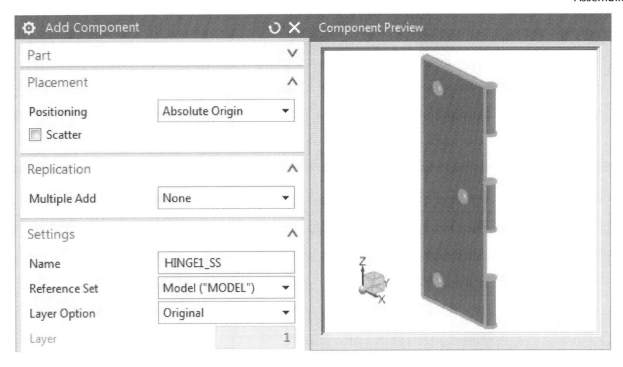

16.4 Reference Sets

In NX 10, a *Reference Set* is a "named group" of geometric items that is used to control the display of assembly components. Reference sets are defined in the part database but are not used until that part is added to an assembly. A common application is to filter out all of the construction geometry required to create a complicated part (datum planes, sketches, tool solids, etc.) and only display the resultant solid model. There are three pre-defined reference sets: Model, Entire Part, and Empty. All other reference sets are user-defined.

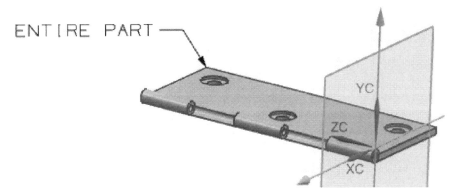

You may recall that in order to create the solid model of the hinge part, you created several datum planes and sketches. In many cases you can choose Model reference set, which mainly consists of the solid or sheet body, but for different uses you can define different reference sets, especially in the case of parts with multiple solid bodies.

You can define a reference set to display only the desired solid geometry in an assembly. A component's displayed reference set may be easily changed (using Assemblies / More / Replace Reference Set).

In the following project, you will first create reference sets in your *hinge1* and *hinge2* parts from a previous project and assemble them together using bottom-up techniques.

Note: *If you do not have the files available,* http://designvisionaries.com/goodies/workfiles/ *contains the completed parts for your reference*

- Open the part file *hinge1* that you created in Chapter 5.8. Even though it is open within *hinge assembly*, you can still open it independently. More on this later.
- Select the Assemblies tab.
- Select More / Reference Sets.

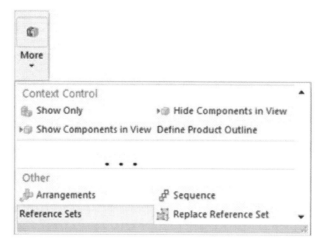

- The Reference Sets dialog box appears as follows.

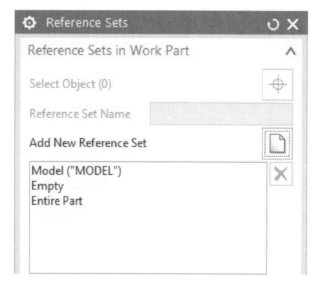

- Select the Add New Reference Set icon.
- Type SOLID and hit [Enter].
- Select the hinge solid body (be careful to not select any other geometry).
- You have now successfully defined a reference set named SOLID. It should appear in the list displayed in the 'Reference Sets' dialog box.
- Choose Close.
- Save *hinge1* and navigate back to *hinge assembly*.
- Right-click on *hinge1* in the Assembly Navigator and select Replace Reference Set / SOLID.

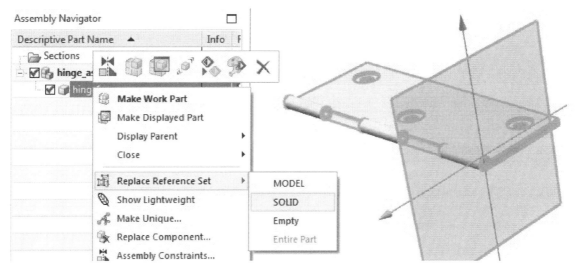

- Now, the only part of *hinge1* that appears in the assembly is the solid body. You can confirm this by going to the Show and Hide menu ([Ctrl]+[W]) and clicking the "+" next to *All*.

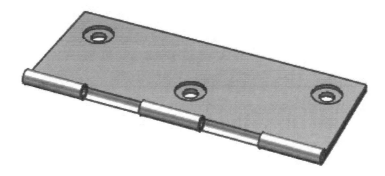

- Save your assembly file.

16.5 Assembly Constraints

To fully constrain a component, you must specify a set of Assembly Constraints. Each constraint removes one or more degrees of freedom from the component's movement. As an example, consider the Touch/Align constraint, which attaches two components together. It removes the ability of one component to move independently of the other. Some of the most commonly used Assembly Constraints follow:

Touch	Entities coincident; surface normal vectors in opposite directions
Align	Entities coplanar; surface normal vectors
Infer Center Axis	Aligns the center axis of cylindrical parts
Concentric	Make circular edges coincident
Fix	Hard fixes a component in the position it is in according to the WCS
Angle	Entities oriented with an included angle
Bond	Fixes components together to act as one
Parallel	Entities constrained to be parallel
Perpendicular	Entities constrained to be perpendicular
Center	Entities centered
Distance	Entities parallel with a specified offset
Fit	Constrain two parts to fit together
Prefer Touch	Similar to Infer. NX guesses the mate/touch with other components

The order in which components are selected when applying Assembly Constraints is important. If you wish hinge2 to inherit its position from hinge1, the first face selected must be from the "follower" component, not the "leader" component.

Note: *You can mate faces, edges, datum planes, datum axes, points, lines and curves*

Continue working in your hinge assembly, and add another part to it using Assembly Constraints to constrain it parametrically.

- Select the Assembly Constraints tool from the Component Position group on the Assemblies tab.

- Select the Fix constraint and click on *hinge1*. You will see a small Fix icon appear on top of *hinge1* in the Graphics Window. The Select Object prompt on the menu will remain highlighted in yellow and with a red asterisk – the Assembly Constraints tool allows you to specify multiple constraints before confirming the change with either OK or Apply. In this case, the Fix constraint is enough, so click OK to confirm.

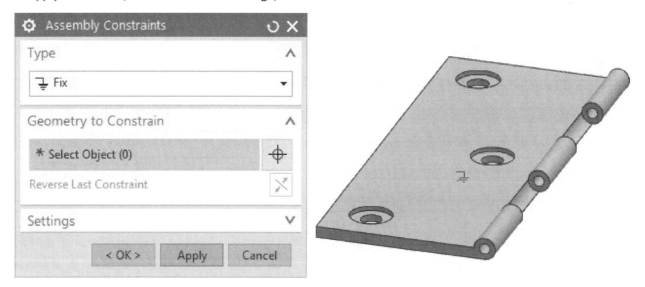

- Select the Add Component icon from the Component group on the Assemblies tab.

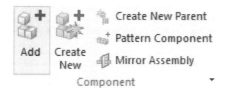

- Select *hinge2* and fill out the rest of the Add Component dialog box as shown below.

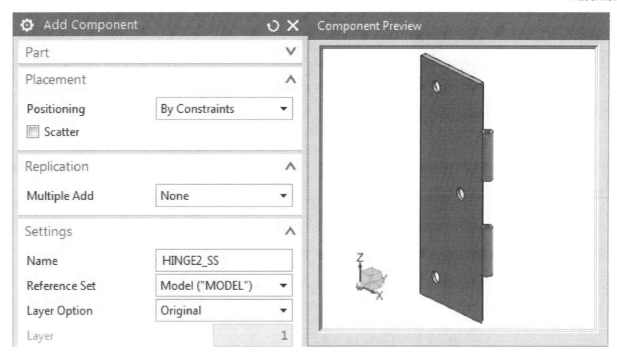

- The Assembly Constraints menu will appear when you click OK.

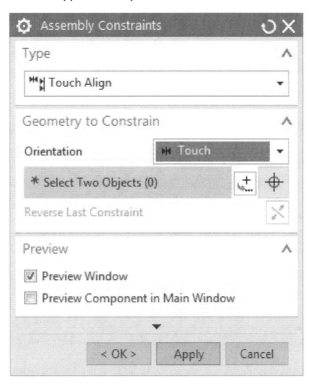

Read the Cue – NX 10 is prompting you to select your first object.

- Select the Type as: Touch Align, and the Orientation to Touch shown above.
- Zoom in on *hinge2* and select the inner planar face of the cylindrical hinge as shown below.
- Now, select the opposite face of *hinge1* as shown. Click OK to exit the menu.

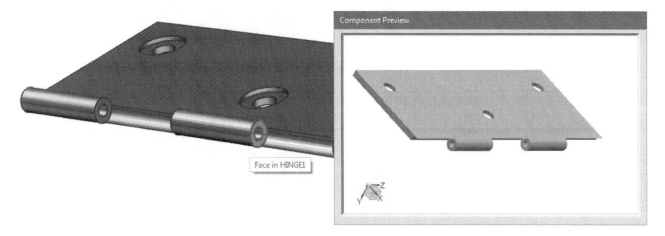

- Select **Move Component**, click on *hinge2*, and select **Specify Orientation**.
- A dynamic CSYS should appear. Clicking and dragging the arrows of the CSYS tells you exactly what degrees of freedom *hinge2* still has. *You will learn a bit more about moving components later on.*
- Select the **Assembly Constraints** tool again. In the **Assembly Constraint** window, the **Type** should be **Touch/Align** and the **Orientation** should be Infer **Center/Axis**.

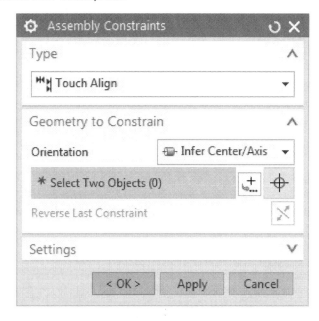

- Hover over the edge of the leftmost cylinder of *hinge1*, shown next with an arrow. An axis should appear. Select this axis, called the *Centerline in hinge1*.

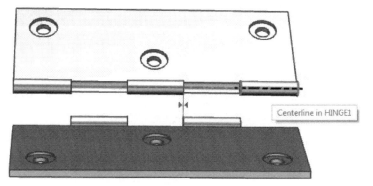

- Use the same method to select the centerline in *hinge2*.
- Compare your results to the following figure.

318

- If you Move Component again, you should see the hinge properly constrained.

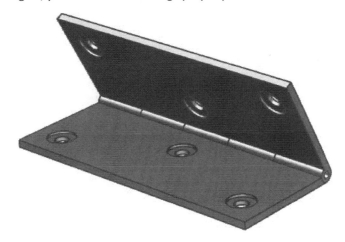

- Save your assembly file.

Note: *You can also initiate the assembly process by simply dragging an existing part straight from its folder and onto the Graphics Window of an open part.*

There are many different constraints that can be used to position parts in assemblies. This project only covers a few of them. Play around with the assembly constraints to see what other cool tricks you can do in assemblies!

16.6 Create New Component

To perform top-down assembly design in NX 10, you must create parts using the Create New Component tool. Once you have a new empty component, you can proceed to add geometric features to it.

Note that when you create a component in this manner, it inherits its units from the parent assembly. If you wish to use different units, you must create it outside the assembly and add it using bottom-up assembly design techniques.

The ability to create components directly within an assembly is a very powerful tool. To grasp this concept fully, you must first understand the concept of *Work Part* and *Displayed Part*.

16.6.1 Work Part vs. Displayed Part

The *Displayed Part* is the part that is currently displayed in the Graphics Window. The *Work Part* is the part to which any command is applied (i.e. **Extrude, Edge Blend, Chamfer... etc. etc.**).

In this project, you will create a new hinge pin component in your *hinge_assembly.prt* and define its geometry using Top-Down design techniques.

- Select Create New Component from the Component group on the Assemblies tab.

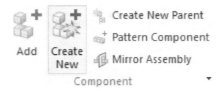

- Type in the new model file name: *hinge_pin_<your initials>.prt*.
- The Create New Component window appears.

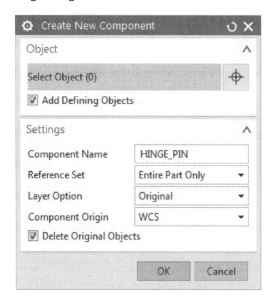

- Click OK without selecting any objects.
- **Right-click** on *hinge_pin* in the **Assembly Navigator** and select **Make Work Part**.

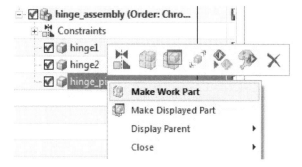

- The other parts in the assembly will change their color to indicate that they are not the Work Part.
- Insert a sketch on the YC-ZC Datum Plane.
- Create the sketch shown next.

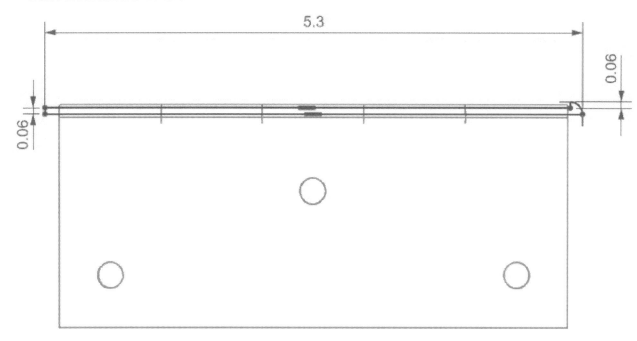

- Create the hinge pin solid by revolving the sketch 360° about the hinge center axis.
- Your pin may not be in exactly the right spot. We'll get to the positioning a few sections from here.
- Make the *hinge_assembly* the work part. Compare your results to the figure below.

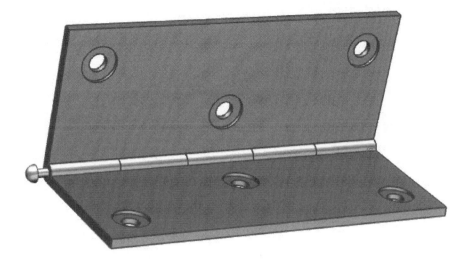

- Save your assembly file.

16.7 **Component Position**

Components may be repositioned in many degrees of freedom unless they are parametrically constrained by applying *Assembly Constraints*. Normally, three constraints are required to fully constrain a component, although you may apply fewer and allow the component to be under-constrained.

You are not required to apply any Assembly Constraints to the first part of an assembly but it sure helps. If all components are fully constrained, the positions of all the components will update when the first component is repositioned.

You can reposition any components that have not been fully constrained, subject to the existing constraints. When you move a component, NX will constrain the component's motion according to any existing constraints.

Change the color of your components and reposition the *hinge2* part.

16.7.1 **Move Component**

- Open your *hinge_assembly* part (if required) and select the Assemblies tab.
- Use Edit Object Display to give *hinge_ pin*, *hinge1*, and *hinge2* all different colors.
- Select Move Component.
- Select your *hinge_pin* part and click on Specify Orientation.

If you select one of the arrows, the component will be constrained to move along that axis only.

- **Left click** and drag *hinge2*. Notice that it will move around only the cylindrical axis. Drag the hinge into the position shown below.

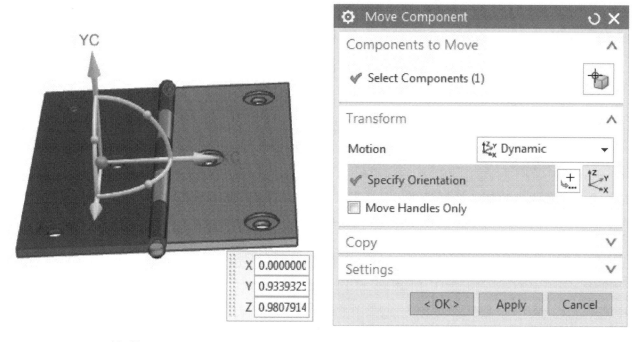

- **Save** your assembly file.

16.7.2 **Concentric Constraint**

In this project you will fully constrain your *hinge_pin* component by adding a concentric constraint between the hinge pin and the hinges.

- Open your *hinge_assembly* part and select the **Assemblies tab.**
- Select **Assembly Constraints** .
- Select the **Type: Concentric.**
- Select the edge from your *hinge_pin* and the edge of *hinge2* parts as shown below.

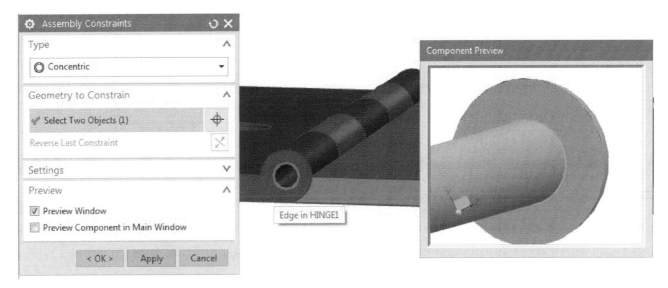

- Compare your results to the figure below.

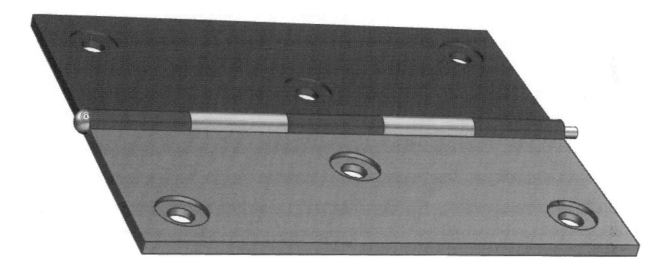

- Save your assembly file.

16.7.3 Angle Constraint

You have learned that you can move a component in any degree-of-freedom in which it is not constrained. In some cases, you may wish to further constrain this movement and vary it using a parameter. This can be accomplished by adding Assembly Constraints that have offset parameters.

In this project you will add an angular dimensional constraint between the two hinge parts and vary its value.

- Open your *hinge_assembly* part (if required) and select the Assemblies tab.
- Select Assembly Constraints.
- Select the Type as Angle.
- Select the faces from your *hinge1* and *hinge2* parts as shown below.

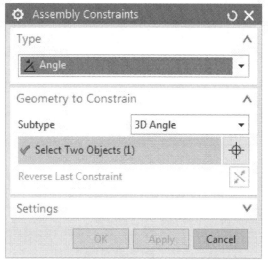

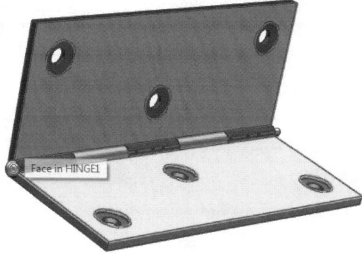

- Enter an angle of **150**.

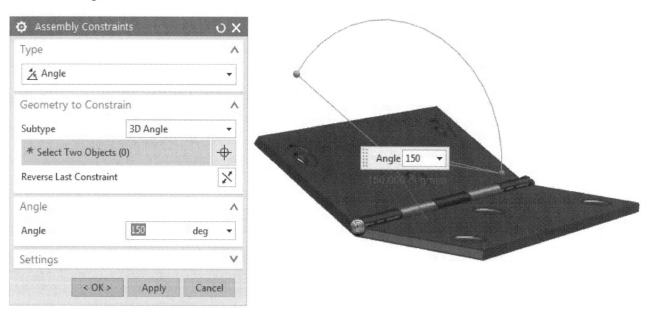

- Compare your results to figure above.
- **Save** your assembly file.

16.8 **Modifying Assembly Components**

NX allows you to modify assembly components in many ways. You have already learned how to **Move** components and to add **Assembly Constraints** to existing components. You may also modify existing **Assembly Constraints** by deleting them, suppressing them, or changing their type. Components may themselves be deleted, suppressed, or modified. Some of the commonly-used techniques are covered in the next few paragraphs.

16.9 **Deleting and Suppressing Components**

Assembly components may be deleted or suppressed. Just as in modeling mode, a *Suppressed* component may be *Unsuppressed*, but a deleted component is gone forever. A suppressed component will retain its **Assembly Constraints**, so you may choose to first suppress a component until you are certain that it no longer will be used in the assembly. It is important to note that deleted components themselves are not removed from the hard drive – they are simply deleted from the assembly file.

To suppress a component, select Assemblies Tab / More / Suppress Component. Similarly, to Unsuppress a component, select Unsuppress Component from the same menu. You can delete a component by Right-Clicking and selecting Delete or clicking the large X that pops up when selecting a component.

16.10 Suppress and Deleting Assembly Constraints

You can suppress an Assembly Constraint by unchecking the box next to the constraint, as shown below. The system remembers the suppressed constraint, so you can restore it by simply checking the box again.

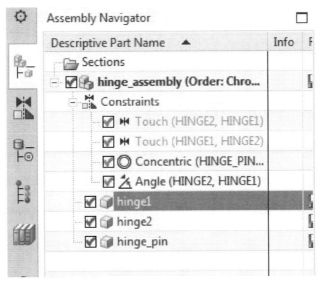

If you are certain that you want to completely remove an Assembly Constraint, you may delete it by right-clicking on the constraint and selecting Delete.

16.11 Changing Properties of a Constraint

You can change the property of a constraint by selecting the Right Click / Convert To option as shown in the following figure. For example, you can convert a Touch constraint into a Distance constraint, thus enabling you to specify an offset value for the constraint.

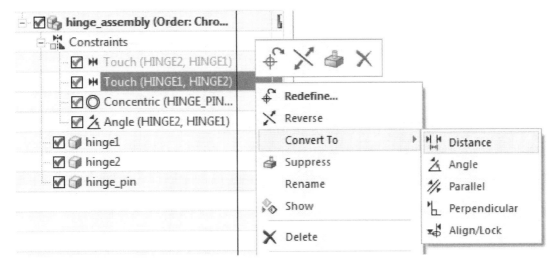

16.12 **Design-In-Context**

You can edit any part's feature in the assembly by making it the Work Part. When a component is set as the Work Part, you have access to most of the NX 10 modeling functionality, with the added benefit of seeing the part within the context of its parent assembly. This process is known as *design-in-context*.

In this project you will adjust the length of the hinge pin in the assembly, in context.

- Open your *hinge_assembly* part and select the Assemblies tab (if required).
- Set your *hinge_pin* part as the Work Part.
- Select Modeling under the Application tab.
- Select Sketch.

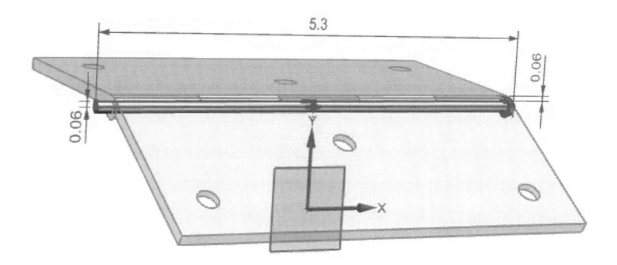

- The figure above shows the original sketch. Edit the sketch to make the pin **5.00in** long from the end of the pin to the shoulder of the pin head.

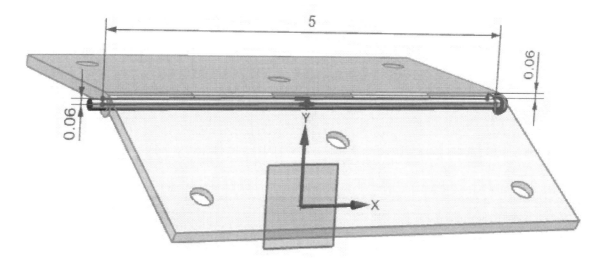

- Compare your results with the figure below.

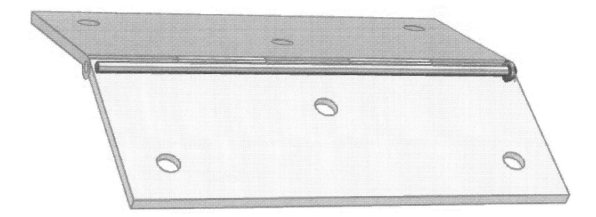

- Make the assembly file the work part.
- Save your assembly file.

16.13 Changing the Reference Set

By assigning a Reference Set to a part, you can load only the features of a part that you need into the assembly instead of the entire part. NX 10 gives you an option to use Reference Sets when you add an existing component to the assembly. Most of the time, using the Model Reference Set is sufficient unless you have solid / surface bodies that you don't want to load in the assembly. You can also create and replace Reference Sets after a part is assembled.

- Open your *hinge_assembly* part and select the Assemblies tab (if required).
- Set your hinge_pin part as the Work Part.
- Select Assemblies Tab/ More / Reference Sets.
- Select the Create icon from the Reference Sets window.
- Enter the name: SOLID, and choose only the revolved solid of the pin.
- The Reference Set named SOLID will be added to the Reference Sets list box, as shown in the following figure.

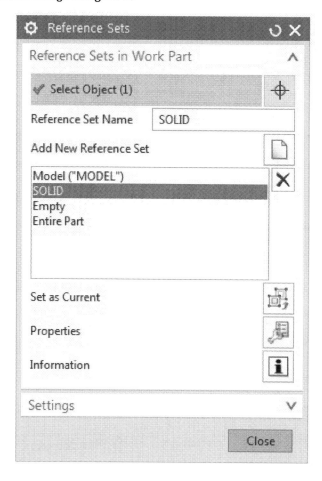

- Make the hinge assembly the workpart.
- Right-click on the hinge_pin part in the Assembly Navigator and select Replace Reference Set/ SOLID.

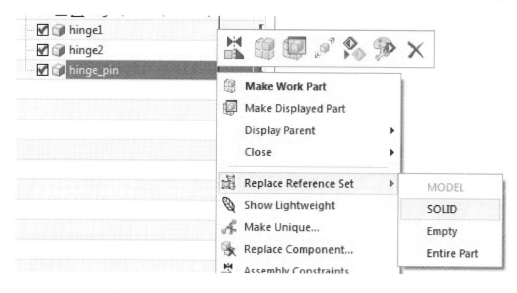

- Save your assembly file.

16.14 **Adding Translucency to a Component**

Adding Translucency can be a great help in visualizing complex assemblies. Before you add translucency to a component, make sure that the Translucency option is toggled on from the View Tab / More menu.

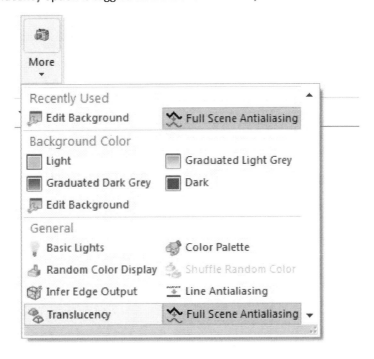

- Open your hinge_assembly part (if required) and select the Assemblies tab.
- Select View Tab / Edit Object Display.
- Select the hinge2 component and choose OK.
- Move the Translucency slider bar to 50 in the Edit Object Display window, as shown in the following figure.

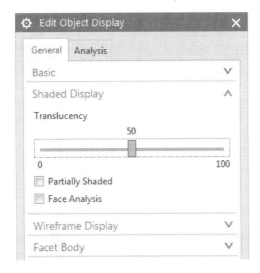

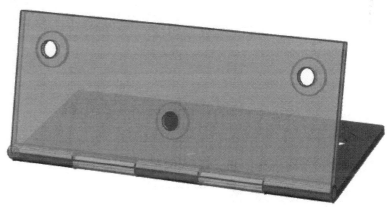

16.15 **Exploded Views**

Exploded views allow you to *"explode"* parts away from their assembly location to better show how parts are assembled and/or used in assemblies. These are helpful for assembly schematics and instructions.

You can create an exploded view of the assembly components. They are stored as a *"snapshot"* of the assembly that includes the exploded positions of the components. Exploded views can even be used for display in assembly drawings.

In this project you will create an exploded view of your hinge assembly components.

- Open your hinge_assembly part (if required) and select the Assemblies tab.
- Select Exploded Views / New Explosion.
- Choose OK to accept the default name 'Explosion 1.'

- Select Exploded Views / Auto-explode Components.
- Select your hinge_pin component.
- Enter Distance = 6 as shown next.

- Choose OK.
- Compare your results with the following figure.

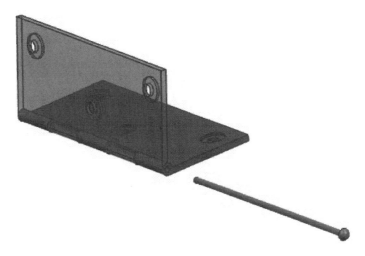

- Select Exploded Views / Edit Explosion.

The Edit Explosion window appears, as shown in the following figure.

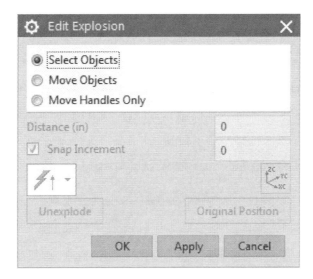

- Toggle the radio button to Select Objects, and select your hinge2 component.
- Toggle the radio button to Move Objects.

The Dynamic WCS appears, as shown below.

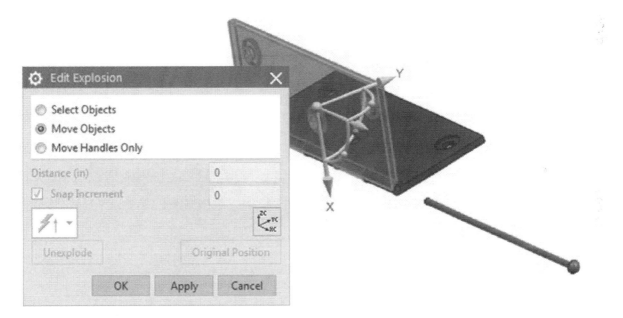

- Drag your hinge2 part up a short distance.
- Choose OK to finish editing the Exploded View.
- Compare your results with the following figure.

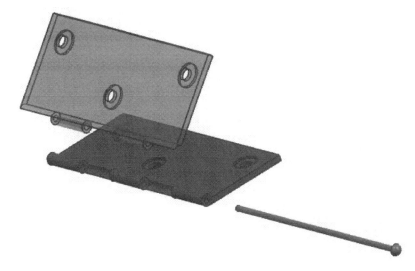

- Select Exploded Views / Unexplode Component.
- Select your hinge_pin part, and choose OK to unexplode the selected component.

- Select Exploded Views / Hide Explosion to return the assembly to the unexploded state.
- Save your assembly file.

16.16 Project – The Do-Nothing

Now you have the skills to do nothing! No really; this next toy is called the *"Do Nothing."*

16.16.1 Building and Constraining an Assembly

In this project we are going to use Assembly Constraints to create the following assembly. This is a small mechanism, often used as a children's toy. If we use the assembly constraints properly, we will be able to show the motion of the mechanism without having to do a complicated motion simulation.

Luckily for you, the parts are already created. All you have to do is create the assembly.

- Start with File / New to create a new assembly file.
- Name the new assembly *cool toy.prt* as shown in the following figure.

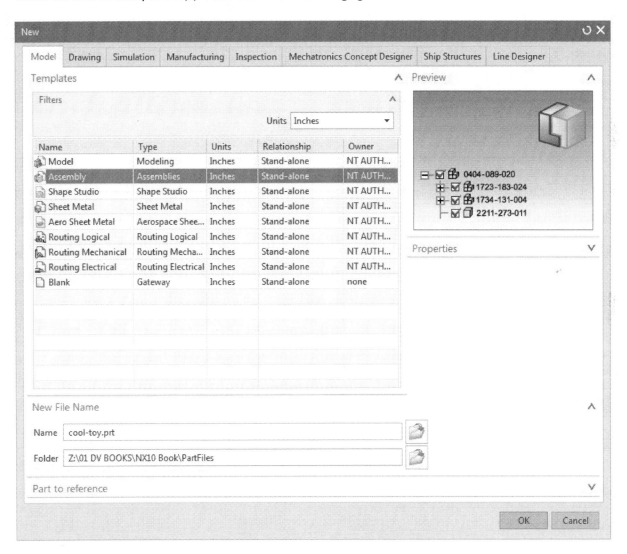

The first window that shows up is asking if you would like to add a component. Click on the folder button next to Open, navigate to the directory where your parts are (downloaded from the *Design Visionaries* website) and then select *Base.prt*. Once the part is loaded, it will show up in the Component Preview window, as shown in the following figure.

- Select Absolute Origin in the Add Component window for its placement, as shown in the next window.
- Then Select OK to fully import the part into your assembly.

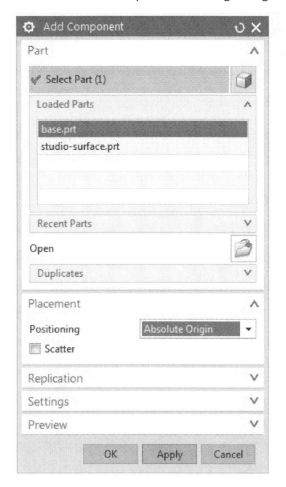

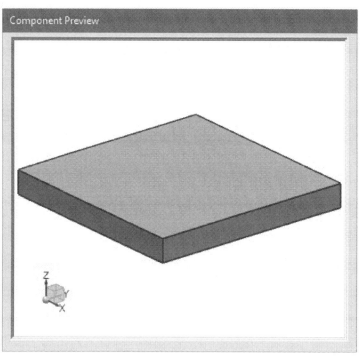

Before we start adding new components to this assembly we have to *Fix* the first component. If this is not done, the base part is likely to move around.

- To *Fix* the component, go to *Assemblies tab/ Assembly Constraints*. Or click on the assembly constraints button in the *Assemblies* toolbar, as shown in the following figure.

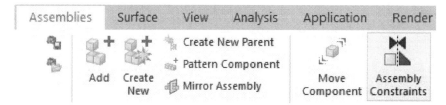

This will show you the *Assembly constraints* window as shown in the following figure. The drop down arrow shows all the constraints available.

- Select the *Fix* constraint, and then click on the base in the graphics window. You will now see the *Fix* symbol attached to the base in the following figure.

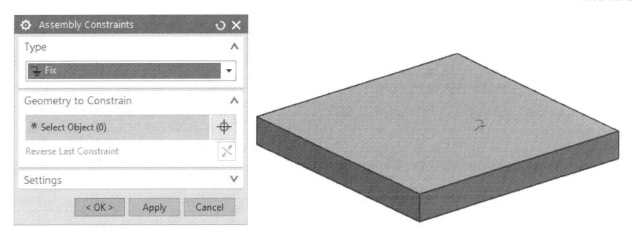

You can add or remove these little constraint indicators by right clicking on the constraints tab in the assembly navigator and selecting or deselecting **Display Constraints in Graphics Window**. We prefer to turn them off, as when the assembly gets more complicated it gets messy with them there!

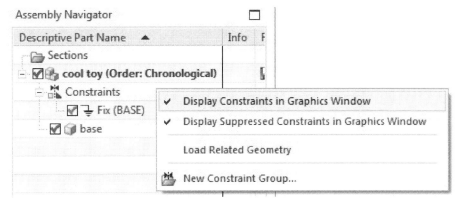

- Now we will add the next component. Go to **Add**. Click the same button as before to navigate to another part file. This time choose *body parts.prt*.
- In the placement section of the **Add Component** window, select By Constraints, as shown in the following figure.

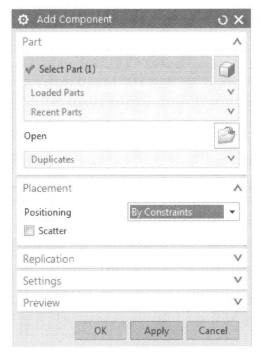

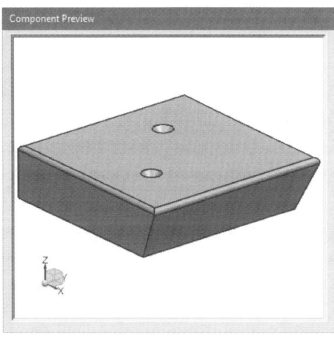

- Once you hit **Apply**, the **Assembly Constraints** window will appear with the preview window.
- Select the **Touch Align** constraint and set the orientation to **Touch**.
- First, select the bottom face of the body part, as shown in the following figure.

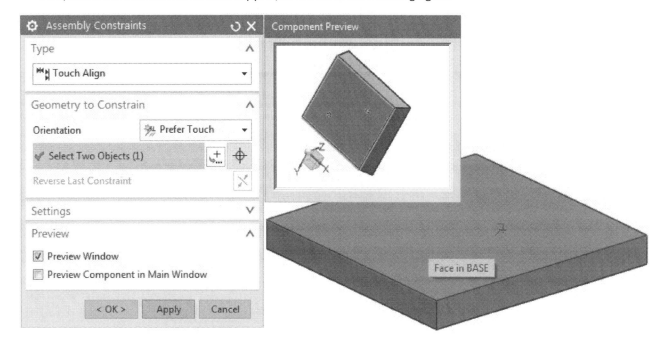

- Then select the top face of the base. You do not have to click apply or **OK** yet; only do that once your model is fully constrained.

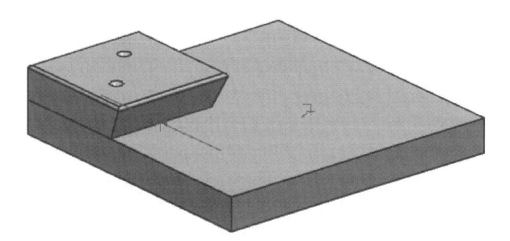

- The model will now jump into position. If your model flips the wrong way, you can **right-click** the constraint and select **Reverse**, as shown in the following figure.

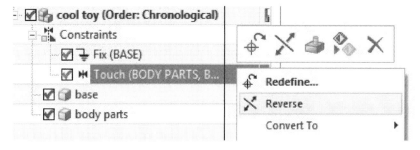

The model is not fully constrained yet – we have two left to do. The next two are Align constraints. Make sure the orientation is set to Align. Select coplanar faces shown in the following figure, then do the same for the perpendicular faces.

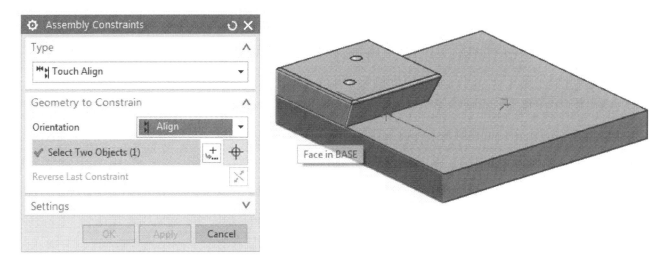

Note: *You don't have to choose the model in the preview window, though it is useful when you can't see the model clearly in the normal graphics window.*

- Repeat this process, adding three more body parts.prt to the base as shown in the following figure.

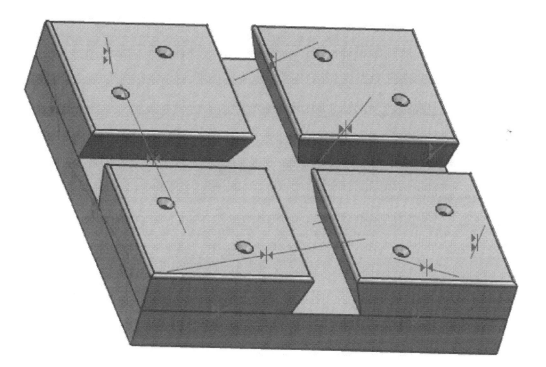

- The next step is to add a new component. This time add the *slider.prts* using placement By Constraints.
- The first constraint will be a Touch Align between the large bottom surface of the slider and the top surface of the base, as shown in the following figure.

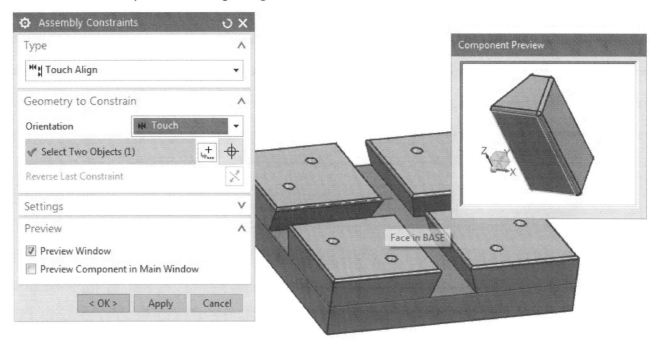

- Then Touch a Side Face on the Slider with the Side Face on Body Part.
- Repeat this process with another slider.prt so that you get the following model.

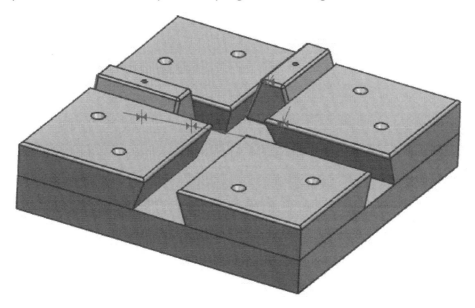

- Next, add the *crank.prt*, using the Touch Align placement. However, this time, choose the infer center/axis command.

- Connect the pairs or faces shown in the following figure by clicking on the cylindrical face of the slider to the cylindrical inner face of the crank.

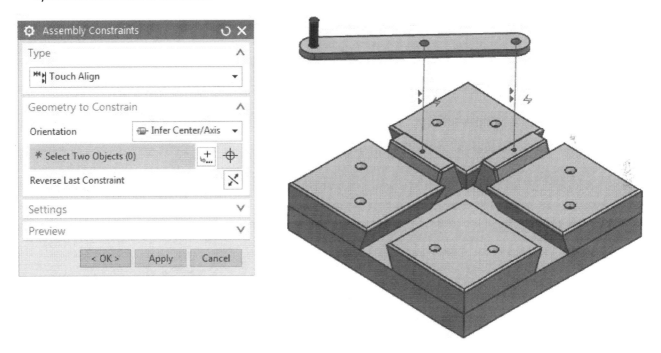

- Then use the Touch Align constraint, specifying the touch command, shown in the following figure.

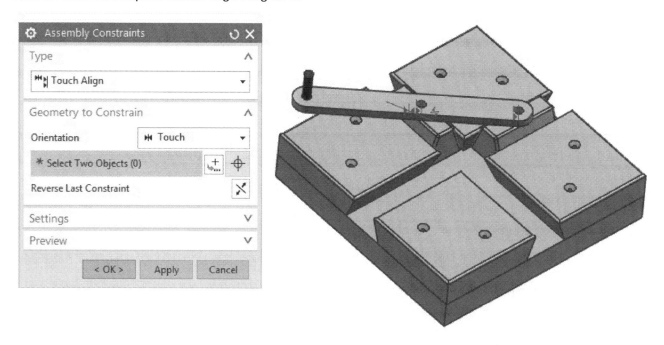

- Let's add screws to this model, since there are screw holes! We will screw in the crank first.
- Go to **Assemblies tab / Add** and open *screw.prt* from the folder.

- For Positioning, choose **By Constraints**.
- Choose the **Align and Lock** assembly constraint.
- Like the concentric constraint choose the bottom circular edge of the screw head and the top circular edge of the hole in the crank as shown.

You may have to flip the direction to get what you want; if you have done it correctly you should have something similar to the following figure.

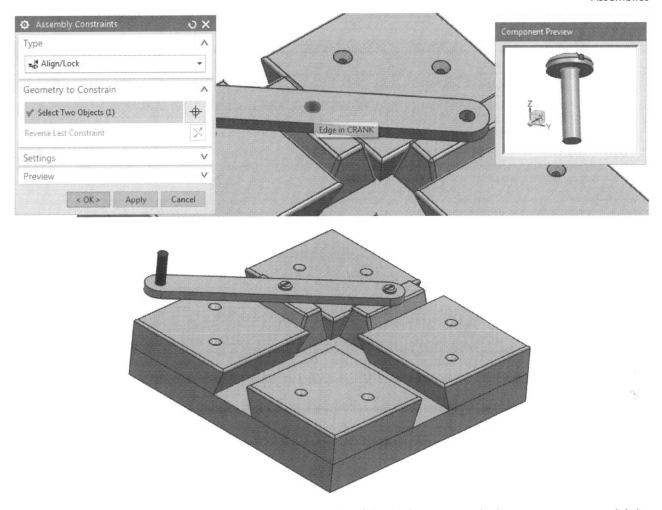

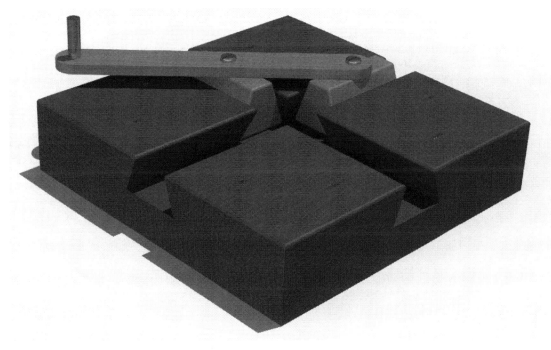

- Last but not least, assemble *wood screw.prts* in the holes of the body parts exactly the same way as you did the other screws. Your model should look like the following figure. When you choose Move Component to rotate the crank, you'll see the beauty of the Do Nothing.

16.17 **Make Unique**

The *Make Unique* command is an extremely useful ability that is available in NX 10. A good way to describe it is a way of dealing with the situation that arises when you have an assembly with a number of components that you first thought would be all identical, but then you subsequently found it necessary to make some of them different. For example, if you have a table that has four identical legs, and then you decide that two of the legs should have casters on them so you could just tilt the table and roll it away.

The BOM for the typical table would have all four of the legs be identical as shown below. Notice that the table leg has as quantity of 4.

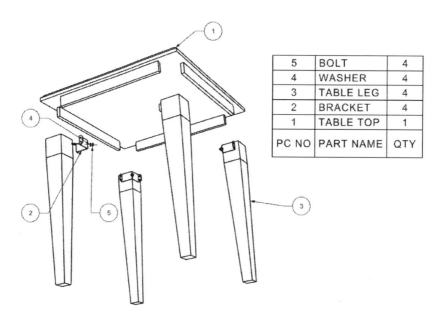

PC NO	PART NAME	QTY
5	BOLT	4
4	WASHER	4
3	TABLE LEG	4
2	BRACKET	4
1	TABLE TOP	1

Using the Make Unique command all you need to do is select the two legs that you want shortened and select the command. Assemblies Tab / More / Make Unique. The following menu appears.

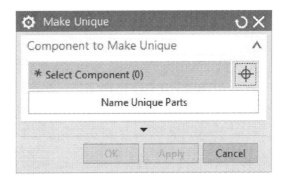

You may have to *Unpack* the components in order to select them individually, you can do this by right clicking a set of components (usually with the suffix X and a number) and select *Unpack.*

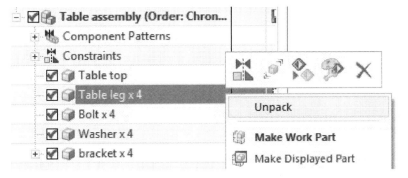

With the assembly work part, you are prompted to select the components that you want to alter. Once selected, you click on the **Name Unique Parts** button. You are prompted to enter a new component name. In this case *"Table leg Shortened"* was chosen. You must type it into the **Name** box and select OK.

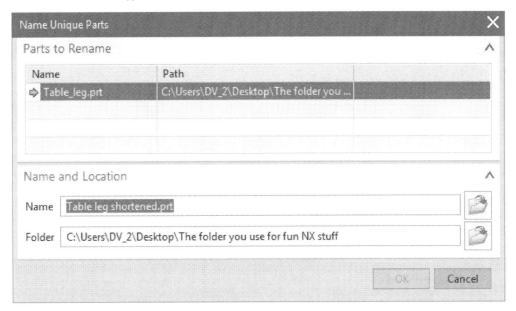

Then you make the shortened leg the work part and chop the end of it off where the caster will go. Finally you assemble the casters onto the end of the shortened legs and you're good to go. The new assembly is complete.

The bill of materials updates to reflect the new structure.

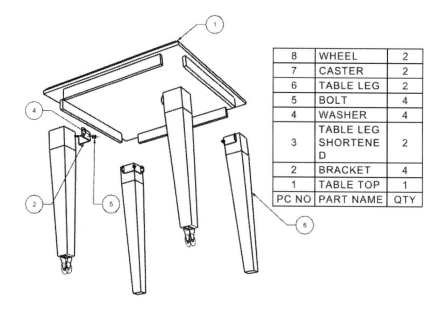

8	WHEEL	2
7	CASTER	2
6	TABLE LEG	2
5	BOLT	4
4	WASHER	4
3	TABLE LEG SHORTENED	2
2	BRACKET	4
1	TABLE TOP	1
PC NO	PART NAME	QTY

The Make Unique command can be found in the Menu / Assemblies / Components menu. To give it a try download the Make Unique Table Assembly. It is a zip file that contains the original table assembly plus the caster. You will have to shorten the two legs by 3.25 inches.

16.18 Arrangements

When an assembly is created especially an assembly that has moving parts there is a great way of viewing it so you can see those components in various positions. For example, if you have an assembly of a door in a laptop you may want to view that door in its open position as well as closed. This is easily done with an assembly technique called arrangements. You begin with the assembly of the components and you navigate to the arrangements menu Assemblies Tab / Arrangements from the General Section of the Ribbon.

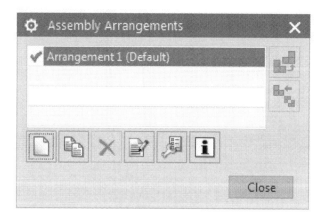

You will see that there is a default arrangement called Arrangement 1. This will correspond to the initial position of your assembly components. For example in the simple assembly below the Handle on the housing is in its closed position. You may want an arrangement that shows the open position.

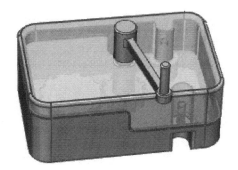

Next you may make a new arrangement that you call open. You select on the New arrangement button and input the new name. The new name can be edited to read *"open"*. Also double click on it to make it the active arrangement. You will see a green check mark to the left of the new arrangement name.

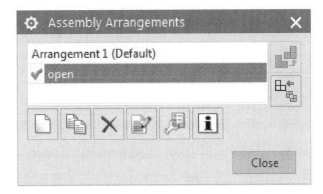

Next you may change the position of the component or components that you want in the new arrangement using the Move Component command with the arrangement setting set to Apply to Used as shown below:

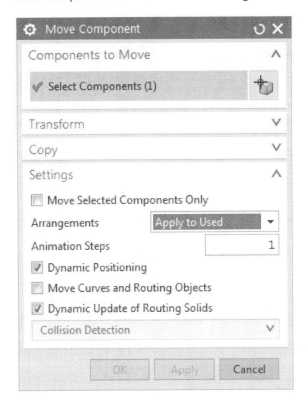

Once done with the move, you will be able to go back and forth between the two arrangements, checking clearances and other aspects of the assembly. This can be done by navigating back to the arrangement menu and double clicking on the old arrangement, or you may right click on the assembly name in the Assembly navigator window and use the arrangements menu that appears. You will notice when using assembly constraints that there is an Apply to Used option. This affords you the ability of creating constraints that are dependent on your arrangements.

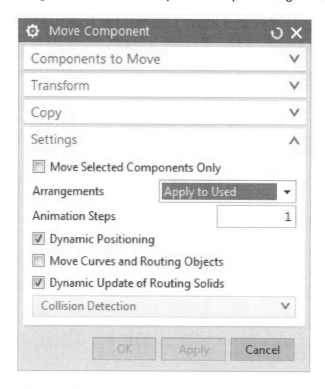

The key to creating arrangements is to not forget the Apply to Used option.

16.19 **Assembly Load Options**

Since assembly components are stored in separate files, managing the data becomes a little more complex. You must consider modifications to each part as well as to the assembly. If you save the Top-Level assembly, NX 10 will save all of its modified components – which may lead to versioning problems. The three Load Options are From Folder, As Saved, and From Search Folders. All three are accessed from the File / Assembly Load Options (under Preferences in the right column) dialog box. You can also define these options by clicking Options located in the bottom left corner of the File/Open command.

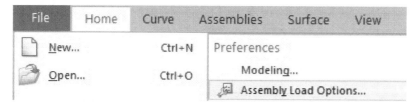

In order to fully load an assembly, NX 10 must be able to load all of its component parts. An easy way to accomplish this is to store all files in the same directory and to set the Load Method to From Folder.

Note: NX 10 will not search in embedded folders when this option is chosen; therefore, the directory with the assembly file must also contain all of the components.

For the forward-thinking, there is the As Saved option. This requires that each component of an assembly remain in its original saved location.

If component part files are moved or stored in different directories, the From Search Folders option provides the most flexibility. Select Add Folder to Search to bring up an expanded menu that allows you to create one or more Search Directories. Any added search directories are only effective in the current session of NX 10. To make your changes permanent, choose the Save option.

Note: *To search all subdirectories of a specified directory, use an ellipsis (three periods) "..." at the end of the chosen directory pathname. Otherwise, NX 10 only searches in the specified directory.*

17 Basic Drafting

17.1 Introduction

Once you have a solid model of a part or assembly, you can use it to create an engineering drawing. Drawings are defined using the 3D data, and are updated whenever you update the associated solid model. Many types of drawings can be created in NX 10; however, in this manual we will discuss only detail part drawings.

17.2 Creating Drawings

To enter the drawing mode, select the Application/ Drafting. If no drawing exists, NX 10 will prompt you to create one. You may have as many drawing sheets as you require, however you may view or edit only one at a time.

NX 10 enables you to define standard drawing templates that can be imported into any drawing. Typically, a template may contain a drawing border, title and revision blocks, and other standard information. Setting up templates is a useful technique to standardize engineering drawings across a company, but this is an advanced topic not covered in this manual. You can ask your CAD System Administrator for information about your company's standard drawing templates.

17.3 The NX 10 Drawing Environment

As always, drawing functions are invoked by clicking on an icon or selecting from the top tabs. Several different sections on the ribbon will appear that are specifically tailored for the drafting mode. You can right click in the toolbar area and customize it. You can also drag and drop icons on the ribbon at your desired locations.

17.4 The Drawing Process

Every drawing is created with a process much like this:

1. Create a solid model
2. Create drawing sheet 1
3. Import the company-standard drawing template
4. Add views to drawing sheet 1
5. Add dimensions
6. Add GD&T annotations (if required)
7. Add drawing annotations (notes, symbols, etc.)
8. Add drawing sheet 2, and repeat the process

Note: *You may begin creating a drawing at any time during the design process. Because the drawing views and dimensions are associative, they will update as the model evolves.*

17.5 Defining the Drawing Parameters

Before you start adding views to a drawing sheet, you should define the drawing name, units, scale, size, and projection angle. You may change these parameters at any time; however, you may need to re-arrange the views and annotations quite a bit as a result.

17.5.1 Creating a Drawing

- Create the model shown in the following figure and start a drawing of it.
- Create a new part. Save it and rename it as: *drw_block_<your initials>.prt*.
- Change all dimensions to match those shown in the figure below. The size is **3in x 2in x 1in** with a **0.75in** diameter hole at the center and a **1in x 1in** corner **Chamfer**.

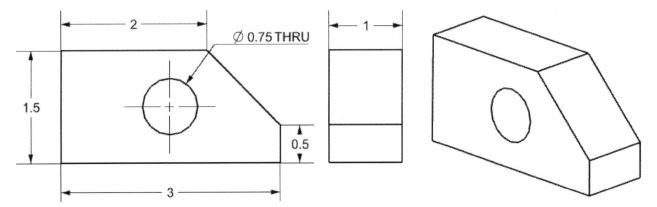

- Save your part model.
- Select **Application tab / Drafting.** A new drawing sheet dialog box appears as shown below.

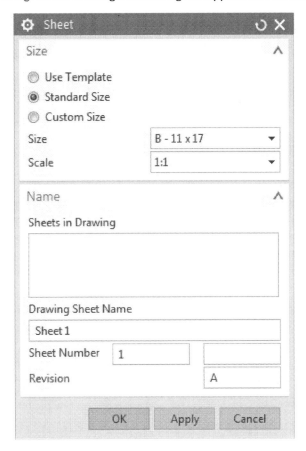

- Enter the drawing sheet name if you don't want to use the default name.
- Select the drawing size, units, and projection angle options according to the figure above.
- Enter **Drawing Scale = 1:1**
- Save your drawing file.

17.6 **Drawing and Modeling Layer Standards**

Most companies have standard procedures for modeling and drafting. An important component of these standards is layer conventions. Usually, a range of layers is reserved for modeling entities and another range for drafting entities. It is good practice to organize your work in this fashion. Please contact your CAD System Administrator to obtain more information on how this should be done at your site.

17.7 **Creating Drawing Borders**

If your company has standard drawing borders, you can import them into a drawing or you can use the border template depending on your company policy. The procedures for this vary widely between companies, so no further discussion of this would be appropriate in this manual. Please contact your CAD System Administrator to obtain more information on how this should be done at your site.

17.7.1 **Creating Drawing Borders**

In the following project you will learn how to create a border and save it in order to use it as a template or import it into the current drawing. If you already have drawing borders from your company you can skip this project.

- Create a new part *"B_size_in_SH1.prt"* part and select **Application Tab/ Drafting.**
- To create a border select **Drawing Tools Tab / Borders and Zones**, as shown in the following figure.

- A dialog window will be presented containing many different options how to style the border as shown in the following figure.

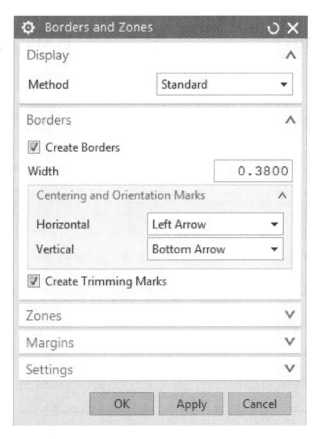

- By pressing OK a default border will be created in NX.

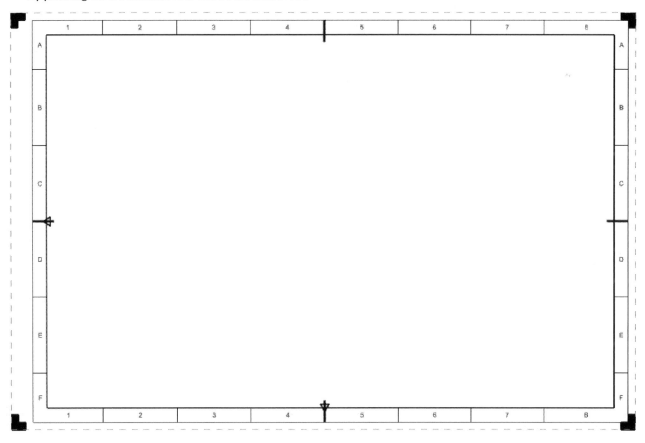

- In order to create a title, a table must be created. Select Tabular Note from the Home Tab. When selected the following dialog window will be presented.

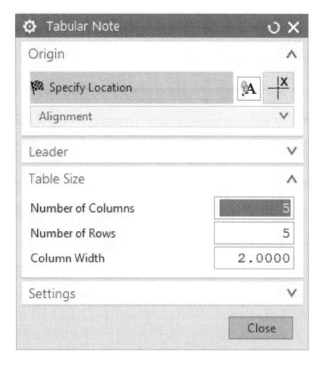

- Read the que: NX is asking for the location to place the table. Select a point inside the border that aligns the table on the left. Set the Number of Columns to 3 and the Number of Rows to 4.

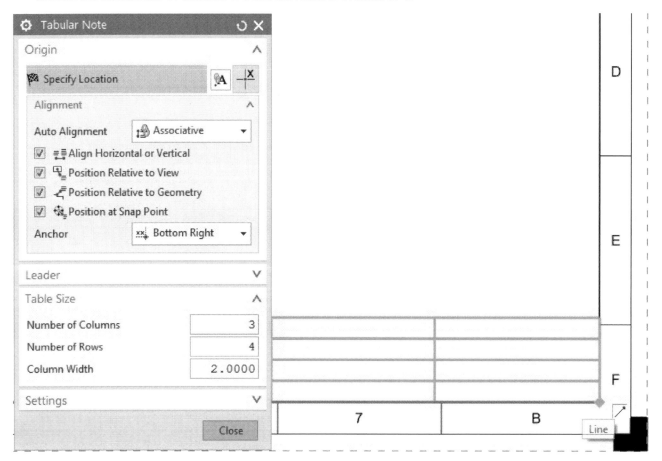

Note: By left clicking and dragging the mouse on the dividers between cells and rows, the table can be resized to the styles of data the must be inserted.

- Each cell of the table can be clicked and information can be added. Now that there is a table in the drawing a title can be added. Select Drafting Tools Tab / Define Title Block.

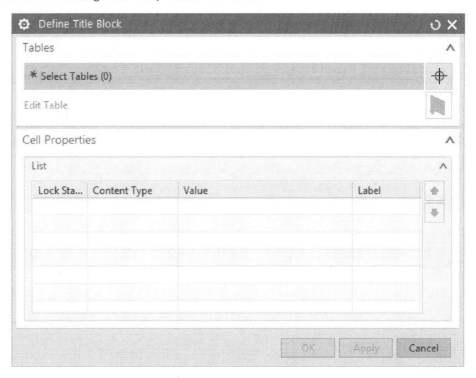

- Select the table that was previously created. Below labels can be entered into the list. Create a label for Title, Revision and Designed By as shown in the following figure.

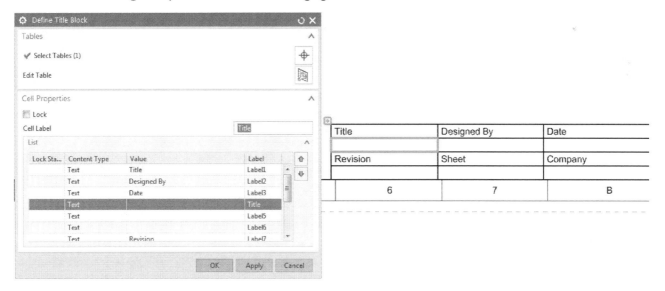

- Double click on the table, a new dialog window appears allowing you to populate the fields of the table. Populate the table as shown in the following figure.

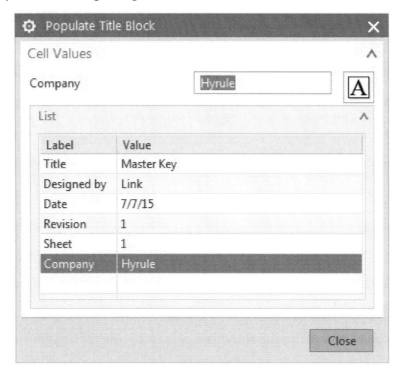

- Create a new folder *"Drawing_Borders_Import"* and save your file.
- You just created a file that can be used to import into your current drawing. A better way to create drawing templates is to create a file with all the sheets and basic views that you usually need. You can create several of these files and save them into a folder that you can define as a template folder, but using this method you cannot add a drawing border to the part file you are already working in.

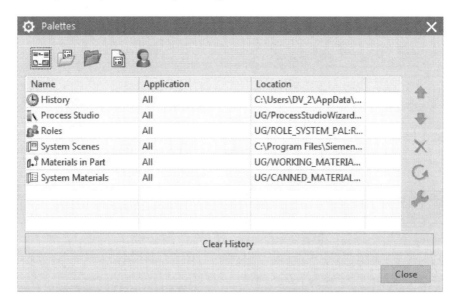

- Create another file with two sheets. Add borders and titles and then save it. Re-name it *"B_size_in_<your initials>.prt"*, and place it in another folder *"Drawing_Border_Templates." Later you can add some views to it.*
- Select **File / Preferences / Palettes** and click **Open Directory as Palette** as shown in the figure above.
- Browse to folder *"Drawing_Border_Templates"* and select it. You will notice that it is added to the list as well as to the resource bar.

17.7.2 Importing Drawing Borders

In the following project you will learn how to import the drawing border into your current drawing.

- Open your previous drawing from earlier in this chapter and select Application Tab/ Drafting.
- Select File / Import / Part.

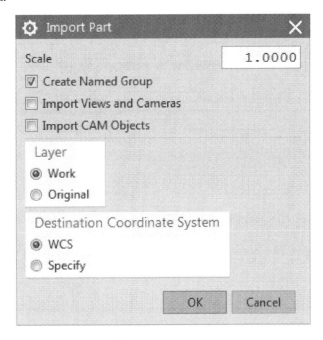

- Leave the default options as shown above and hit OK
- Select the template file you just saved and hit OK
- A Point Constructor menu pops up; make sure that XC, YC and ZC are set to zero. *You can use the* Reset *button to set it back to zero if they are not.*
- Hit OK.
- You should see your drawing border in this part file.

17.7.3 Importing Sample Palettes

In the following project you will learn how to import the sample palettes provided by NX 10. Adding your own files to palette files requires editing or creating an xml file with the *".pax"* extension, which is a more advanced topic to be covered in our future books.

- Select Menu / Preferences / Palettes and click the Open Palette File icon as shown in the figure below.

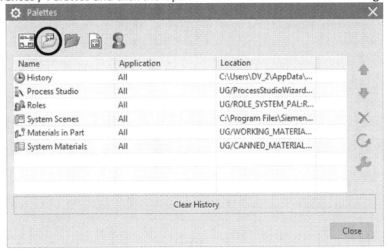

- Browse to the location where NX 10 is installed (usually "/Program Files/Siemens") and select the file *"NX_drawing_templates.pax"* from folder *"\NX 10\UGII\templates"*.
- Hit **OK**.

You will notice that it is added to the palette list as well as to the resource bar.

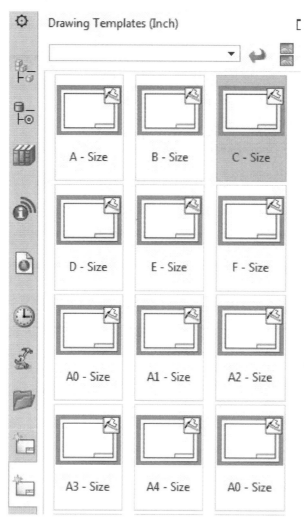

You can add other sample palette files available in the same folder in the same way.

- Open any part file containing some geometry that you have created in one of the previous projects.
- Click the icon **Drawing Template (inch)** as shown in the following figure to open the template and click on the file *"B size"*.

Drawing Templates (Inch)

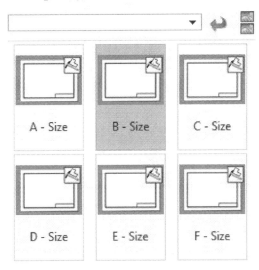

A - Size   B - Size   C - Size

D - Size   E - Size   F - Size

- This will automatically create a new file with your base part assembled in it. Notice the Assembly Navigator and the Title Bar. This is the concept of master modeling that we will be discussing in Chapter 19.
- Open the Part Navigator and notice how the drawing sheets with the drawing border and the standard views defined in the template file have been automatically added to this new part file. *This is a very fast way to produce drawings and lets you work independently in a separate file without making any changes to the original file.*

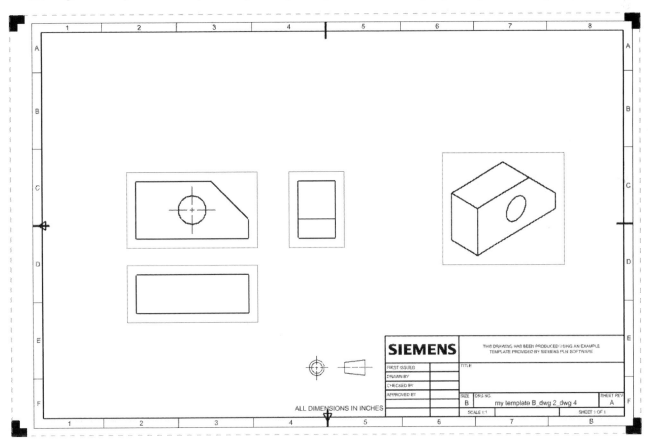

- Save the file.

17.8 Adding Basic Drawing Views

In NX 10, views of the solid model may be added to drawings using several methods, including:

- Importing pre-defined or saved model views
- Adding projections of an existing drawing view
- Adding a section view based upon an existing drawing view
- Creating an enlarged detailed view of an existing drawing view

Drawing views may be moved, edited, and deleted using functionality that will be discussed in a later part of this chapter.

17.8.1 Layer Masks and Drawings

The Layer Masking functionality is used in Drafting mode to control the visibility of items in drawing views. Layer Masks are accessed through the View Tab / More / Layer Visible in View (see the following figure). This allows you to control which layers are visible in every view and drawing sheet contained in a part file. Manipulating these settings allows you to control the display of your drawing views.

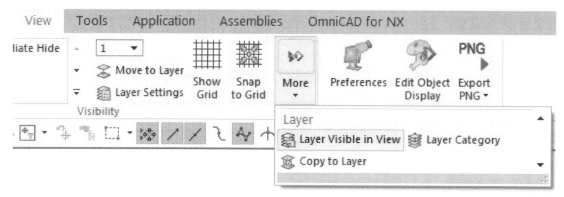

By default, when you create a new drawing, NX 10 sets the Visible in View status to Global for the drawing sheet according to the following rule: all layers that are marked Selectable become Visible, while all others are Invisible. The same thing occurs when you import a view. What this means is that any entity on a Visible layer can be seen in the drawing. Often, you will need to modify these settings to get the proper geometry displayed on the drawing.

Follow these rules to reduce errors and problems related to the Visible in View functionality:

- Place the resultant solid geometry on a specific layer, and don't change it
- Move any construction geometry to layers that are Invisible before adding views
- Create all drawing entities on a specific layer or layers
- When possible, all drawing views should have the same layer mask
- Assign a layer mask to all finished drawings to isolate them from layer settings changes

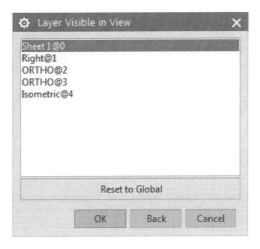

17.8.2 Updating the Drawing Views

The NX 10 drawing is created using views of the 3D model. When you add, change, or delete a feature from the model, the drawing views become "Out of Sync" with respect to the model. If this happens, you will see an OUT-OF-DATE message appended to the drawing sheet name when you enter the drafting application. It is important to keep the drawing views up to date. To update the drawing views at any time, select Update Views from the Home tab and select the views you need to update or select one of the options shown in the figure below. You can also select a view and Right Click to open a pop-up that has a list of commands including update views.

17.8.3 Importing the Base View and Orthographic Views

The first view added to a drawing sheet must always be imported from the model. You can use one of the pre-defined views (TOP, FRONT, RIGHT, etc.), or you may use a view that you have saved. The first view is commonly referred to as the Base View, since it becomes the basis for the remaining drawing views.

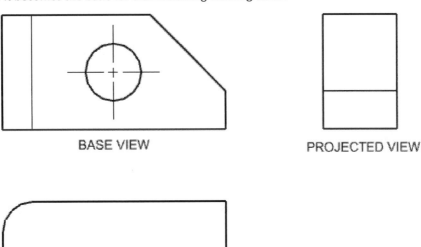

BASE VIEW

PROJECTED VIEW

PROJECTED VIEW

Once you have added the Base View, you can create projected views using the Projected View command. Projected Views are created by selecting the Base View as the Parent View, and using either the 'First-Angle' or 'Third-Angle' projection method, according to the drawing settings. As such, the Base View essentially becomes the 'Front' view on the drawing sheet, and all of the projected views become the 'Top,' 'Right,' 'Bottom,' etc. views.

You may define projected views using any view type as the Parent View (although in some cases this would be a fruitless task!). All projected views are aligned to the parent view. By default, they also inherit its Layer Mask.

Here you will create the Base View and several projected views. Move all your construction curves, sketches, and datum planes to invisible layers, and display only the solid body on the drawing.

- Open any part you have with a solid body and datum planes (In this example we have used a solid from a previous exercise and added a datum plane to trim the solid) and select Application Tab / Drafting.
- Select Base View from the Home Tab.
- Select the TOP view from the list.
- Select scale 1:1.
- Move your cursor onto the drawing sheet, and place the view by left clicking. Notice that when you move your cursor, NX 10 automatically generates another view based on the one you just placed.
- Choose OK or middle click to let NX 10 know you are done placing views.

You should see that a view has been added to your drawing sheet, as shown in the figure below. If your TOP view does not match this, delete it and add the Base View again, this time importing the FRONT, RIGHT, or any saved view that gives you this result. If the orientation doesn't match you can click on the Orient View icon and reorient your view.

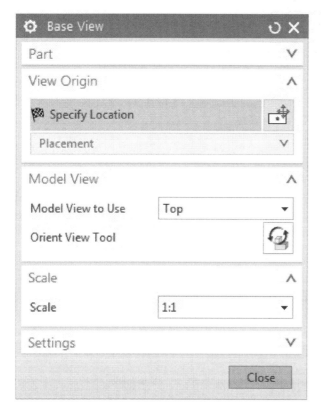

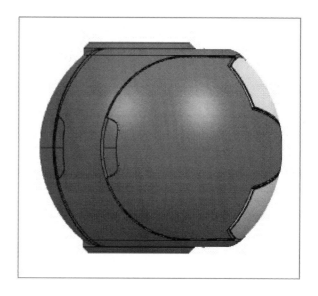

Notice the rectangle around the view – this is the View Boundary. It is updated automatically, based upon the size of the model displayed in the view, and does not show up in the final printed drawing. You can hide/unhide the view boundaries from File / Preferences / Drafting / View / Display Borders. The entities displayed in your Base View may be different, depending upon the Layer Mask. If the solid body is on a layer by itself, and the construction entities are on hidden layers, you will not see them in the drawing.

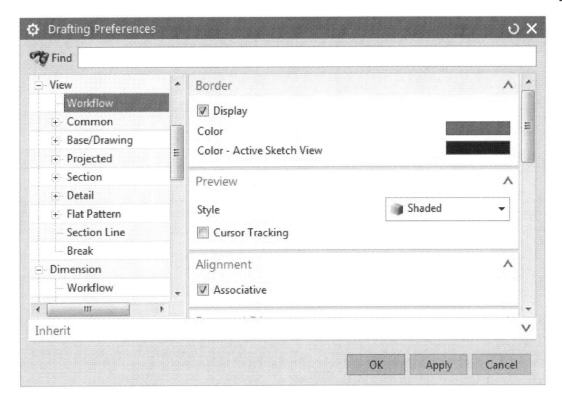

- Select **Application tab / Modeling**.
- Select **View Tab / Move to Layer**.
- Select the solid body and choose **OK**.
- Enter **10** for the **Destination Layer** and choose **OK**.

361

The solid body should disappear, since it was moved to a layer that is hidden. Follow the next steps to make Layer 5 the Work Layer, mark Layer 1 Invisible, and make Layer 10 Selectable.

- Select View Tab / Layer Settings.
- In the Show drop down, choose All Layers.

- Double-Click 5 to convert it to the Work Layer.
- Click on Layer 1 and mark it as Invisible.
- Click on Layer 10 and mark it as Selectable, and choose OK.

Notice that there are some construction entities visible in your base view; however, the solid body is no longer visible. The next steps will correct this problem.

- Select View Tab / More / Layer Visible in View.
- Select your base view and choose OK.

The Visible Layers in View dialog box appears. Use it to mark all layers except layer 10 Invisible.

- Select the ALL category.
- Select Invisible to mark all layers as Invisible.
- Double-click on layer 10 to mark it as Visible.

Notice that an OUT-OF-DATE message appears at the lower left corner of the Graphics Window. This indicates that one or more drawing views has been modified, and requires an update.

- Select Home Tab / Update Views.

The solid body should now be displayed, and all construction entities should be invisible. Notice that the View Boundary is updated to reflect the entities shown in the Base View. Now, proceed by adding several projected views.

- Select Home Tab / Projected View.
- Notice that an arrow appears from the parent view. This arrow can be rotated 360 degrees around the base view to create projected, secondary views on the drawing. Move the cursor to the right of the Base View, and click to create the projected Orthographic View shown in the figure below. NX 10 will *snap* the view horizontally in place.
- Create the remaining three projected views using this technique, as shown in the following figure.
- Save your drawing file.

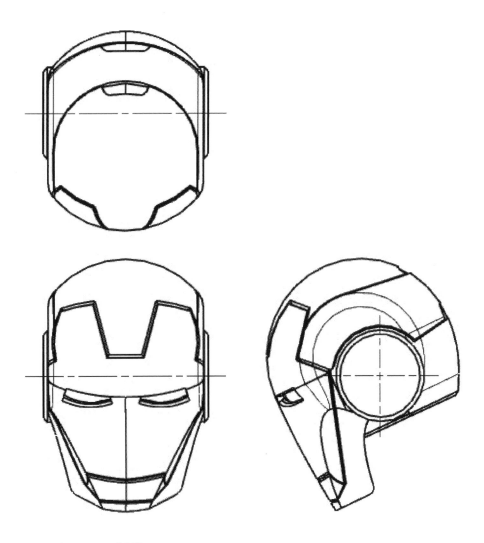

17.9 **Editing Drawings and Views**

Creating engineering drawings is really an art form. The intent is to clearly communicate the function and/or manufacturing dimensions of a product. To accomplish this usually requires some iterations of the drawing, especially in the early stages of documentation.

17.9.1 **Editing Drawing Sheets**

You can change options of existing drawings using Home Tab / Edit Sheet dropdown menu under New Sheet. A common operation is to increase or decrease the size and/or the scale of a drawing. Note that if the size is decreased, any existing drawing views must fit within the new boundaries, or the operation will fail.

17.9.2 **Edit View Style**

You can edit drawing views by selecting Layout Tab / Edit Settings and then selecting an object to modify. You can change its Angle, Scale and other parameters from the menu shown below.

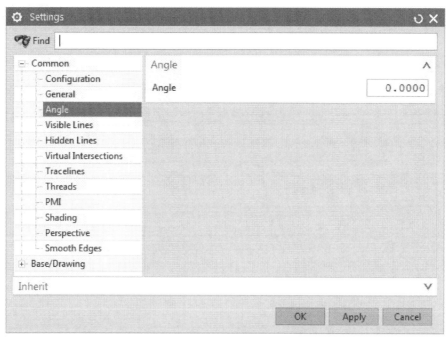

You can also add or remove the View or Scale Label of a drawing view, change parameters such as Hidden Lines, Visible Lines, Smooth Edges, and Threads, and Virtual Intersections using this dialog box.

17.9.3 **Move View**

One or more Drawing Views may be moved using Home Tab / Move/Copy View under the Update Views drop-down menu (see the figure below).

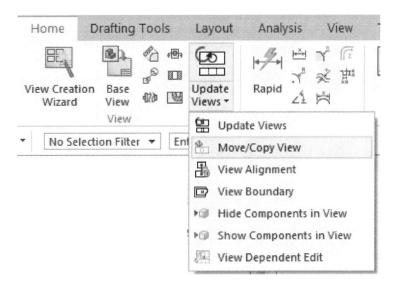

The movement of the drawing views may be free or restricted to certain directions, such as either horizontal or vertical. You can also move a view just by clicking and dragging it.

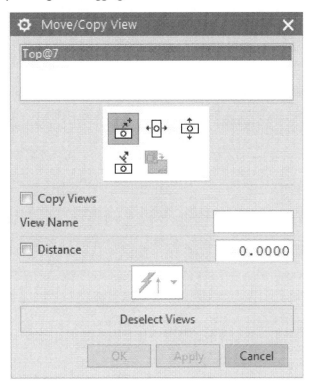

You may also duplicate drawing views or move them to another drawing sheet using the Move/Copy View dialog box. Whenever you copy or move a drawing view, all dimensions, notes, and symbols associated with the view move along with it. You can also move a view from one sheet to another by simply cutting and pasting it.

17.9.4 Remove View

To delete a drawing view, simply select the view(s) that you wish to delete and hit Delete on your keyboard or right click the view and choose the delete option. You can also select the Menu/Edit/Delete (Ctrl+D) option or delete the view from the Drawing Navigator. When you remove a drawing view, all dimensions, notes, and symbols associated with the view are also deleted.

17.9.5 **Align View**

Drawing Views can be aligned using Home Tab / View Alignment under the Update Views dropdown. Views may be aligned horizontally, vertically, or perpendicular to a line. There are three alignment methods available when the Overlay Method is selected: To View, Model Point, and Point-to-Point. NX 10 also shows dotted alignment lines if you click and drag a view to align it.

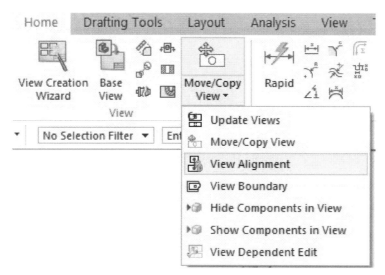

The most frequently used alignment method is Model Point, which allows you to select an entity from the 3D model that serves as the alignment point for all selected views. The Point-to-Point method is similar, except that you must select the corresponding point from each view to be aligned. NX 10 also lets you align the views by simply dragging them to approximate locations with respect to other views. A dotted line with arrows appears and the view snaps in to align with the other views.

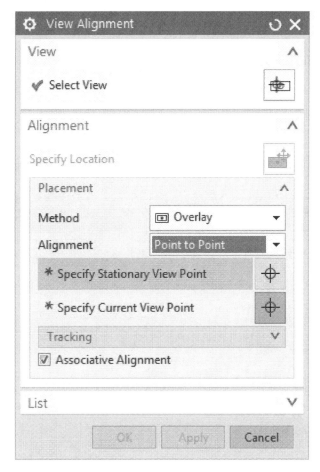

Remove several extra views from your drawing, change the drawing scale, and re-arrange the remaining views.

- Open the part from previous project (if required) and select Application tab / Drafting.
- Select the Top and Left projected views and delete them.
- Select Move/Copy View.
- Select the three remaining views, and select the To a Point icon.
- Move the views to the lower-left corner of the drawing and click to drop them.
- Select the Bottom projected view, and select the Vertically icon.
- Move the view up and click to drop (see following figure).

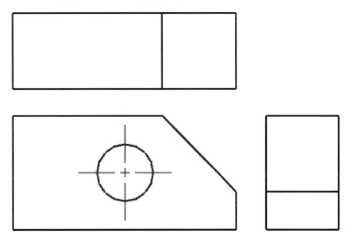

Now intentionally misalign the right projected view, and then re-align it...

- Select the right projected view, and select the To a Point icon.

- Move the view so that it is no longer aligned to the Base View.
- Select View Alignment.
- Select the Stationary Model Point as shown in the following figure.
- Select the View to be aligned, as shown in the figure above.
- Select the 'Inferred' alignment icon.

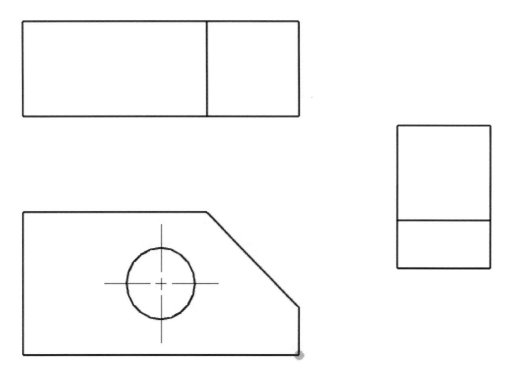

The misaligned view should become re-aligned to the Base View. You may need to use Move View to change its horizontal location.

- Save your drawing file.

17.10 Advanced Drawing Views

You have learned how to create and manipulate basic drawing views. To complete most drawings, you will be required to create more advanced view types, such as Section and Detail Views. Each of these view types requires a Parent View, just as for Projected Views.

17.10.1   Projected Views at an angle

Auxiliary Views are projected views along non-orthographic directions, as shown in the figure below. They are very useful to show the form of a model that has features located on angled surfaces.

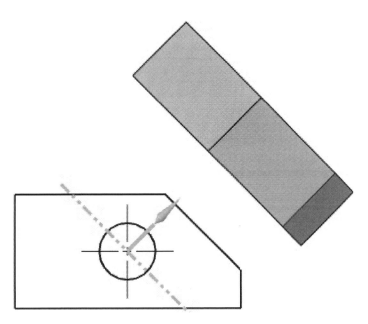

In NX 10, the projection direction of Auxiliary Views is controlled by a Hinge Line. The Hinge Line is usually a linear model edge that is normal to the desired projection direction (*Hinge Line Vector*), although it may be defined using other techniques. If the Hinge Line is defined using model geometry, the view angle is parametric; thus, the view orientation will automatically update if the angle in the model is modified.

The direction of the Hinge Line Vector determines which side of the model is visible once the auxiliary projection is done. If it is in the wrong direction, you can select the Reverse direction option.

17.10.2   Simple Section Views

NX 10 has the ability to create Section Views of solid models. The section cuts are automatically generated, and updated along with the solid geometry. Section Views are a very effective technique for illustrating internal geometry of complicated parts. There are several types of Section Views available in NX 10; here we will discuss only Simple Section Views.

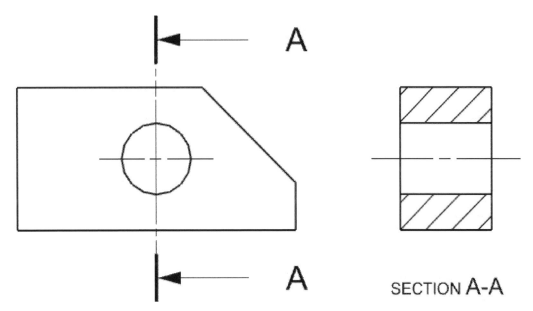

Simple Section Views are similar to Projected Views in that they require a hinge line. In addition, you must specify a Cut Position and the Section Arrow Direction, as shown in the figure above. NX 10 creates the section cut by constructing a plane that is parallel to the Hinge Line and passes through the Cut Position.

The location of the Section View Arrows is automatically determined by NX 10 if you don't select it. You can modify these locations, as well as the Arrow Direction and Cut Positions of existing section views using Home Tab / Section Line. The Section View Label display, View Letter, and Crosshatch Parameters can be changed via various Preference settings.

17.10.3   Detail Views

Detail Views are essentially enlarged regions of existing drawing views. You are able to specify the boundary and scale, and NX 10 creates a set of parametric view entities as shown in the figure below.

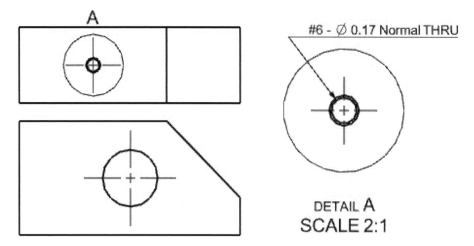

Detail Views are useful for illustrating small features of a model. Any changes to the solid model are automatically cascaded through the Parent View and into the Detail View. The Detail View Label display, View Letter, and View Boundary options can be changed via various Preference settings.

17.10.4   Adding 3D Views

You can add 3D views of a model to a drawing by using the Base View option. You can insert one of the standard views (i.e. Isometric or Trimetric), or you may import a customized orientation. If you save a view in the modeling application, you can then use it in the drawing. In NX 10 you can also add an image (i.e. jpeg, png and tif) in to a drawing. To add an image use Image from the Annotation section of the Home Tab.

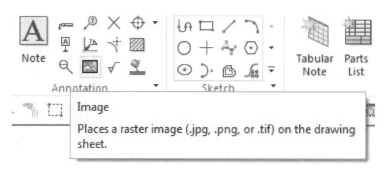

17.10.5   View label

When you add a view, if the View Label and Scale Label boxes on the Settings dialog box (see the figure below) are checked, the View Name and Scale will be shown on the drawing.

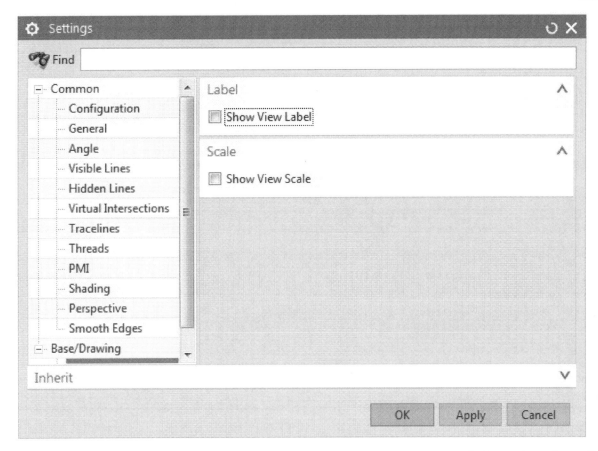

You can change these options for views that have already been created using Layout Tab / Edit Settings. If you display the View Name, you may also wish to assign a meaningful name to it.

You can modify the View Labels with in the same menu, as shown in the same figure. There are different options available for Section, Detail, and Other views.

Some commonly used options are to change the existing View Letter and modify the Scale display format. Labels on existing views may be turned on or off using Edit Settings.

Add several features to your solid model and update the drawing by adding three new views. Then modify an existing view to add a section cut.

- Open the part from the previous project (if required) and select Application tab / Modeling.
- Rotate your model into a good 3D orientation.
- Right-Click Model Views and select Add View.
- Enter NICE into the as the view name.

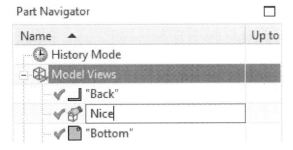

You have now saved a view that can be used later on for a drawing view.

- Add a 0.20in chamfer to the existing hole, and add a 0.125 x 1.0 hole in the top, as shown in the following figure.

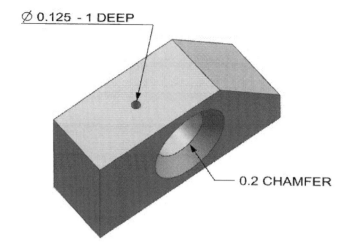

Ø 0.125 - 1 DEEP

0.2 CHAMFER

- Select **Application tab / Drafting.**
- Select **Update Views.**
- Select **Projected View.** A preview of the projected view appears.
- Move the cursor to the right of the **Base View** and click to create the **Auxiliary View,** as shown in the following figure.

Note: NX 10 will align the projected view to the angled edge by "locking" the view in place. Move the cursor around near the angled edge until it locks. The orthogonal face will highlight when locked.

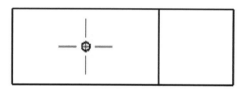

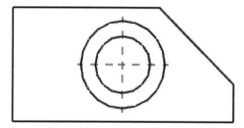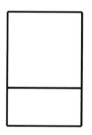

Now, add a **Detail View** of the small hole.

- Select the **Detail View.**

Read the cue. NX 10 is prompting you to select the detail center on the **Parent View.**

- Select the center of the small hole as the detail center and move your cursor slightly above the top edge of the block to define the size of the **Detail View Boundary.**
- Select the scale **2:1** from the menu displayed in the top left corner.
- Place the center of the **Detail View** as shown below.

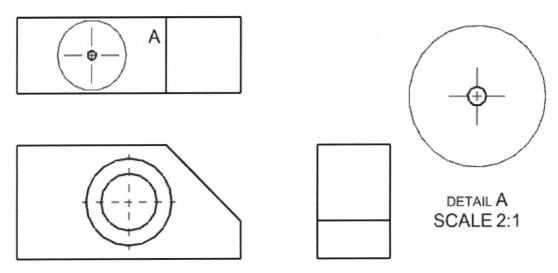

DETAIL A
SCALE 2:1

- Click near the edge of the circular block surrounding the Detail View Boundary.
- Compare your results to the figure above. Now, add a Section View through the middle of the block.
- Select Section View.
- Select the top projected view as the Parent View by clicking.

Read the Cue. NX 10 is prompting you to define the Cut Position.

- Click the center of the small hole to define the Cut Position.
- Move the cursor above the top projected view and click to create the Section View, as shown in the following figure.

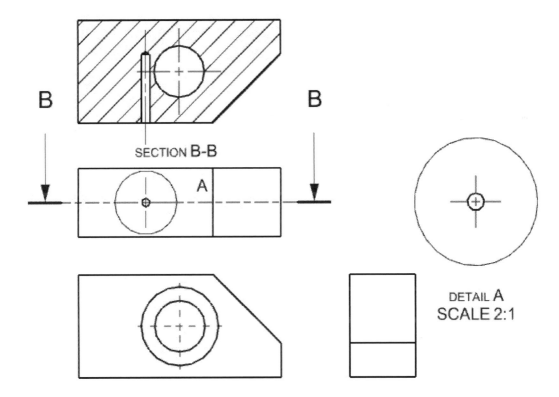

SECTION B-B

DETAIL A
SCALE 2:1

Compare your results to the figure above. Now add a 1:1 scaled 3D view of the model.

- Select Base View.
- Select Scale 1:1.
- Select the 'NICE' view from the drop down list of available views.

- Click on the style button and check the Scale Label box to add a Scale Label.
- Move your cursor into the Graphics Window and place the view as shown below.

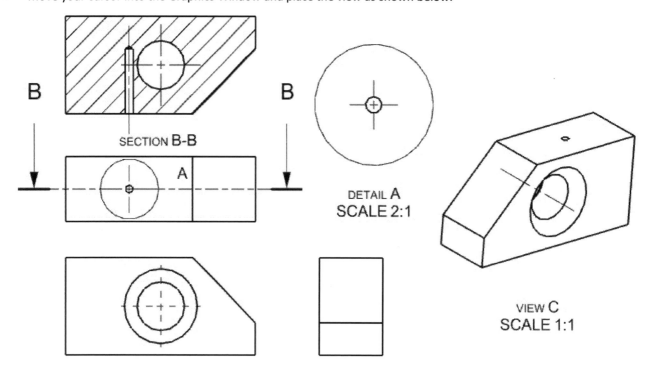

17.11 Creating Dimensions

Placing dimensions on a drawing is very similar to dimensioning a sketch. In drawing mode, you can also include information related to the part's manufacturing and inspection processes, such as the number of decimal places and tolerance specification.

There are a number of dimension icons available in NX 10, including Horizontal, Vertical, Diameter, Radius, Perpendicular, Parallel, etc. In this manual, we will discuss the Inferred option, as its function encompasses most of the others.

17.11.1   Rapid Dimensions

The Rapid Dimension dialog box is shown in the figure below. You can find Rapid Dimension in the Dimension section of the Home Tab.

A general outline of the dimension creation procedure is as follows:

- Select the Dimensions Tab, and set to Place Automatically.
- Set the Tolerance Type and Dimension Precision.
- Add Appended Text (if required).
- Select the entity (or entities) to be dimensioned.
- Place the dimension in the Graphics Window (by left-clicking).
- If the dimension requires modification, select it and change the desired settings.

You will find that the units, text justification and extension line/arrow settings are not frequently modified once you have started a drawing.

17.11.2   Moving / Modifying Existing Dimensions

Existing dimensions can be moved at any time by simply clicking and dragging them to a new location. You can also modify the attributes of existing dimensions using the Dimension dialog box. Simply select one or more dimensions, change the desired attributes.

17.11.3   Orientation and Location

The figure below, found by clicking File / Preferences / Drafting, shows several icons that allow you to place text in various orientations on a dimension. You may add appended text to one, or all of these locations.

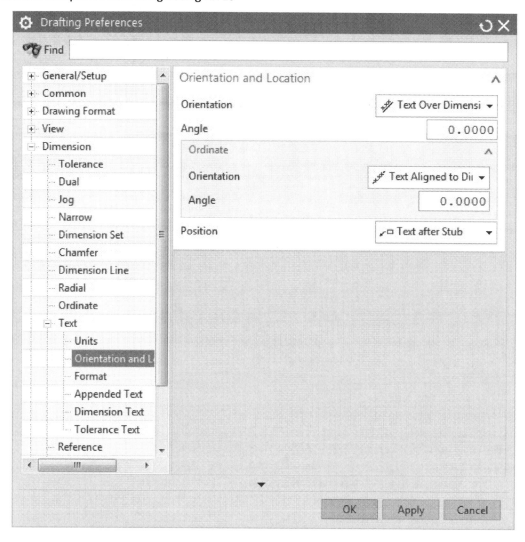

This option is useful for adding notes, GD&T callouts, and special drafting symbols. The functionality of the Annotation Editor will be covered in more detail later in this chapter.

17.11.4   Dimension Placement and Leader Direction

In general, the Automatic Placement option yields good results; however, some dimensions require manual placement. There are two types of manual placement options: Arrows In and Arrows Out. If you set the Dimension Placement to one of these options, you may also specify either the From Left or the From Right leader placement method. You can change these options from the Dimension Style menu.

17.11.5   Drawing-Related Preferences

Many properties of NX 10 drawings are set using Preferences. Select File / Preferences / Drafting to set the Drafting Preferences. See the figure below.

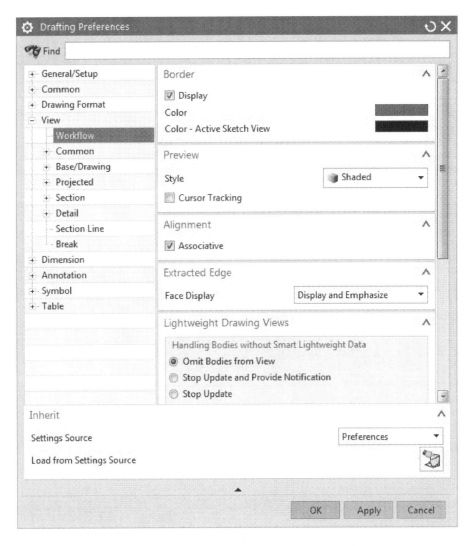

The default values for most Preference settings are controlled by the settings in the NX 10 Customer Defaults file. Most Preference settings are stored in the part database, so your changes will remain after you have saved the part. It is good practice to verify all Preference settings before creating any drafting entities, thus avoiding a lot of tedious re-work.

Other commonly used preferences are Origin, Section Line Display, View and View Label. You can find it in Preferences menu. To change the preferences of a drafting object follow this procedure:

- Choose File / Preferences / Drafting
- Select the object(s).
- Change the desired Preference Settings.

The figure below shows another portion of the Drafting Preferences window. Here you can control many settings for Dimensions, such as Line / Arrow Style, Lettering Sizes, Units, etc.

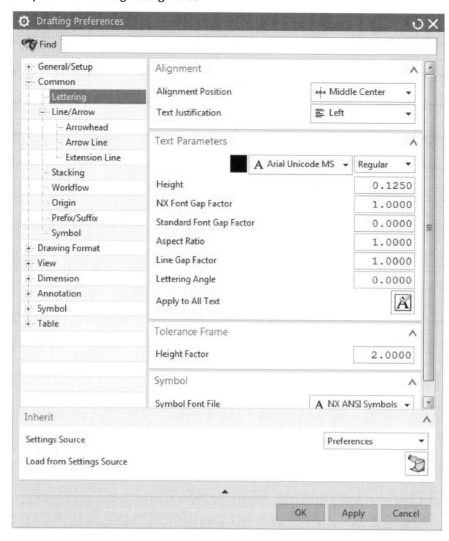

You will also notice that certain Preference settings are duplicated in other dialog boxes. This provides for convenient access to commonly used functionality, such as changing the dimension tolerance mode or text height.

17.11.6 Preference Finder

You may have noticed the binoculars icon at the top of the preferences window. The text field to the left of this icon is a search field where an option that may be hard to find can be typed in. NX 10 will generate a list of the possible options that match the search query making it much easier to change the desired options.

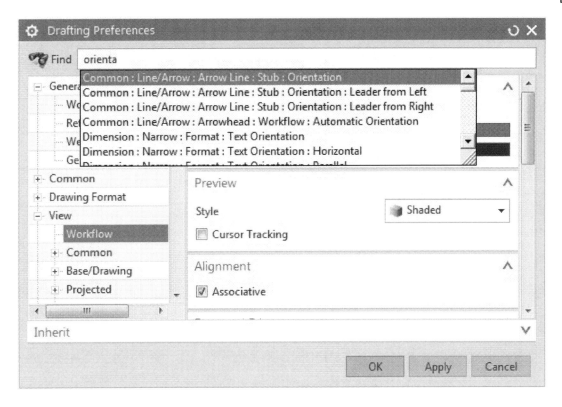

17.11.7   Preferences Action Buttons

Most drafting-related preference dialog boxes have a set of buttons on the bottom that can be used to synchronize the settings of the current Preferences dialog box.

Use the Rapid Dimension tool to add several dimensions to your drawing, as shown in the figure below. Use the View Label Preferences to re-name the drawing views.

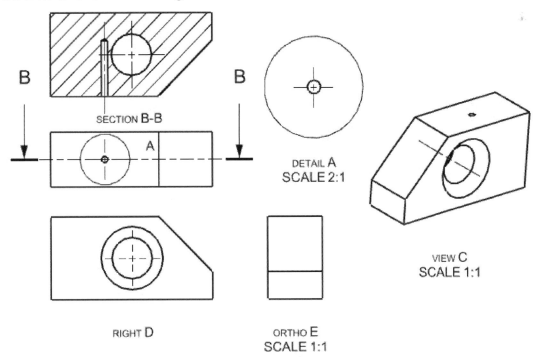

- Open the part from last project (if required) and select Application tab / Drafting.
- Delete the right projected view and add a section view.

- Turn off the View Boundary Display.
- Select File / Preferences / Drafting.
- On the View tab, uncheck Display Borders to turn off the view boundary display.
- Set up the default dimension style.
- Now expand the Dimension Tab.
- Select the No Tolerance setting from the Tolerance Menu.
- Insert 3 in the Decimal Places box.

Note: You may also change these Settings from the Rapid Dimension dialog box.

- Select Rapid.
- Create the width and height dimensions of the block, as shown below.

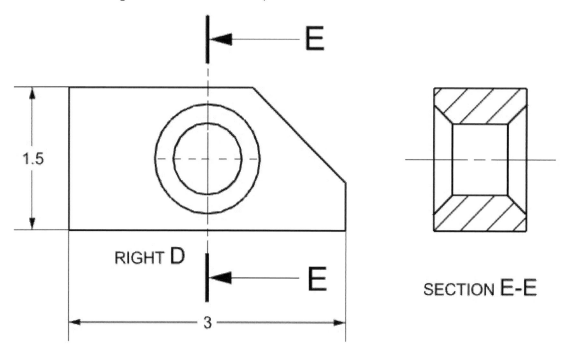

- Click on the bottom edge of the block (selecting it once is enough).
- Move the cursor into the Graphics Window to preview the dimension placement.
- Click to place the width dimension.
- Select the left edge of the block and create the height dimension.
- Create the thickness dimension of the block.
- Select the top edge of the block in Section E-E and click to place the thickness dimension.
- Now, create the Hole Callout dimension on the small hole.
- Click on the Radial icon in the dimension toolbar.
- Change the Method to Hole Callout.
- Select the edge of the small hole in the detail view.

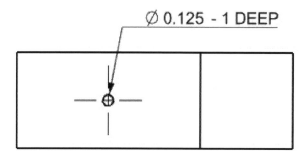

Create an angular dimension on the side chamfer. Use a counter-clockwise selection order to get the dimension orientation correct.

- Select the edges as shown below, and place the angular dimension.

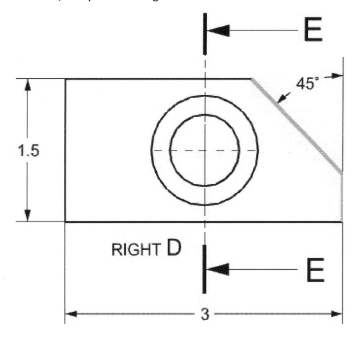

- Create a diameter dimension on the large hole using the Cylindrical Method from the Linear Dimension command.
- Select Cylindrical in the Method drop down.
- Select the edges as shown in the figure below and place the diameter dimension.

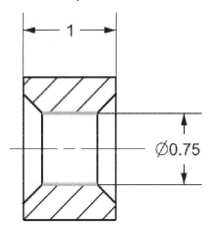

- Create a dimension to the center of the small hole using the Perpendicular method.
- Select Perpendicular in the Method drop down menu.
- Select the edges as shown in the figure below.

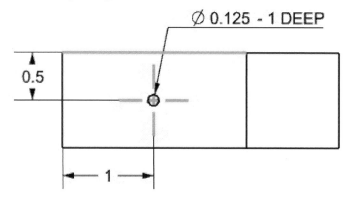

Ø 0.125 - 1 DEEP

0.5

1

- Place the perpendicular dimension as shown in the above figure.
- Hit Escape.

Now we will modify the View Labels for Section E-E and Detail F.

- Double-click the Detail F and View Label Style window will pop up.
- Set the Value Format pop-up menu to Ratio.
- Set the Label on Parent display to Label.
- Change the Letter to A .

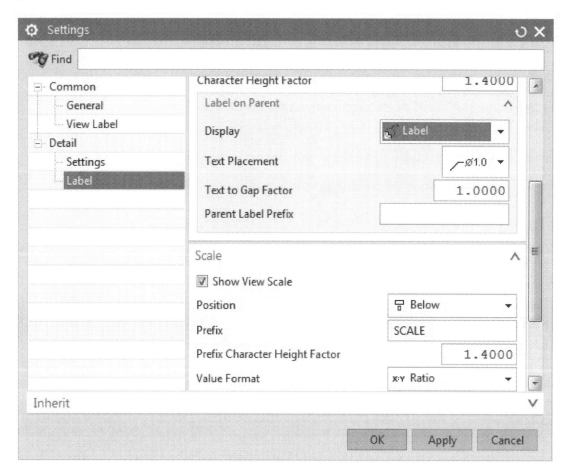

- Double-click the Section E-E view label.
- Change the Letter to B as shown in the figure below and choose OK.

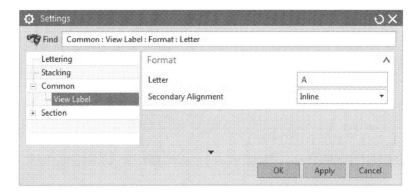

- Now we will add a View Label to the Projected View.
- Double click on the Projected View.
- Check the Show View Label box.
- Choose Apply.
- Compare your drawing to the figure below.

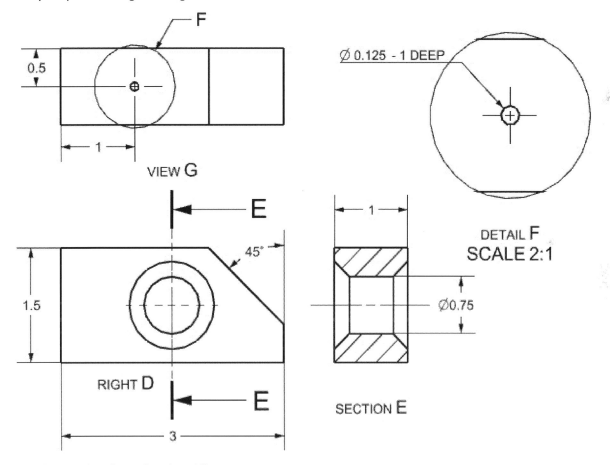

- Practice creating dimensions by adding more.
- Save your drawing file.

17.12 Creating and Editing Notes

Adding various types of notes is an important part of creating an engineering drawing. With them, you can add explanatory text to dimensions, features, and drawing views. The text may contain a variety of standard drafting symbols as well as alphanumeric text. In NX 10, you may define notes with or without leaders, depending upon your requirements.

17.12.1 The Annotation Editor

In NX 10, you can create or edit notes using the *Annotation Editor*, shown below. All note text is entered in the center area and can be previewed in the area immediately below. You can enter special characters by using one of the various symbol palettes, such as the Drafting Symbols, GD&T Symbols, or User Defined Symbols. If you have a note that is stored as a text file, you can import it into the Annotation Editor, and then place it on the drawing.

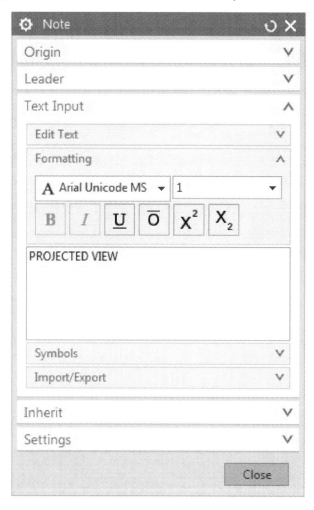

To insert a note, follow this procedure:

- Select Note. The window above appears.
- Type in the note text, including any special symbols.
- Expand the Edit Text, Formatting and Symbols sections if you need more options.
- Place the note in the drawing at your desired location. If you want to create a leader, check Create with Jogs under Leader section in the Note window.

The Text Editor may also be used to edit existing notes. This is done by double clicking on the note to be edited.

17.12.2 Free Note Placement Options

Free notes (with no leader) are placed using the Origin Tool dialog box shown in the figure below. The Alignment section allows you to specify the alignment of the note relative to its origin. Three of the most commonly used origin options are:

- Drag – place the note anywhere on the drawing.
- Offset View – place the note relative to a drawing view.

- Offset Character – place the note relative to a dimension or symbol.

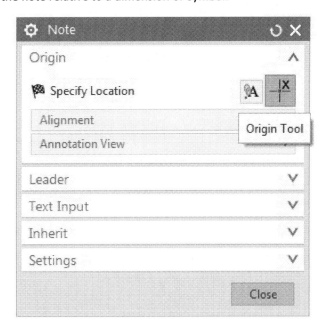

If you select Associative from the Auto Alignment drop down option, the note will be tied to the selected entity. Using this option is a recommended practice, since dimensions and drawing views are rearranged frequently.

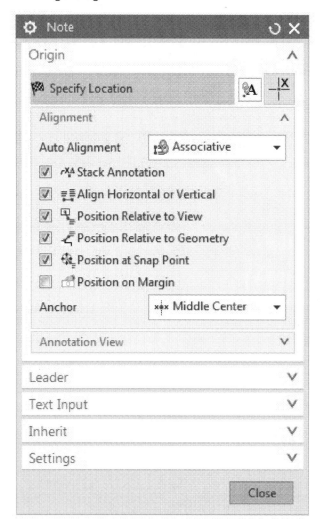

17.12.3   Leader Note Placement Options

Notes with a leader are placed using the Leader section of the Note toolbar shown in the figure below. You can select one of five leader types:

- Plain – Left- or Right-Hand leader
- All Around – same as Plain, but with an All-Around symbol
- Flag – leader which extends parallel from a model edge
- Datum – leader that extends perpendicular to an edge
- Dot Terminated – leader that terminated to any point you select.

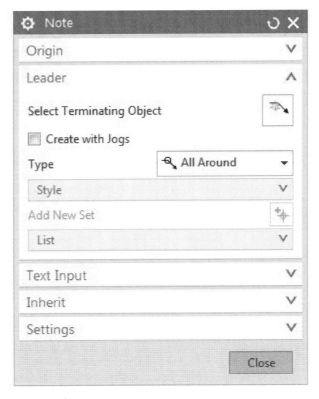

In this project we will use the Text Editor to create several notes on your drawing.

- Open the part from the previous project (if required) and select Application tab / Drafting.
- Select Note.

The Text Editor will appear.

- Under Settings Section, select the Settings icon .
- The Annotation Style menu allows you to change many attributes of a note, including the lettering type, color, character size, and lettering angle.
- Enter Height = 0.375 and hit OK.
- Click in the white text box and type *"BIG NOTE"*
- Move your cursor into the Graphics Window and place the note as shown below.

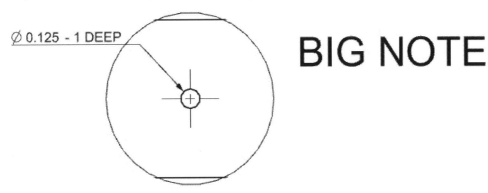

Now we will add two notes that are associated to the 3D view.

- Select the Load from Settings Source button to restore all of the text settings (located in the Annotation Style menu). Click in the white text box and type *"BREAK EDGE"*.
- Under Leader, hit the Select Terminating Object button.
- Select the Plain Leader type

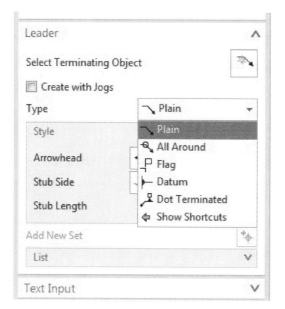

- Move the cursor into the Graphics Window and select the edge as shown below.

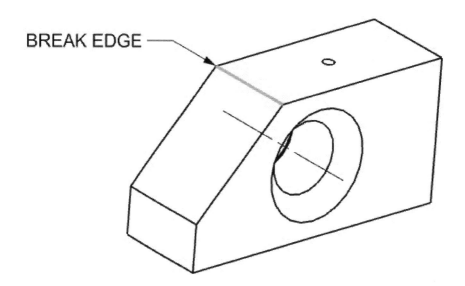

- Choose OK and drag the note to the location shown above.
- Click in the white text box and type *"REFERENCE VIEW"*.
- Select the Origin Tool (button next to Specify Location at the top of the Note dialogue box) and select the Relative to View icon.
- Select the 3D view, and place the note as shown in the following figure.

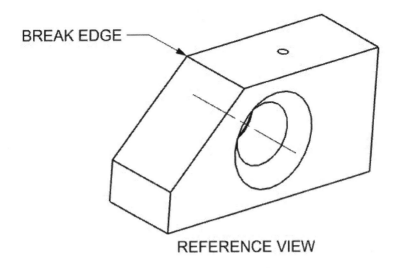

BREAK EDGE

REFERENCE VIEW

- Move the 3D view to a new location.
- Both notes will move along with the drawing view.

Now we will use the Text Editor to add Appended Text to a dimension.

- Double-Click the dimension for the small hole.
- Select the Appended Text icon.

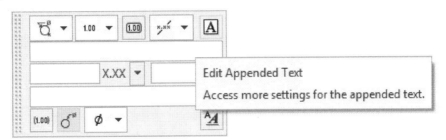

Edit Appended Text

Access more settings for the appended text.

- Select After spot from the Appended Text window drop down.
- Click in the white text box and type "x 1.0," then click the Depth Drafting Symbol as shown in the following figure.

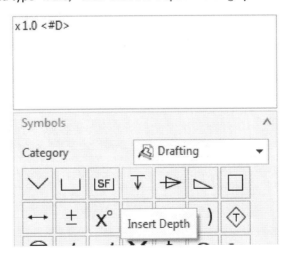

- Choose OK to close the Text Editor.
- Click and drag the dimension to the lower right corner of the view, as shown in the following figure.

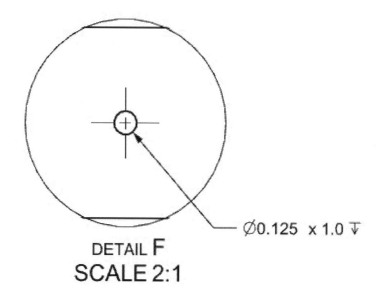

DETAIL **F**

SCALE 2:1

17.13 **Drawing Symbols**

In NX 10, you can add several types of symbols to drawings that help you to document the engineering intent. Two of the most important are *Utility Symbols* and *ID Symbols*. The same dialog boxes are used to create or modify existing drawing symbols.

17.13.1   **Utility Symbols**

You can add certain pre-defined symbols such as Center Mark, Bolt Circles, and Target Points found under the Center Mark drop down in the Annotation section of the Home Tab.

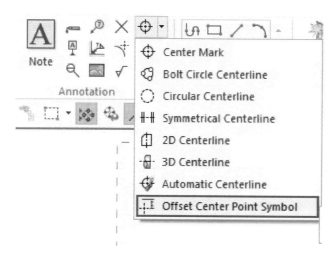

Each Utility Symbol has a set of parameters that control its appearance. The default values are set at the time the part is created (inherited from the NX customer defaults file) and are stored in the part database. The defaults may be modified in the same manner as Drawing Preferences.

To add a Utility Symbol to a drawing, simply select the desired symbol, then place it using the appropriate drawing entities. It is important to read the cue when adding Utility Symbols so that you understand what NX 10 expects you to select.

17.13.2 ID Symbol

In NX 10, ID Symbols are geometric shapes (such as circles or hexagons) that are often used in conjunction with drawing notes to annotate features. ID Symbols may be created either with or without leaders, just like drawing notes. The menu in the figure below appears by selecting Balloon.

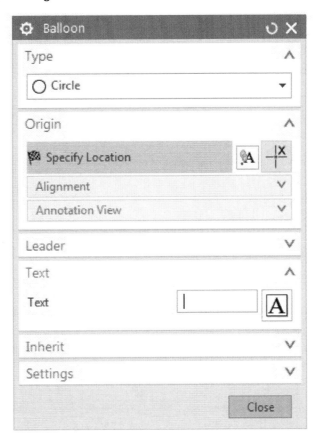

17.13.3 User-Defined Symbols

NX 10 allows you to define customized symbols. *User-Defined Symbols* are useful for automating the creation of commonly used items, such as company logos or standard drawing items. They can be used in NX 10 by selecting User-Defined. Check with your company's CAD System Administrator to see if you have a symbol library.

17.13.4 Weld Symbols

You can define different weld types by adding weld symbols in your drawing. To create a weld symbol select Weld Symbol and specify weld type, size, finish and any other parameters you need to define a weld.

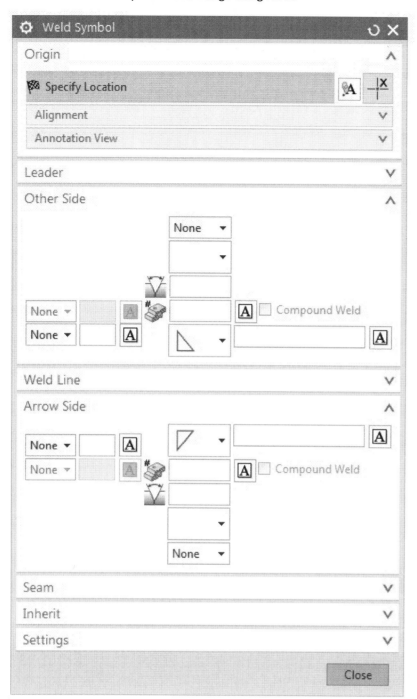

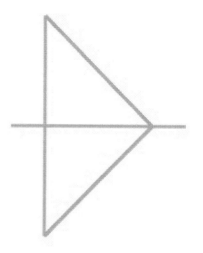

Create several Utility Symbols and ID Symbols on your drawing.

- Open the part from the previous project (if required) and select Application tab / Modeling.
- Add a R0.5 Edge Blend to the model, as shown in the following figure.

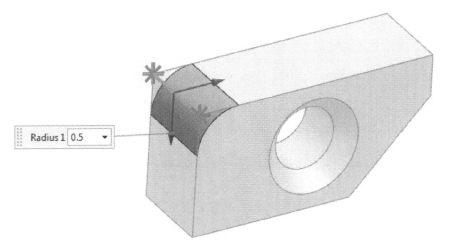

Radius 1 0.5

- Select **Application tab / Drafting.**
- Select **Update Views** to update the drawing sheet. Notice that any dimensions that referenced the edge removed by the Blend are now incorrect, as shown in the following figure.

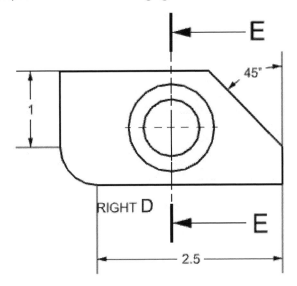

- Delete any incorrect dimensions.
- Select **Intersection Symbol.**
- Select the two edges as shown in the following figure to create the intersection symbol.

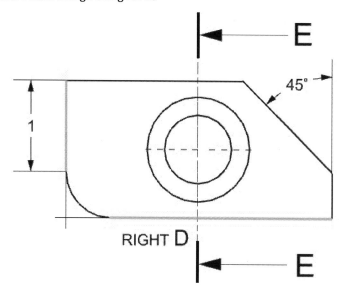

RIGHT D

- Re-create any dimensions that you deleted, and add a dimension to the new Edge Blend feature.
- Select the Automatic Centerline icon.
- Select the view shown below and choose Apply.

Notice that a centerline symbol appears on the large hole

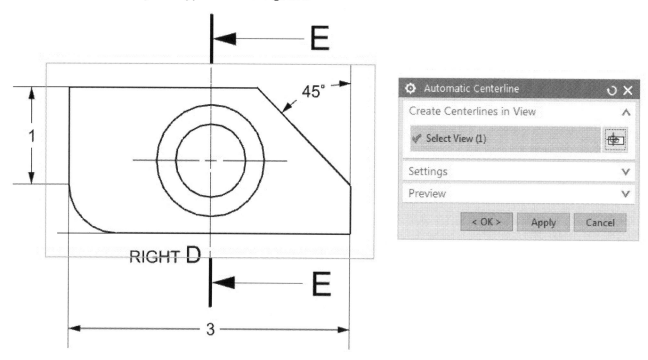

- Select the Top and Right projected views and choose Apply.
- Select the 2D Centerline icon.

Read the Cue throughout the symbol definition process. NX 10 is prompting you for the first side edge object of the block centerline.

- Select the 3D View's two defining edge sides, as shown below.

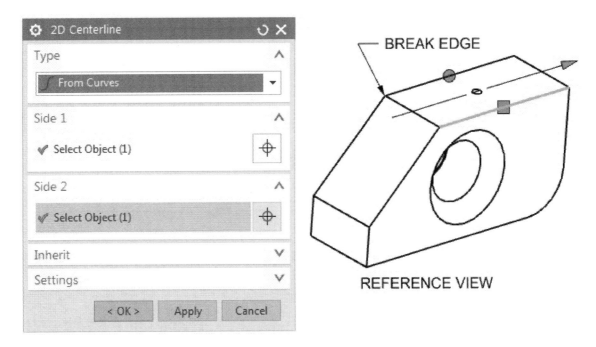

REFERENCE VIEW

- Create ID symbols that annotate part features. First, create one with a leader.
- Select **Balloon**.

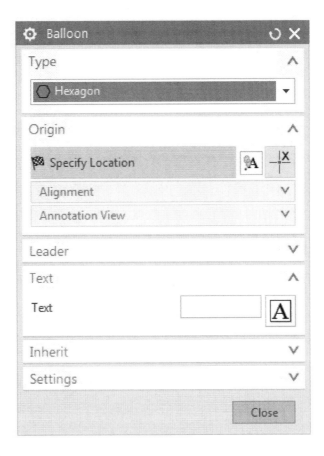

- Select the **Hexagon** Type.
- Enter **Text** = **3** and **Size** = **0.75** in the dialog box as shown above.
- Select the small hole in the **Top** projected view.
- Drag the cursor into the Graphics Window and place the ID Symbol below the view.

Now we will create an ID symbol without a leader.

- Enter Text = 2 in the dialog box.
- Move your cursor into the Graphics Window and place the ID Symbol near the BREAK EDGE note.
- Compare your results to the following figure.

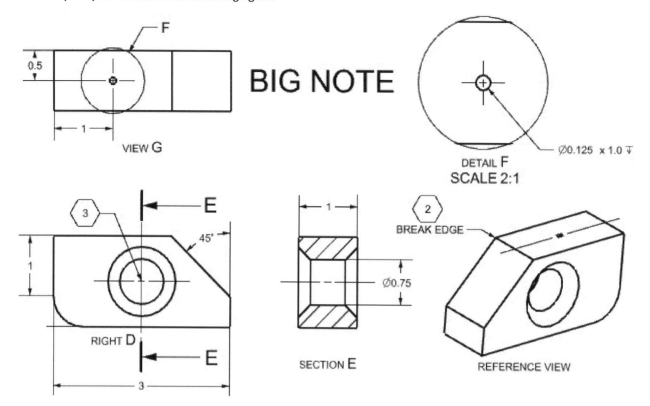

18 Master Modeling

18.1 What is a "Master Model?"

Master modeling is a simple technique that enables concurrent engineering. It is best understood by an example. Suppose you have a model of a modem unit, just the outside surfaces or the ID, and in other files you had all the other components that were related to the outside shape of the master model file. Every time you change the master model file, everything related changes – that illustrates master modeling working for you.

The following figure shows the master model along with each part created directly from the master model. The last figure shows what happens to all the components when the master model is changed.

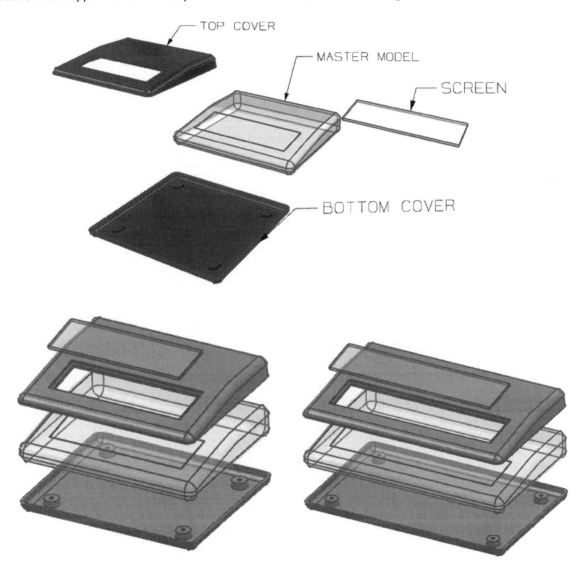

18.2 **How to make an Associative Assembly using a Master Model**

As depicted in the previous figures, Master Modeling can begin with a single part file that captures the main form of the geometry. Then you can add as many non-master part files that use that geometry. All you have to do is create your master part, create parts that reference the geometry of your master, and then your master modeling will be complete.

- Create a new part file and call it *Master*.
- Create a simple sketch that has the geometry and dimensions shown in the figure below.

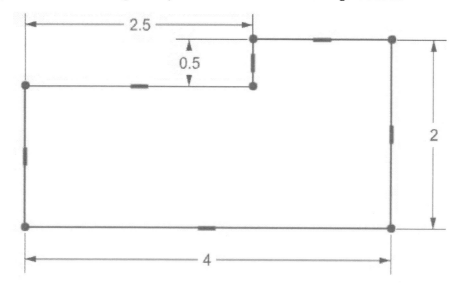

- Extrude it **1in** in the Z direction with a **10** degree draft.
- Extrude it **2in** in the –Z direction with a **10** degree draft.
- Unite them to create a model similar to the one shown in the following figure.

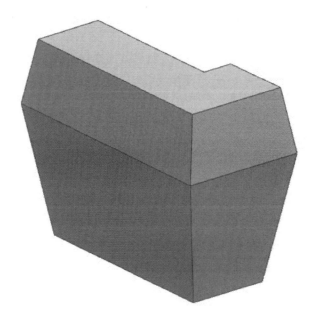

- Make sure the Assemblies application is turned on (Application tab / Assemblies).
- Now go to Assemblies tab / Create New Parent.
- Call the new component Assembly.
- Next Create a new *Blank* component called *Top Cover*

- Make the *Top Cover* the work part and you're ready to steal the geometry you need to create your new component.
- Select Home / More / WAVE Geometry Linker. Select Body as your type.
- Select the entire top body (as shown in the following figure) and click OK. Now that body will be linked to your Top Cover part file. Make sure that the Associative box is checked, as shown.

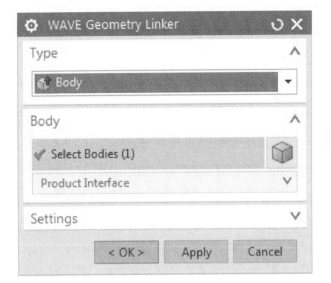
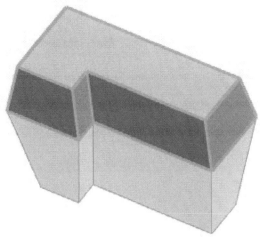

- When you hide the master part file you will see that you have a stolen body to work with, as shown in the following figure.
- Now Blend all the edges with a 0.1in radius and shell the bottom face with 0.05 in wall thickness.

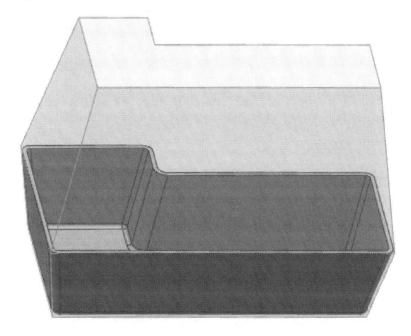

- Next repeat this process. Create a new part called bottom case. Steal the bottom body using the WAVE geometry linker from the master model. Hide the master body first. Blend the edges and shell it using the same values as the top cover. The bottom cover should look like the following figure.

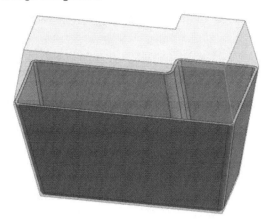

- At this point you should have three different part files: Master, Top Cover and Bottom Cover. The top and bottom covers rely on the master for its overall dimensions.

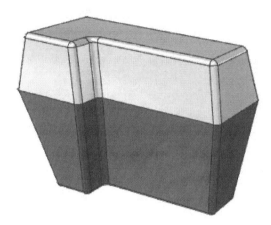

- Now change the length of the original sketch in the Master part file to 7. The corresponding model will appear as shown in the figure below.

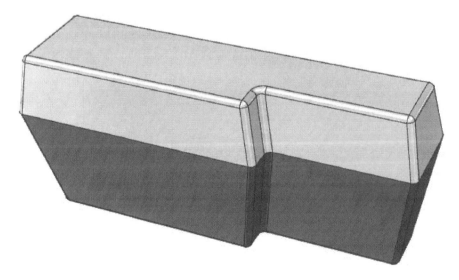

18.2.1 Master Modeling for Various Applications

The most common application of master modeling is when it is used for drafting. NX 10 is one of the only CAD packages that gives you the choice to perform your drafting in a separate non-master part file or right there in the actual component part file. Imagine having a component part file, such as the top cover of the modem housing mentioned above as your master part file, and a separate non-master part file for the drawing data. The top cover geometry is assembled into the drawing part file and all the drafting is performed in it. This way, the drafter and the modeler can work at the same time without overwriting each other's changes.

18.3 Wave Geometry Linker

Here we are going to use the Extract Virtual Curve tool to create a centerline on a part in an assembly. Then we will use the parametric centerline to create a wire that will run between two identical parts in the assembly. During this exercise we will use the WAVE Geometry Linker to create links between parts and create a fully parametric assembly.

- Begin by creating the following component named *'flange.'*

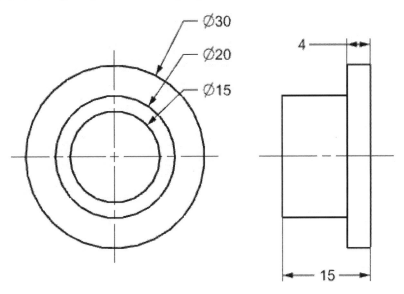

- Now create this component named *'container.'*

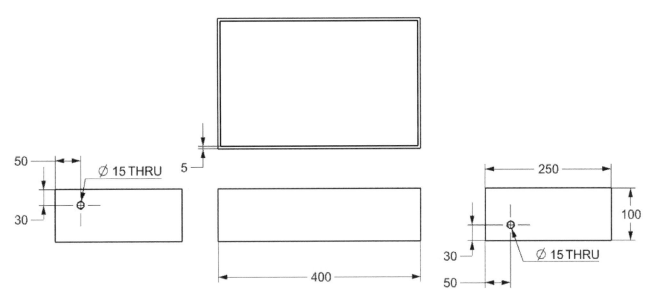

Now that you have created both of the parts, put them into an assembly. Use Assembly constraints to Fix the container. Then constrain the two flange components inside the container at the hole locations as shown in the following figure (*one is hidden in the following view*).

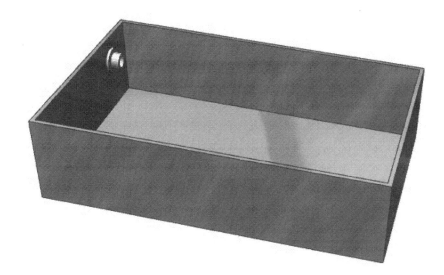

- Make the *flange* the displayed part. Select Curve Tab / More / Extract Virtual Curve from the Edit Curve section. Select Rotation Axis as the type, then select the cylindrical face shown below and click OK. You will now view your extracted curve, shown in the following figure.

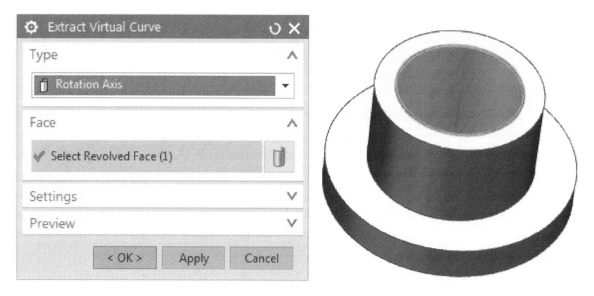

- Now select Assemblies / More / Reference Set. Click the Add New Reference Set button. Type in *"Extract Curve"* for the name, select the solid body and the extracted curve to include in your new reference set, and then press Enter on your keypad to complete.

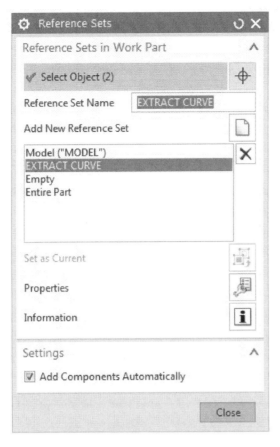

Note: *Automatic centerlines may already have been created upon view insertion in your drawing depending on NX 10 defaults. If you already have centerlines, skip ahead to the insertion of ID symbols on the next page.*

- Go back to the assembly. Right click on the *flange component* and select **Replace Reference Set / Extract Curve**. Now you will see the extracted curve as well as the flange solid in the assembly, as shown below. Repeat this for the other flange in the assembly.

- While in the assembly, select Create New Component from the Assemblies tab. Name the new component *Wire* and click OK.
- Make the new component the Work Part and select Wave Geometry linker.
- Choose Composite Curve as the type and then select the extracted curve from the flange component.
- Under settings make sure Associative and Fix at Current Timestamp is checked.
- Click Apply, then repeat the process for the other flange part in the assembly.

Note: Reference sets are one way to control what you see of a part file at the assembly level.

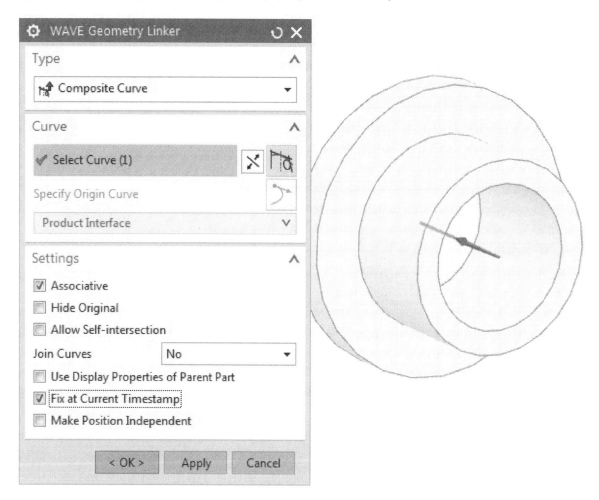

- Now select Curve Tab / Bridge Curve. We are going to use a Bridge Curve to connect the WAVE'd lines from each flange. Zoom up on one of the flanges and select the line.
- Now select the line from the other flange in the assembly and you will see the curve that connects the two flanges, as shown in the following figure. Click OK.

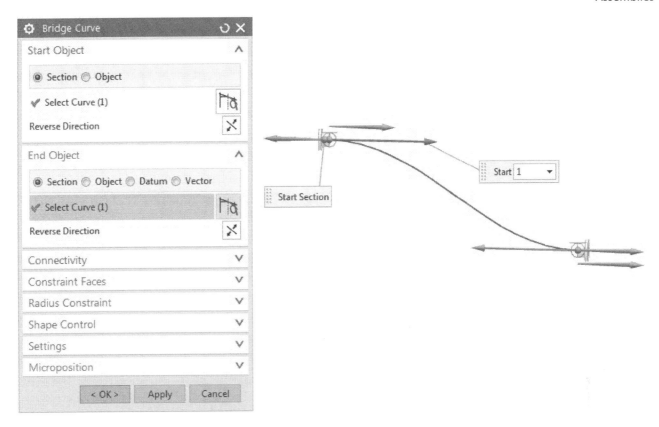

- Finally select **Tube**. Select the bridge curve with an outer diameter of **15**.
- Your assembly will now look like the following figure.

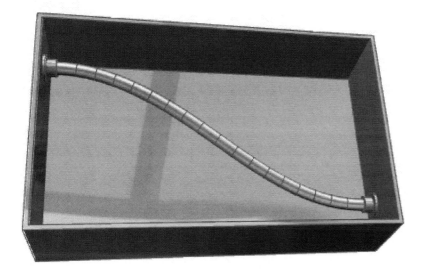

19 Sheet Metal Features

19.1 Introduction

To create sheet metal parts you have to use the NX Sheet Metal module found under the Applications tab.

Sheet Metal tools let you add details that are parametric, can be added to any solid model, and can show bending and distortion due to forming. Using Sheet Metal tools, you can create flanges, beads, bends, brackets and other geometry that are commonly used in sheet metal operations.

19.2 Tabs & Flanges

Start all the projects in this chapter by going to the Application tab and selecting the Sheet Metal icon. To create a flange, select Flange. You can create a simple flange by selecting the edge of a solid block, then choosing the direction and attachment face as shown in the following project.

In this project you will create a flange and define the width using options.

- Select the Tab tool.

- The Tab tool asks for either curves to create a tab or a plane on which to sketch the profile of your tab. It is effectively Extrude, but where the extrusion distance is specified by the Sheet Metal material thickness parameter.
- Click on the XY axis and sketch the following sheet metal Tab using a rectangle that is 5in x 2in.
- Edit the thickness to 0.05in in the Tab window after you have finished the sketch.

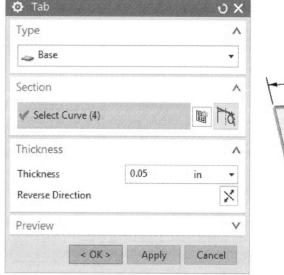

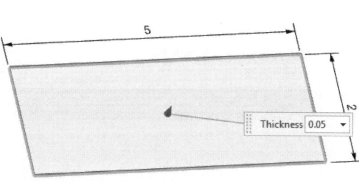

- Select Flange.
- Select the top edge of one of the long sides as the Bend Edge.
- Type in the Width Option, Length, and Angle, as shown in the following figure.
- Set the Width Option to At Center. This will center the flange on the edge that you selected.
- Also set the Inset to Bend Outside.

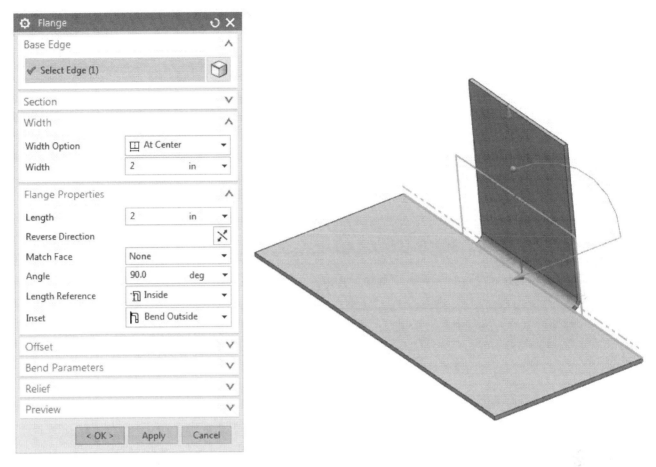

- You can also add reliefs to the sides by choosing an option from the Relief tab in the flange menu. Try creating a 0.1in round relief.

19.2.1 Inset Flange

Using this option, you can insert a flange on any planar face. This is different from the Flange option because Flange adds the geometry on a planar face, while the Inset options in the Flange insets it. See the figure below.

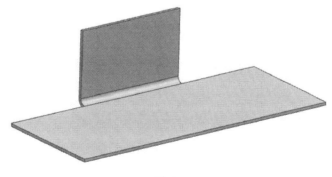

Flange

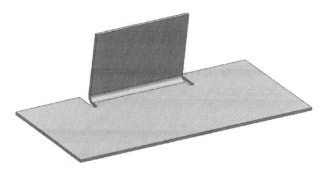

Inset Flange

In this project you will create a flange using inset flange with relief on the edges.

- Create a tab with dimensions 5in x 2in x 0.05in.
- Select Flange.
- Create a flange with a length and width of 1.5in. Change the Width Option to From End. Choose the left edge and give it a distance of 1 in. This is the distance away from the edge your flange will be placed.

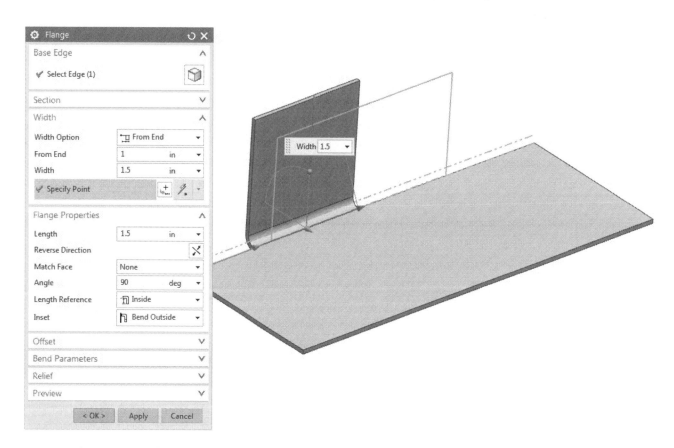

- To make it an inset flange, change the Inset options under Flange Properties to Material Inside as shown in the following figure.

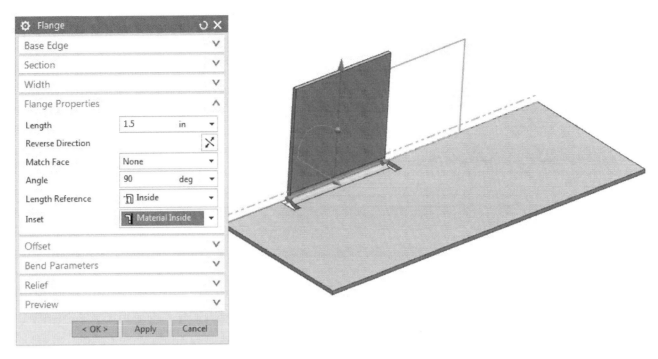

- Finally, change the Relief option to have a Round of 0.1in in width and depth.

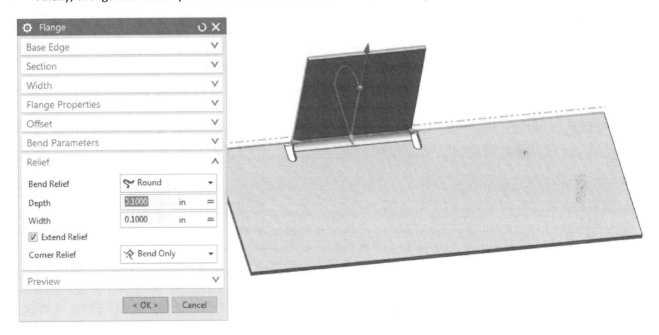

19.3 Sheet Metal from Solid

Sheet Metal from Solid is used to create a sheet metal feature using reference geometry. This is a really good technique especially when you have a part that needs a sheet metal inlay or something to that effect. You simply select the faces that are to be included and sheet metal is generated.

In this project you will create a sheet metal part using the reference geometry.

- Create geometry by extruding the sketch shown in the figure below by 2 inches.

Note: You can create this in the NX Sheet Metal environment – there is no need to enter the Modeling application!

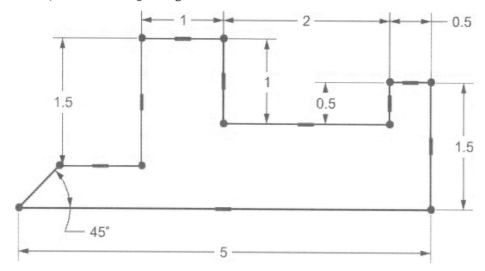

- Select **Sheet Metal from Solid**.
- Sequentially select all the faces on the outside of the solid, as shown below, from one side of the part to the other. After you click the second adjacent face, the sheet metal will begin creating.

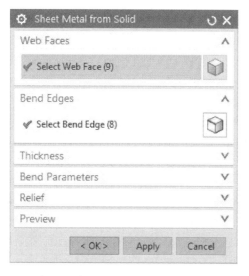

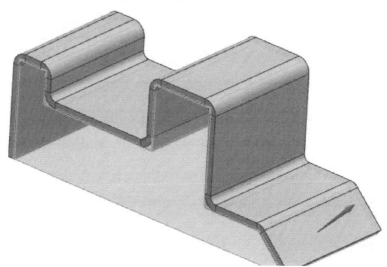

- Change the thickness of the sheet metal to **0.05in**.
- Your sheet metal will now look like the following figure.

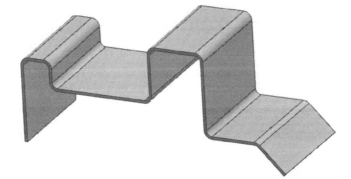

- The **Sheet Metal from Solid** can also be used to create a sheet metal enclosure.
- Try selecting both side faces and then the top face on the highest point.

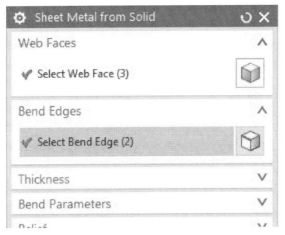

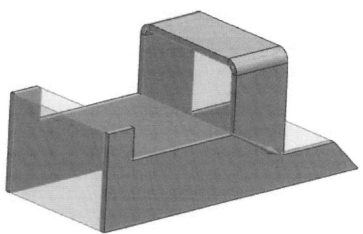

- Next select the back face, NX is alerting that the bend edges must be resolved.

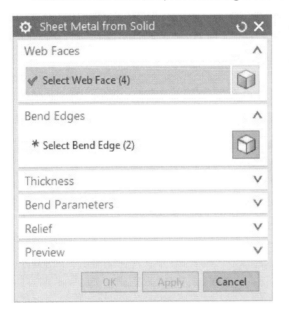

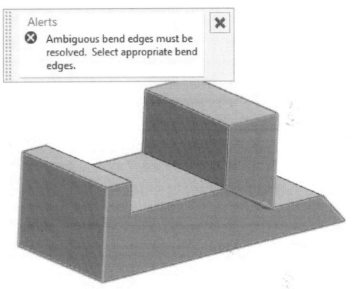

- Select the vertical edge on one side of the back face.

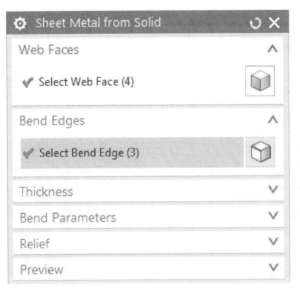

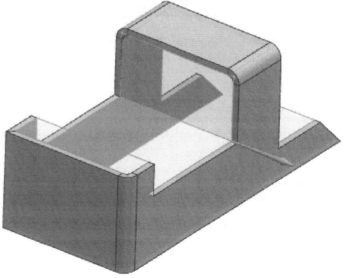

- The same step can be applied to the front of the solid.

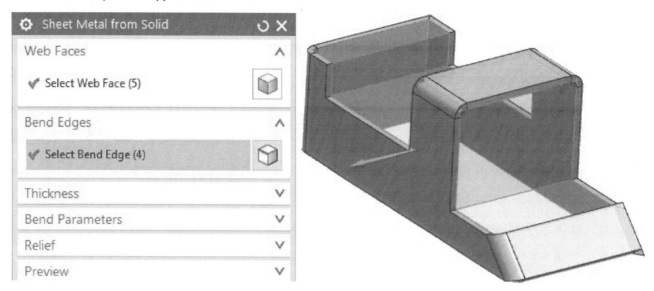

- Continue until you have an enclosure around the majority of the solid.

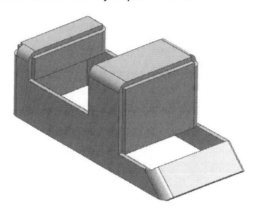

19.4 **Contour Flange**

The Contour Flange is a great tool that can create a custom flange around the entire perimeter of a tab.

In this project you will create a Contour Flange with a custom profile.

- Create a Tab that is 10in x 5in x 0.1in.
- Select Contour flange.
- Choose Secondary as the Type. The next stage is prompting you to select an edge to sketch your custom flange profile on. Select the edge shown, define the position as 50% along the edge in the following figure, and you will be thrown into the sketch environment.

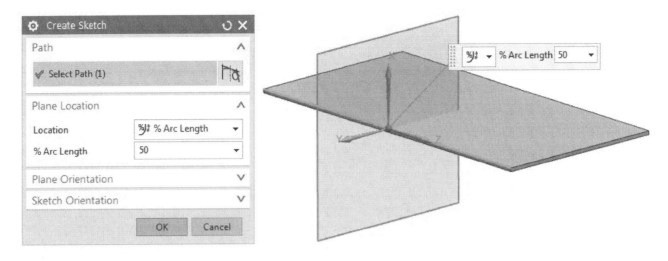

- Draw the profile shown in the following figure.

Note: Start the profile from the edge that you selected for the flange in the previous step.

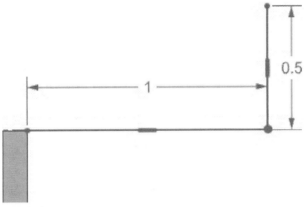

- Click Finish to move onto the next step.
- At the Width step, select Chain as the option.
- NX is now prompting you for edges – specify all four edges of the top face of the t ab. The flange will be created around the perimeter, as shown in the following figure.

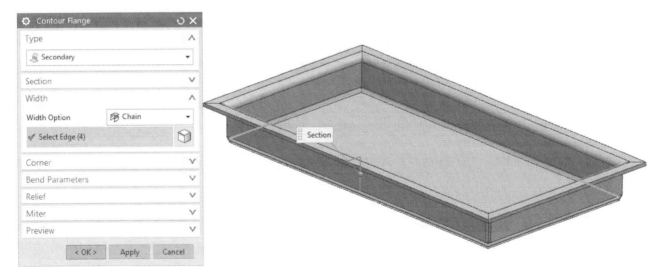

- Your model will now look like the following figure. Note that the edges are automatically mitered!

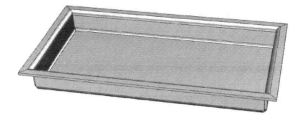

19.5 Bead

Beads are created using open-ended curves as centerlines. These are fully associative with the body. You can create U-shape, V-shape and circular beads.

In this project you will create a U-shape hollow bead and then pattern it.

- Start with a 5in x 3in x 0.1in Tab.
- Select Bead.

- Select the top face of the tab and you will be thrown into the sketch environment.
- Sketch a centerline to create a bead as shown in the figure below.

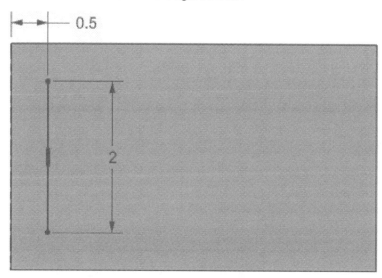

- Choose U-shape as the Cross Section shown in the following figure.

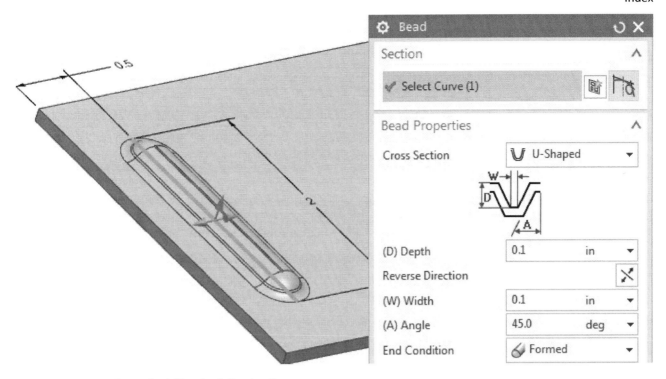

- Your model will now look like the following figure.

- Use **Pattern Face** to repeat the beads as shown in the following figure.
- Select all the faces that make up the bead feature.

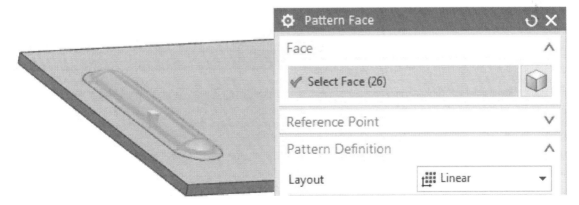

- Choose the long edge of the top tab as the X and the short edge as the Y.
- Make the number along **X = 5**. Specify a 1in pitch for X. Your model should now look like the following figure.

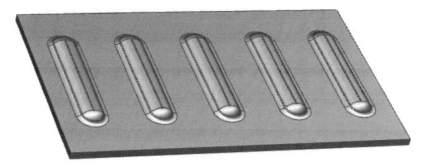

19.6 **Drawn Cutout**

Drawn Cutout is one of the many tools available in the Punch group. You can also use the solid punch tool that will be shown in a later exercise.

Use the embossed punch to create a sunken area with a flanged cutout.

- Create a tab and offset the boundary of the top face by 0.5 mm inward.
- Select Drawn Cutout.
- Select the edges of the offset curves as the section. Change the Depth to 0.2in.
- Check that Round Section Corners and Round Cutout Edges are both checked.

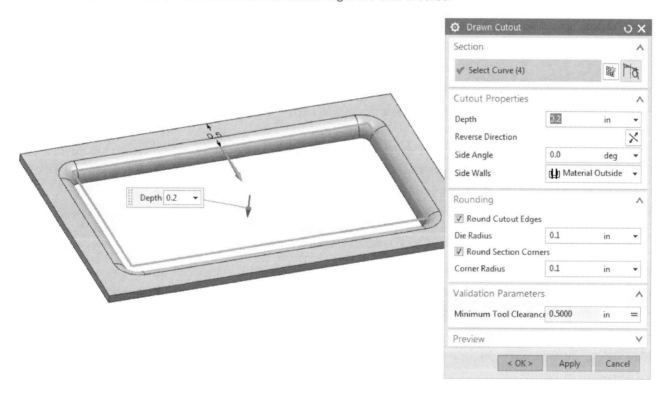

19.7 **Closed Corner**

The *Closed Corner* feature can be used to create *Butt, Machinery, Simple Miter* and *Full Miter* corners between two flanges.

In this project you will create a corner between two flanges.

- Create a tab, 6in x 4in x 0.05in.
- Create a 1in high flange on all four sides as shown in the following figure.

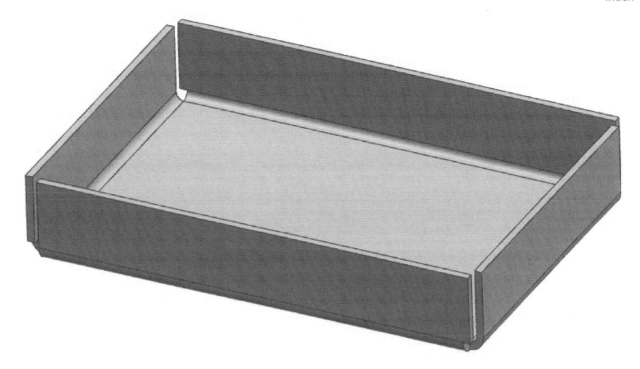

- Select Closed Corner.

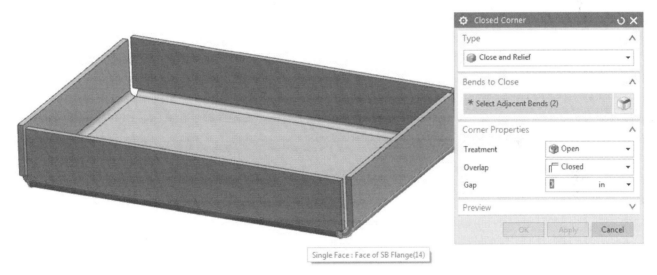

- Choose Close and Relief as the Type and the Treatment step as Open.

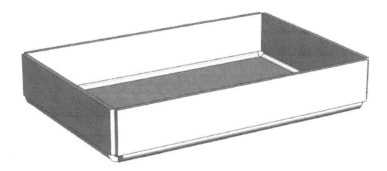

19.8 **Unbend/Rebend**

Unbend/Rebend can be used to form or unform self-forming features. This is a time-stamped operation so you can Unbend a flange, go through an operation where you need a flat surface, then Rebend the flange after.

- Using the previous project.
- Select Unbend.
- Select a Stationary face (as shown below).

- Select the bends that you want to Unbend.

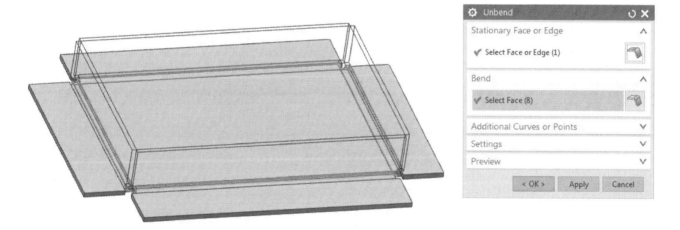

- Compare your results with the figure above.

19.9 **Relief**

In NX 10 you can create reliefs within the Closed Corner tool. You can create a Circular, U, V, and Rectangular Relief features between bend areas that are fully associative with the part.

- Use the part file from the last exercise and delete the Unbend operation and the Closed Corner operations.
- Now we are going to create new Closed Corners, this time with reliefs.
- Select Closed Corner.
- Select the two bends around one of the corners.
- For Treatment, choose Circular Cutout and copy the dimensions shown in the following figure.

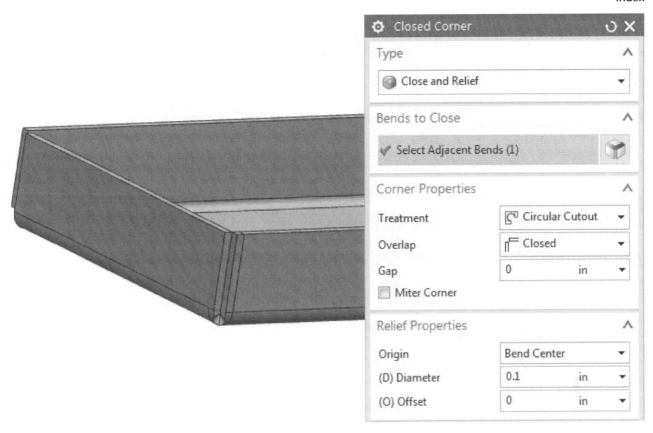

19.10 **Solid Punch**

A Solid Punch can be used when you want to inherit a shape from a tool body.

- Use the part file from the previous exercise.
- Create a tool solid, as shown in the figure below.

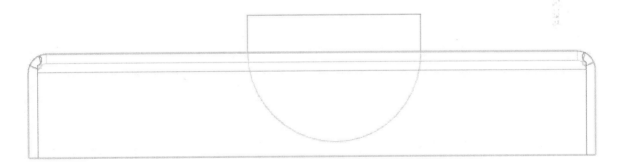

- Select Solid Punch.
- Select the Top Face as the Target Face and Tool Body as shown in the following figure.
- Check the Hide the tool body option, along with Infer Thickness and Auto Centroid.

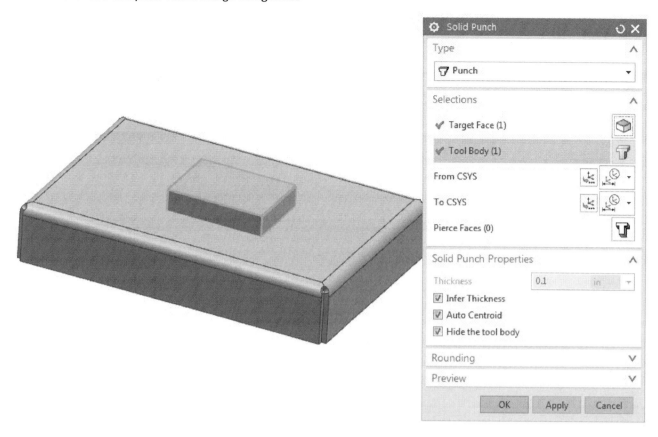

- Compare your results with the following figure.

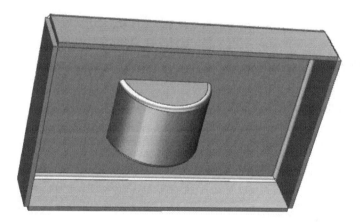

19.11 Bend

You can bend a solid body of uniform thickness along any straight curve using the Bend option.

- Create a 5in x 5in x 0.05in tab, sketch the curves so your model looks like the following figure. The curves are going to be used to create the bends.

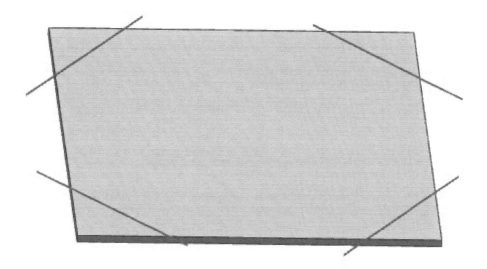

- Select **Bend**.
- Select one of the bend lines and a bend will be automatically created.
- Make your model look like the following figure.

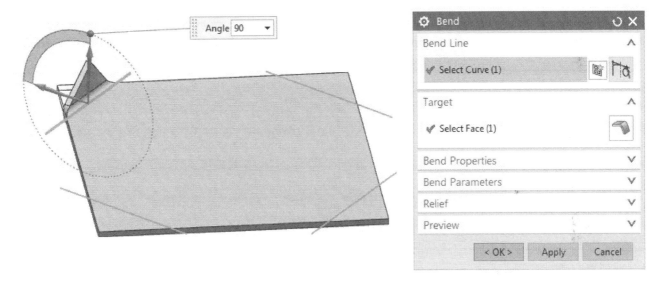

- Repeat the process for the other lines, changing the bend direction for each bend.
- Your model should look like the following figure.

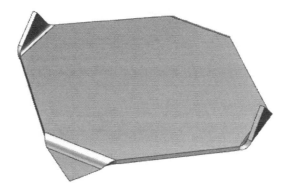

Note: *The Reverse Direction button will change the direction of the Bend. The Reverse Side button will change what side of the line is to be bent.*

421

20 Index

Z

Made in the USA
Lexington, KY
27 June 2017